4820

①

I 036726 004 E1

D1439127

ZOOLOGY SERIES

Editor: F. KINGSLEY SANDERS, M.A., D.PHIL.

ANIMAL ECOLOGY

AIMS AND METHODS

ANIMAL ECOLOGY

AIMS AND METHODS

BY

A. MACFADYEN, M.A.

Senior Lecturer in Zoology, University College of Swansea

LONDON
SIR ISAAC PITMAN & SONS LTD.

First published 1957
Second edition 1963

SIR ISAAC PITMAN & SONS LTD.
PITMAN HOUSE, PARKER STREET, KINGSWAY, LONDON, W.C.2
THE PITMAN PRESS, BATH
PITMAN HOUSE, BOUVERIE STREET, CARLTON, MELBOURNE
22–25 BECKETT'S BUILDINGS, PRESIDENT STREET, JOHANNESBURG

ASSOCIATED COMPANIES
PITMAN MEDICAL PUBLISHING COMPANY LTD.
46 CHARLOTTE STREET, LONDON, W.1
PITMAN PUBLISHING CORPORATION
20 EAST 46TH STREET, NEW YORK 17, NEW YORK
SIR ISAAC PITMAN & SONS (CANADA) LTD.
(INCORPORATING THE COMMERCIAL TEXT BOOK COMPANY)
PITMAN HOUSE, 381–383 CHURCH STREET, TORONTO

200509
591.5 AR

MADE IN GREAT BRITAIN AT THE PITMAN PRESS, BATH
F3—(T.696)

I am a firm believer that, without speculation there is no good or original observation.

C. DARWIN, Letter to A. R. Wallace, 22nd December, 1857.

We cannot too carefully recognize that science started with the organization of ordinary experiences. . . . It confined itself to investigating the conditions regulating the succession of obvious occurrences. . . .

A. N. WHITEHEAD, *Science and the Modern World* (1926).

Que l'écologie soit une science historique au premier clef, cela ne fait à mes yeux aucune doute. Au même titre que l'histoire humaine, elle doit être considérée beaucoup plus comme la résultante des liaisons et des attachements secrets qui en sont la traduction apparente. Elle est, à ce titre, avant tout centrée sur les relations des êtres entre eux dans les milieux naturels et c'est à cela que tient la grande importance de la biocénotique.

C. DELAMERE DEBOUTEVILLE, *Microfaune du Sol* (Paris, 1951).

Some concepts are more fundamental than others, but even those which turn out to be only rough pictures of what really happens often retain their usefulness. They are sketches as compared with finished pictures, and if details are not needed the sketch is often clearer.

G. THOMPSON, *Adv. Sci.* (Cardiff, 1960).

PREFACE TO THE SECOND EDITION

ECOLOGY is an expanding science and the task of expounding its principles is both an exacting and exciting one. In the short space of time since the first edition of this book was written a remarkable proliferation of ideas and results has occurred and it is only when one looks back that their range and importance can be appreciated. It is particularly satisfactory that, as against the "fragmentation" which is supposed to beset modern science as a whole, much has been done in Ecology, not only to synthesize the results of many separate inquiries but also to bridge the gaps between aspects and approaches which were formerly quite distinct. These trends are reflected in the new edition; it now seems ridiculous, for instance, to separate the "population" from the "energetics" approach to ecological productivity, and the integration of topics such as these has required the rearrangement of most of the chapters in the second and third parts of the book. A new chapter, on ecological aspects of metabolism, has been included in Part I and about one-third of the book has been completely rewritten. The rest has been revised in the light of publications up to the end of 1961. The book was not primarily intended as an undergraduate text-book and makes no claim to impartiality or complete coverage, as explained in the original preface. However in response to evidence that it has been used in this way I have doubled the number of line diagrams and included more illustrative examples. The references have been brought together in a single bibliography at the end, and authors' names are more widely quoted in the text. These and other improvements and corrections result from the comments of many correspondents to whom I am truly grateful but in particular I would like to thank in this respect C. S. Elton, F.R.S., Dr. C. B. Goodhart, Dr. M. Heine, Dr. A. J. Nicholson, R. S. Miller, and Prof. G. C. Varley. A. M.

PREFACE TO THE FIRST EDITION

ECOLOGY is fortunate, even among biological sciences, in having many friends, acquaintances and helpers. Few of these, however, regard themselves as ecologists. Whole armies of amateur naturalists help to collect ecological information while professional biologists, working in other fields, frequently encounter ecological problems. Much applied and economic biology is concerned with ecological material even when the approach and outlook are different. To many of these people, one suspects, ecology is a vague or even difficult subject with an elaborate jargon, an obsession with theories and with mathematics and an incomprehensible fondness for the study of populations, when all one needs to worry about, surely, are individual animals.

It is more particularly for those on the edge of ecology, for the naturalist, the student and the layman who want to know what ecology is about and how the ecologist goes about his work, that this book has been written. It deals with the kinds of problems that are currently occupying the minds of ecologists, the principles governing their approach, the methods they use and the results they obtain and hope to obtain. Because it is a short book, and because there is no book more exasperating to read than that which deals only with general principles *in vacuo*, I have tried to give a few easily remembered examples of the principles discussed, some concrete surveys of techniques, choosing especially those which are missing from the review literature, and fairly full lists of references at the end of each chapter so that points and ideas raised can be followed up.

Text-books can be classified into three categories: first the elementary text-book which is concerned with presenting factual information simply to the beginner; in this type of much maligned book the author usually avoids controversial issues or makes dogmatic statements about them. Secondly, the authoritative or encyclopedic type of text-book which aims to cover the whole field of a subject, quoting all important results and opinions. There is, however, a third type of technical publication for which the term "text-book" is an inadequate description. This is a book which claims neither to offer a comprehensive treatment nor to cater simply for the elementary student. Its scope is at once wider and more limited; limited to a few special problems and unashamedly more one-sided, but wider for the very reason that these problems are considered in a broader and more critical way. Such a book should appeal to the layman, the student and to the worker in the field under consideration. To this category I believe that this work belongs. In the field of animal ecology we have now a number of elementary text-books, an excellent modern encyclopedic work (Allee *et al.*, 1949) to which all will refer for facts and figures, and rather fewer books of the third category. An outstandingly successful example of this class of book was Elton's *Animal Ecology*, which has probably inspired more ecological research than any other work. The present volume comes at a time when the ideas put forward by Elton and his contemporaries have taken root and are bearing fruit; this volume itself is in a sense part of that fruit and describes more of it. Such books, if they are not to fall between two stools, should first present the ideas and information which are interesting research workers of today, in such a way as to stimulate thought and interest, and secondly they should review the standard methods and techniques so that they can be critically appraised.

The present work is therefore concerned mainly to build on earlier foundations a frankly controversial text which includes my own background of assumptions, hypotheses and methods. I have given as fair a treatment as possible to rival views and theories and have tried to differentiate between themes which are widely current and those which are my own. However, as any historian of science will know, even those theories which come to be labelled with a man's name are usually widely discussed long before they are clearly formulated and the attribution of ideas to one person is an invidious and usually inaccurate practice.

I have tried to provide a book which will tell the student how animal ecologists in general go about their self-imposed task of determining why a given organism is found where and when it is, and of learning to predict the future behaviour of populations. At the same time, because I believe the two are inseparable, I have examined the basic assumptions and ideas which lie behind our approach to these phenomena; in this way I hope to demonstrate that the subject of animal ecology has a set of unifying theories and characteristic techniques and is a profitable means of investigating such practical problems as concern us daily in our relations with the plant and animal kingdoms on which we depend for our food, clothing and other necessities of life.

Of course we are only beginning to sense the existence of these principles and it is as well to be honest and to admit that all biologists are studying a marvellously complicated subject about which they know almost nothing. The current tendency to extol the achievements of biology is very misleading, but this is no excuse for an alternative cynical attitude.

I have made no attempt in this book to provide a balanced selection of examples from all groups of the animal kingdom; there is a bias towards the ecology of terrestrial and freshwater invertebrates and I hope that this will be considered justifiable for four reasons. First, I am most familiar with these fields myself; second, invertebrates are very much neglected and should be better known—moreover there are many excellent books about vertebrates and a book in the present series is planned to cover marine ecology; third, invertebrates, by their universal distribution and dense populations, are often more suitable for the study of animal populations than larger animals and, fourth, the principles arrived at in this book apply equally to all groups of animals. I have been careful to maintain an even balance of theories and have supported these, where necessary, with examples from many different animals.

Scientific work involves the collection, by means consistent with observation by more than one observer, of reports of incidents and the classification of such reports so as to reveal their common factors. Once a sufficient number of similar sets of behaviour have been accumulated, hypotheses can be formulated, taking the form that, given certain sets of events, other events may be expected to ensue. Armed with his hypothesis the student returns to the field of observation to test its validity and, if need be, to modify it. The fitting of a given report into a system of classification is an "explanation" of observed events. That practical applications of scientific results are possible is due to our ability to relate consequences hitherto uncontrollable, to factors over which we have some control.

Ecology concerns itself with the interrelations of living organisms, plant or animal, and their environments; these are studied with a view to discovering the principles which govern the relationships. That such principles exist is a basic assumption—and an act of faith—of the ecologist. His field of inquiry is no less wide than the totality of the living conditions of the plants and animals under observation, their systematic positions, their reactions to the environment and to each other, and the physical and chemical make-up of their inanimate surroundings. The boundaries of the older scientific disciplines are demarcated by their known subject-matter and to no small extent by the history of human thought. What of this parvenu among sciences which seems to be all facts and no theory and which suffers, apparently, from a surfeit of observations and from a lack of principles by which to classify them? Is there such a thing as a science of ecology?

It must be admitted that the ecologist is something of a chartered libertine. He roams at will over the legitimate preserves of the plant and animal biologist, the taxonomist, the physiologist, the behaviourist, the meteorologist, the geologist, the physicist, the chemist and even the sociologist; he poaches from all these and from other established and respected disciplines. It is indeed a major problem for the ecologist, in his own interest, to set bounds to his divagations.

One of the aims of this book is to show that ecology is a science in its own right, with its own themes and basic principles which cannot be derived from the contributory sciences enumerated above. It is hoped to satisfy those interested, scientist and layman alike, that the ecologist is justified in his belief that the interrelations of living organisms conform to clear principles, that these principles can be discovered, and that they will enable us to predict how many organisms live, where and when they are to be found there, and why.

In the early 1920s the generally accepted definition of ecology, when the term was used at all, was "scientific natural history." This implied the recording of observations on the occurrence of organisms and, sometimes, the rather conjectural linking of these records to environmental factors. A new phase in the development of the subject began with the appearance of Elton's *Animal Ecology*, for it shifted the emphasis from the individual organism to the animal population as the appropriate unit of study. Just as the attention of the chemist is concentrated on the behaviour of molecules, of the cytologist on that of cells, and of the morphologist on that of organisms, so the natural and the most profitable unit for the study of ecology is the population of organisms.

This thesis is still not recognized by all students of the subject and the reader is not expected to accept such an assertion without question, but a further object of this book is to present evidence for this view.

The "population dynamics" approach to animal ecology has allowed us to expand the scope of the subject from the "scientific natural history" theme in a number of directions. In the first place it has allowed us to make quantitative statements about ecological phenomena. Biologists as a whole have a lively distrust of the application of mathematics to their science and this is certainly justified by many examples from the history of the subject. A further aim of this book will be, however, to demonstrate that, in the particular field of animal ecology, mathematical techniques provide a set of most potent weapons and that such techniques are indispensable to the study of many aspects of the subject. Decisions about what animals occur where and when are not, as was once thought, purely matters of qualitative correspondence between the tolerances of an organism and the environmental features of its "niche," but the result of a constantly changing set of forces whose interplay results in a balance which can only be measured in quantitative terms. We shall see, however, in the simplest experimental situations involving populations of one or two species, that the outcome of, for instance, the competition for a single food supply, is more properly expressed in terms of statistical probabilities than simple statements. The process of integrating these concepts of experimental population dynamics with the observations of the field naturalist and with the problems of the practical exploiter of plant and animal husbandry is one of the main occupations of the present-day ecologist. Thus the introduction of the animal population as the basic unit of ecology and statistics as its main analytical tool have allowed us to make not only quantitative statements about animal population phenomena but also qualitative generalizations and predictions of a new order: we can answer questions, not merely about how many, we can provide more precise information about what, when and where.

Equipped with this background of theories and techniques, how in fact does the ecologist go about his job? The answer to this question is partly historical, because the series of techniques evolved at different stages of the subject are appropriate to a corresponding series of different problems. I will trace in the course of this book some of the techniques and the types of problems they aim to solve. The aspects of taxonomy and genetics which are appropriate to ecology are considered first, then the physiological and behavioural characteristics of individual animals which define the ultimate limits of habitats which they can tolerate. This is followed by chapters on the physical environment as manifest in the "microclimates" of habitats, the plant background and its effect on animals, the spatial and temporal distribution of animals and the synthesis possible from such an "autecological" approach. I hope to show in the first part of the book, which is concerned mainly with the "scientific natural history" stage of the subject, that we can by such means only decide why animals are found in certain general types of habitats and that a different sort of information is needed before we can carry the analysis further. Chapters on the practical measurement of population size and the overlap in range of populations of different species are followed by an introduction to experimental and field-population dynamics and the "morphology" and "physiology" of populations. In the third part of the book I have considered some of the principles and theories of animal populations and their structure which have come to light as a result of ecological work, theoretical, experimental and field studies. A chapter is devoted to the concept of the biotic community which for all its faults has probably stimulated more argument and ideas than any other in this field. A chapter on practical applications to human affairs indicates the nature of a vast and expanding field.

In answer to our question "how does the ecologist go about his job?" it will be seen, then, that there are many approaches and many techniques in so wide-ranging a subject, that methods of analysis vary from the largely intuitive approach of the field naturalist to the refined statistical methods of the experimentalist, but that a certain group of ideas, even if seldom discussed, is constantly present, determining which phenomena will be recorded as significant and how they will be interpreted. It is only by fully appreciating this background and its effects that allowances can be made for it and advances in new directions initiated.

A. M.

ACKNOWLEDGMENTS

THIS book owes its existence to the many ecologists who, in their conversation and their writings, have taught me what I know of the subject. It is impossible to list them all and I will therefore content myself with recording my indebtedness above all to Charles Elton, F.R.S., whose book I first read in 1937 and whose ideas have continued to guide my outlook on ecology ever since.

The book has been read in its entirety by my wife, my father and by Professor Thomas Park; each of these has from a different aspect made great contributions to its accuracy and lucidity and if the book should prove useful my readers will have as much cause to thank these patient critics as I have. Dr. Kingsley Sanders and Mr. J. F. Douglas have also made valuable improvements in a muddled manuscript.

To the following I am greatly indebted for reading particular chapters and making valuable criticisms: J. Le G. Brerton, M. J. Davies, E. Duffey, E. D. Le Cren, M. H. Williamson and D. H. Chitty.

I hope and believe that among my readers will be people who have no training as zoologists; I have therefore thought it important to provide illustrations of at least the more important animals whose ecology is described. It is a very great pleasure to acknowledge the ready and generous help which has been given by the following, who provided illustrations and permitted their reproduction: The Pest Infestation Laboratory of the Department of Scientific and Industrial Research, the Director of the Imperial Institute of Entomology, the Editor of the *Journal of Animal Ecology*, Dr. A. Brauns, N. Haarløv, D. A. Kempson, Dr. A. J. Nicholson, Dr. E. Nørgaard, Dr. K. Paviour-Smith, M. E. Solomon, H. N. Southern, Dr. J. Van der Drift, Prof. G. Varley, and Prof. T. Weis-Fogh.

CONTENTS

PART I. THE ECOLOGY OF INDIVIDUALS

PART II. THE ECOLOGY OF SINGLE SPECIES POPULATIONS

PART III. THE ECOLOGY OF ANIMAL COMMUNITIES

TABLES, FIGURES AND PLATES

Part I

THE ECOLOGY OF THE INDIVIDUAL

Chapter 1

THE CLASSIFICATION AND DESCRIPTION
OF THE FAUNA

In this part of the book I shall consider the methods and results of the "scientific natural history" approach to ecology. It will be a fairly short part because the methods are largely well-established and widely-known. They are still used extensively, are applicable in many fields, and are giving rise to new developments, but they are mainly limited to answering qualitative questions about the limits of tolerance of individual animals rather than to providing the background for precise statements and predictions about the relationships of animals.

The Importance of Taxonomy to the Ecologist

The ecologist cannot escape being to some extent a taxonomist; in fact one of the commonest directions in which ecologists become led aside from their subject is towards taxonomy. The taxonomy of the animal kingdom is, from a systematic point of view, very unevenly developed: in groups such as the vertebrates the vast majority of world species is known and named while in others, such as the far more numerous Arthropoda, the majority have yet to be described. The systematist therefore, when he is interested in general problems of wide systematic implication, concentrates on the first groups and ignores the latter—which hardly helps to rectify the present state of affairs. Modern concepts of the sub-species and the evolutionary aspects of species formation have been almost entirely worked out on birds and other vertebrates, so that this already well-known group has become even better known. Unfortunately, ecological studies cannot —except for certain very special investigations—be confined to these well-known groups, and a normal ecological survey cuts right across systematic groupings and tends to include a majority of organisms whose taxonomy is little known. In a grassland soil, for instance, the numbers of the different groups per square metre are of the following orders of magnitude, and only those marked belong to groups whose taxonomy is well enough known for there to be comprehensive books on the fauna.

3

TABLE I

Table to indicate the orders of numbers of invertebrate animals present beneath one square metre of grassland soil, the relative ease with which they may be collected quantitatively and may be identified. Figures are based on Stöckli, A.,[693] but amended, in the case of groups marked with an asterisk, in the light of studies based on more adequate techniques. All figures, being means based on current techniques, are minimal.

Group	Abundance, per sq m	Amenability to Sampling	Amenability to Naming
Bacteria	$1 \cdot 5 - 4 \cdot 3 \times 10^{12}$	no	no
Thecamoebae	$0 \cdot 1 - 0 \cdot 5 \times 10^{9}$	no	no
Nematoda*	$1 \cdot 8 - 120 \times 10^{6}$	yes	no
Tardigrada (bear animalcules) . .	$0 \cdot 5 - 16 \times 10^{3}$	yes	no
Rotifera	$2 \cdot 5 - 7 \cdot 1 \times 10^{3}$	yes	no
Mollusca (slugs and snails) . . .	$0 \cdot 1 - 8 \cdot 5 \times 10^{3}$	yes	yes
Annelida: Enchytraeidae* (pot worms) .	200–20,000	yes	no
Lumbricidae* (earth worms)	30–2,000	no	yes
Myriapoda (centi- and millipedes) . .	900–1,700	yes	yes
Acari* (mites)	$2 \cdot 0 - 120 \times 10^{3}$	yes	yes
Crustacea (woodlice)	100–400	yes	yes
Araneae (spiders)*	180–840	no	yes
Opiliones (harvestmen)* . . .	2–38	yes	yes
Collembola (springtails)* . . .	$1 - 40 \times 10^{3}$	yes	yes
Coleoptera (beetles) adult . . .	500–1,000	yes	yes
larvae . .		yes	no
Formicidae (ants)	200–500	yes	yes
Diptera (flies) larvae*	1,000	no	no

Even in the field of freshwater habitats the situation was no better until recently the excellent series of monographs of the Freshwater Biological Association began to bridge the gap. A brief summary of the main systematic works of use in investigations of British soil and freshwater fauna is given at the end of the book.

Difficulties and Imperfections and Ways of Reducing Them

The high level of perfection reached by students of bird systematics is unlikely to be attained in other groups, especially invertebrates, for many years and, even if it were, it is doubtful whether the ecologist would be able to take part in such studies without them absorbing all his time. At the same time it is becoming more and more evident that the very cursory identifications which have satisfied ecologists hitherto are not simply a minor inconvenience but a serious source of error. Among the Collembola of the soil, for instance, Dr. Gisin[263] has shown how species hitherto thought to be uniform have been split up by modern taxonomists. It is these morphologically very similar species which show the most clear-cut ecological differences.

Thus the well-known species *Hypogastrura armata* and *Onychiurus armatus* have recently been subdivided, the normal form is only found free in soil but the newly-discovered species occur only in compost and the members of the pairs do not survive in their "wrong" habitat. In the case of the pair of species *Folsomia quadrioculata* and *F. multiseta*, which often do occur together, the former is never found in heaps of rotting pine-needles while the latter is regularly present there.

It is thus a serious obstacle to careful ecological work that accurate taxonomy is essential and that such work is most time-consuming. This difficulty can be overcome from two main directions.

First, the ecologist must choose his material to suit his problems and, where possible, study groups whose taxonomy can be learned without too much trouble and from which a number of questions can be answered without having to turn to different taxonomic groups. This is frequently a counsel of perfection.

Secondly, there is the possibility of collaboration in various ways. Specimens may be sent to an expert taxonomist, a method which has only limited success because the primary observer will miss many important observations by not knowing the names of the animals at the time of collection. A better device, which is being developed for instance in Oxford, [207] is to build up an ecological museum of specimens classified by habitats so that a beginner can go into a given habitat forewarned of the majority of species to be encountered and can reduce greatly the drudgery of identification by comparing his specimens with named material. Such collections are not yet at all common and must obviously be used with discretion. Evidently if the facilities for their preparation exist a major step has been taken because the collections can be contributed to and gradually perfected by successive generations of workers.

Ecology, Systematics and Evolution: the Arctic Fox, a Butterfly and a Snail

For certain branches of ecology a more precise knowledge of the systematic position of individual animals is necessary and here ecology, genetics and evolution tend to overlap. An example is the study of migrating populations by their genetical composition, which has been done extensively in studies of Arctic fox populations. [202] Thus, in the Thule region of West Greenland, three- to four-year fluctuations of fox numbers are accompanied by marked differences in the ratios of the different colour types in the population. The Arctic fox has two very distinct colour phases, the white and the "blue" (a dark bluish-grey). The ratio of these two phases, which are genetically distinct but interbreed, varies much over the Arctic, from less than 1 per cent blue in the Canadian Arctic to 50 per cent or more blue in West Greenland. On the whole the low-ratio blue populations occur where lemmings are the main fox food, while high-ratio blue populations feed mainly on sea refuse and seal carcases left by polar bears. It has been possible to show that years when the ratio of blue foxes in the Thule region is low coincide in a general way with the years of very high numbers of Canadian foxes (white) on the far side of Smith Sound. The general inference is that in these "peak" years the Canadian foxes cross the seventy to a hundred miles wide Smith Sound on the ice. This is supported by the observation of McClintock in 1858 of a blue fox about a hundred miles from land on the ice of Baffin Bay.

An example of an investigation made from a genetical point of view, which would have been more complete had ecological considerations been included, is that of H. D. and E. B. Ford. [227] An isolated colony of the butterfly *Melitaea aurinia* was found to show marked fluctuations in numbers over a period of fifty years. During a prolonged increase which occurred from 1920-4 it was observed that "an extraordinary outburst of variation occurred. Hardly two specimens were alike and marked departures from the normal form of the species both in size, shape and colour, were very common." The butterfly, both before and after the period of rapid expansion, was remarkably constant in form, however, although the normal type before and after the period of expansion was different. This is considered by Ford to illustrate the results of reduced intensity of natural selection and the sort of process that can lead to a marked change in a rapidly expanding population and sometimes result in the production of new sub-species. This conclusion has been disputed [817] on the grounds that phenotypic as opposed to genic variation was not excluded and that, while a simple relaxation of selection would increase variability it would not, by itself, result in the observed changes in the mode of the characters studied. Such changes may have been caused by differences in the habitat or the ecological situation or even by hybridization with another population, but these factors were not investigated.

Much recent work points to the interdependence of the genetic structure of populations and factors determining population size. These two properties, however, are not the same thing and it is, therefore, unfortunate that the first (namely differences in survival rates of genotypes in the wild), is called "population dynamics" by the geneticists; this term is used by ecologists to mean changes in rates of increase of whole populations, whether or not they are genetically homogeneous.[392] The expression is used in the ecologists' sense in this book.

Genetic changes have been related to the seasonal cycle in *Drosophila*[180] and in hybrid populations of toads,[579] to changes of environmental factors over the geographical range of the species[180] and to variations in physical factors in the same environment.[695] They have also been correlated with cyclical changes in population size and density in the tent caterpillar, a pest of Canadian conifers,[798] in *Drosophila*,[51] and, more cautiously in the vole,[104] and in these cases the changes in gene ratios are evidently an important factor in the mechanism which determines population numbers (see Chapter 12). Looked at from the other point of view, the effect of ecological factors on the gene ratios of a population is illustrated by Sheppard's[646] account of two species of *Cepaea* living together and sharing a common predator. When the protection of *C. nemoralis* against thrushes improves through changes in shell colour, the selection pressure on *C. hortensis* increases. Sheppard concludes that an influence of this kind accounts for the fact that mimicry in butterflies and other insects is frequently exhibited by a wide range of species where it occurs at all.

Evidently, therefore, both ecological and genetic factors must be considered, or at least allowed for, whenever changes in gene ratios and in population size occur side by side; since both are properties at the population level of organization, neither can be treated in isolation. And for the ecologist it is especially important to remember that the genetically determined interbreeding population is one of the few independently defined population units which exists.[500]

Genetic Drift

Another way in which the details of population size influence evolution is in connexion with the much disputed genetic drift.[825, 826] An appraisal of the validity of this well-known theory is not within the scope of this book, but it seems certain that the existence of small isolated populations provides unusual opportunities for the rapid evolution of new sub-species bearing characteristics which would not be tolerated in the more normal conditions of larger populations among which natural selection is in full operation.

A more ecological approach to this problem has recently been made[454] by studying the course of gene-frequency changes in experimental populations of *Drosophila*; populations of known genetic composition were introduced and the changes were observed as the populations underwent great variations in size. The author concluded that both "genetic drift" and natural selection were involved in producing the observed results.

Ecological Isolation

The possibility of ecological isolation being a factor in the separation of sub-species to produce new species is frequently discussed in connexion with evolutionary theories[87, 88, 341, 452, 721, 722] but again goes beyond the scope of this book. Briefly there were two main arguments: the first is a mere matter of words and due to Mayr's use of the term "geographical isolation" in the special sense of any spatial separation which effectively keeps apart populations of the species in question. Thus adjacent valleys on Fiji are geographically isolated to the Achatinellid snails which are represented by different species in the different valleys. Mayr, however, argues that this type of geographical isolation is the only means by which the initial separation of two sub-species can take place, while Thorpe considers that it is possible for spatially-contiguous elements of the same species to become isolated from each other owing to the development of ecological differences such as the adoption of different food plants or different diapause habits, etc. A good deal of evidence against Mayr's rather rigid attitude (which is indisputably the most usually correct one) has recently accumulated. The development of diapause differences is mentioned by Andrewartha[12] while Skellam's[649] demonstration that the rates of gene-spread are not as rapid as is often thought indicates once more how important it is to consider such questions in their ecological context. He maintains that isolation of elements within the same population can certainly occur owing to low rates of gene-spread.

The Importance of Reliable Identification

From the ecological point of view, however, the main importance of taxonomy is in enabling one to distinguish between closely-related species so that their distribution in terms of different environmental factors can be determined and their repeated association with other species can be detected. The theoretical implications of being able to do this are manifold and stem largely from Darwin's theory of natural selection, as will be seen in Chapters 13, 14 and 15. The practical advantages include the possibility of using certain "vicariant" species as "indicator organisms" (Chapter 13) for the detection both of certain types of habitat and of well-marked living communities (Chapter 12). Thus the species list, which has always been a conspicuous feature of ecological investigations and has sometimes been regarded as an end in itself, is still a necessary preliminary to most ecological studies.

Chapter 2

THE HABITAT

In the last chapter we briefly considered the means of recognizing and describing the animal material which is one side of the animal ecologist's chosen study. In Chapters 3 and 4 the study of the other facet of ecological relationships, the vegetational and physical features of the animal's surroundings, will be considered. Before going on to this aspect of the animal-environment relationship, however, it is desirable to attempt a closer understanding of what kinds of features do in fact characterize an animal's habitat and how these features have been measured and described. From the point of view of the natural historian the occurrence of animals is often unpredictable and we are mainly concerned here with the factors which contribute to that unpredictability.

A topic of this sort should be discussed at a fairly practical level, and for this reason some examples of animal distribution are given first to illustrate the kinds of habitat limits which are observed in nature. It is hoped that the reader's own experience will suggest other examples which are probably more vivid to him.

1. The Grey Squirrel

The story of the introduction of the grey squirrel into Great Britain[455, 647, 648] is fairly well known, although some versions differ somewhat from the true one. Thus it was *not* a single escape from the Regent's Park Zoo which led to the present widespread distribution of the species, but a number of separate, intentional introductions beginning about 1830 in North Wales, followed by one in Cheshire before 1880 and, undoubtedly the most important, an introduction in a private park in Bedfordshire in 1890. There can be no doubt that the spread of this animal was greatly assisted by man, both in allowing the escape of pet animals, and by the intentional release of squirrels in new areas. By 1930, at least thirty-three separate centres had been established and without man's help the advance of the grey squirrel would have been very much slower. Even allowing for this help, however, the spread of the grey squirrel has been a dramatic episode in English natural history; by 1930 it covered 1,400 square miles and, thirty years after it was founded, the Bedfordshire colony alone was slightly larger than this. Shorten gives the ratio between the areas occupied in 1944 and in 1937 as 708 to 274, based on a census of parish records. Her latest records show a further spread of grey squirrels to 199 more areas; the red squirrel has disappeared from 241 more areas since 1945. The success of the species is to some extent indicated by the fact that its density in English woodland is frequently several times that of the red squirrel in former times.

Here, then, is an example of a very rapid spread of an animal in a new geographical area from which it had hitherto been excluded by geographical boundaries. The rabbit in Australia or the corn boll-weevil in America are other well-known examples of the spread of animals all over the world since the improvement of transport methods.

2. British Titmice

In Britain we have six common tits, of which four woodland species live in rather similar situations. [394] The great tit and blue tit live in deciduous woodland, the crested tit and coal tit in conifers. Within each of these pairs the first is the larger of the two and each of the four species has distinct feeding habits. On the island of Tenerife there is only the blue tit, which breeds in conifers as well as deciduous woodland and is intermediate in size between the British great and blue tits, and has a more pointed, larger beak, approaching that of the crested tit. In the Balearic Isles, only the great tit occurs and this lives in both conifers and deciduous woodland. Lack and Southern give many similar examples, for instance in the genus *Phylloscopus*, in which *P. collybita*, the chiffchaff, and *P. trochilus*, the willow warbler, show very clear distinctions in their nesting territories in Britain, but in Tenerife, where only the first species occurs, this nests in vegetation characteristic of both, namely in low scrub as well as in woodland. However, on Tenerife two species of *Fringilla F. leydea* as well as the British *F. coelebs*, the chaffinch, occur and in this case the Tenerife chaffinch's range is more restricted than that of the British bird.

These are obvious examples, of which many more will be known to ornithologists in particular, of variation in the range of ecological characteristics of animals with the presence of related forms occurring in similar kinds of habitats. Continental ecologists use the terms "eurytopic" and "stenotopic" to mean the possession of a wide and a narrow ecological range respectively; evidently these features are not immutable characteristics of species but vary with the animals' circumstances. This sort of thing is most characteristic of living organisms and occurs in all taxonomic groups, although it is more easily appreciated in birds because of their conspicuousness.

3. The House-fly

Few people would dispute that the house-fly is a highly successful insect in the British Isles. Yet this species came originally from tropical latitudes and it still has a temperature optimum in the region of 25°C (77°F).[719] Even after several centuries in temperate regions it spends the greater part of the year dormant and almost confined to the vicinity of human habitations in many parts of its range. The house-fly, then, has extended its geographical range most successfully (it occurs up to the Arctic circle) in a rather special habitat, but still depends on the seasonal "oasis" of high temperature despite many years of living in such conditions.

4. Two British Spiders

It is a common feature of rare species to appear in seemingly surprising places for which even the expert is unable to suggest an explanation. For example, *Oxyptila nigrita* is a spider known locally from sandy places and steep chalk valleys in Britain. However, it was discovered[183] on a turf bank beside a woodland ride in Oxfordshire. These two habitats presumably share some features which are not easily appreciated, but such a very local distribution remains to be explained. *Scytodes thoracica*, another spider previously rare in Britain, is becoming more and more common in houses; on the continent of Europe it is a cave-dwelling species. In this case it is not too difficult to find resemblances between the climate of the English bedroom and a continental cave!

Some Generalizations about Animal Habitats

With the above examples of distribution of animals in mind, a few generalizations about the habitats of animals can be made. The observed range of animals obviously results from the interplay of many forces: in the first place, there is the geographical and historical accident which decided whether a species arrived in a particular area at all and, if so, how recently. This aspect of animal distribution is mainly the province of the zoogeographer, who studies the routes by which animals have moved from one area of the world to another. Secondly, the absence in a given area of a suitable combination of physical factors may preclude altogether, or limit severely the range of, a species there. Frequently a succession of suitable combinations of factors is needed for the full development of the species and it may be able to colonize a region but not breed there, for instance. The locust, *Locusta migratoria*,[741] which frequently invades southern England from Europe has only very rarely bred here in the wild, and the crossbill (*Loxia curvirostra*) frequently invades England but colonies always seem to die out after a few years; it breeds successfully in Ireland, however. A third generalization is that the presence of other organisms, plant and animal, can completely determine whether suitable conditions exist for the species. The range of these effects is very great: from the complete dependence of a herbivore on a particular plant or of a successful competitor in excluding a species from an area, to the relatively slight changes in habit such as those described above in the Tenerife birds.

Two recent examples of the spread of insects introduced by man into new habitats are an Indian beetle, followed by Duffey[182] and the little beetle *Cis bilamellatus* (Fig. 1) which lives in the birch-bracket fungus and has been recorded in detail by Paviour-Smith.[559] As in the case of the grey squirrel, *Cis* was present in Britain, having been introduced from Australia in herbarium specimens of the fungus, for a long time before suddenly starting to spread across the country at a rapid rate. Many further examples of ecological "explosions" of this nature and a discussion of their implications will be found in Elton's book.[204] The long period of "consolidation" which usually precedes the explosion is presumably associated with imperceptible but critical genetic changes on the part of the animal population.

Thus there is no "typical habitat" for an animal species in the strict sense. Clearly the "typical habitat" will vary geographically from place to place and also seasonally and between seasons according to the predominance of other species. Genetical studies have shown how the genetic structure of a population in the wild is constantly changing, for it is the result of an equilibrium involving changes in the ratios of genetic alleles and selective elimination of unsuccessful individuals. Further, the very size of the population influences the rate of spread of genes and the outcome of the balance (see Chapter 1,[454]). Both the

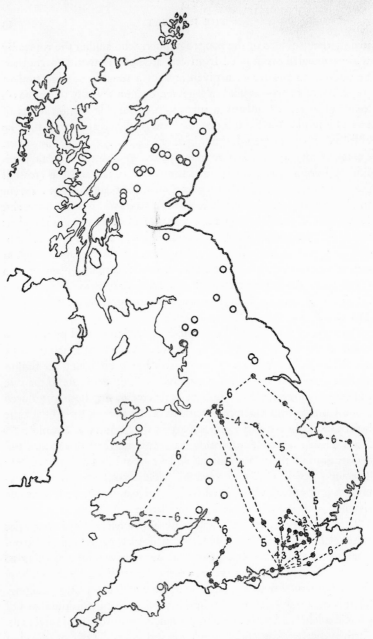

FIG. 1. HISTORY OF THE SPREAD OF *Cis bilamellatus* IN BRITAIN
(After Paviour-Smith, 1960)

O recorded absences – – ● – –, furthermost records for each period, linked
by dotted lines to show apparent spread. 1. 1884–1903; 2. 1904–23; 3. 1924–33;
4. 1934–43; 5. 1944–53; 6. 1954–59.

genetic structure of the population and also the "habitat" it occupies, therefore, are the result of a constantly-changing balance of forces, and the determination of the "typical habitat" of species is an impossible task.

The ecologist who wishes to limit the range of places in which to search for an animal, must detect the relevant factors in its surroundings from the animal's point of view as it were, and it is obvious from the many examples, such as the rare spider *Oxyptila nigrita*, that he is not able to do this as yet. It is often true to say that a good naturalist knows more about this subject, at least within a narrow range of species, than the best-equipped student of the physical environment with all his microclimate apparatus and other devices, and most people who have studied a group of animals will have had the experience of being able to tell "intuitively" that this or that is an area where a given species will be found—and have been right. It is often difficult to explain such intuitions to others and to make them objective.

The particular kinds of factors which determine habitat limits and the adaptations shown by animals are often surprising. External parasites may show strict localization of the areas they occupy, for example the parasites of mice[206] and those of beetles.[343] The Aceosejid mites found on Indonesian millipedes vary in shape according to the form of the spiracular depressions of their hosts.[216] The range of factors which distinguish the niches occupied by *Conus* shells on Hawaian coral reefs has recently been analysed.[371] Some animals occupy two habitats which seem to the human observer to have very little in common; for example the same species of uncommon spiders occur both in heath and fen conditions,[184] while a detailed study of the Lygaeid bug *Ischnodemus sabulei* has failed to show why it occurs not only among the very exposed *Ammophila arenaria* on sand dunes (as its name indicates) but also by the edges of streams and in reed swamps. It seems to occur virtually nowhere else.[728a] A study of ten species of beetles of the family Ciidae by Paviour-Smith[560] showed that five of these predominantly lived, and successfully produced young, in one group of bracket fungi and the other five in a second group. There was a good deal of differentiation within each group on the basis of seasonal succession and physical factors, and the chief factor discriminating the two groups appeared to be the mechanical structure of the hyphal system inside the bracket fungi, through which the beetles have to bore. The group adapted to tunnelling the "tougher" fungi were more often found in fungi of the "wrong" group.

Tolerance Range and Preferendum

Under the general heading of *autecology*, or the ecology of single species, much valuable work has been done on the physical environments of species, especially in support of economic entomology and the prediction of the probable reactions of species to new environments. Usually such work takes two main forms: determination of tolerance limits within which species can survive, and determination of preferenda, or those levels of the various physical factors at which the species congregate, when able to choose, in a range of conditions. The methods employed are well documented in the literature and only one or two typical examples are given here.

Two main types of preferendum apparatus are used: those in which a continuous gradient is maintained, and those in which the animal is offered the choice of two levels of the factor in question and, in a series of experiments, is made to show, by its distribution between two chambers, successively narrower preferences. The most widely-used, continuous-gradient, temperature-preferendum apparatus is that of Nieschulz.[517] This employs a long trough of iron which joins two boxes, one containing hot water and the other ice. The trough is fitted with a gauze floor and has a double-glass lid with an air space between. The animals are placed in the space between the gauze and the lid and the temperature in this space takes up an equilibrium gradient, normally between 10°C and 50°C. The animals are usually left for half an hour to find the preferred temperatures and the positions of the animals along the temperature gradient are recorded. The air temperature is measured by means of thermocouples or mercury thermometers.

The second type of apparatus usually consists of a vertical metal cylinder with a glass top, a metal bottom, and a gauze false bottom with the space beneath it divided vertically in two by a partition. When used for humidity work the two lower hemi-cylinders contain liquids, such as solutions of sulphuric acid or caustic soda of known density, which cause the air above them to reach known relative humidities. (Solomon[671] gives tables of strengths of solutions needed for such purposes. Additional values are given in tables and graphs published by Madge.[445b]) Alternatively, super-saturated solutions of various salts can be used for the same purpose[525]; these are more stable than acid and alkaline solutions but do not give a continuous range of humidities. The humidities achieved are most easily measured by means of Solomon's cobalt thyocyanate papers (Chapter 3), or one of the other microclimate measuring devices mentioned there. A great variety of devices has been made for testing repellent and attractant qualities of air-borne vapours and particles. These are based on the principle of offering the animal a choice of stationary or moving air masses and are thoroughly reviewed by Dethier.[173a]

The choice-chamber type of apparatus gives clear-cut results in cases where the continuous-gradient type does not, and is particularly useful where active animals such as spiders and ants are the subject of investigation.

An improved preferendum apparatus and many practical points in its operation are discussed by Van Heerdt et al.[747] and a more sophisticated version suitable both for gradient and choice experiments on several factors simultaneously by Platt et al.[580] The animal chamber in this case is in contact with three separate water baths each with its own circulation, and humidity is controlled by glycerol-water mixtures which are claimed[350] to maintain the same relative humidities over a wide range of temperature. This is an important point, for otherwise the relative humidity along a temperature gradient varies inversely with temperature, a factor which invalidates much experimentation in this field.[747] Special difficulties in making temperature preference measurements with small Arthropods are discussed by Madge.[445a] Other factors which must be fully understood include the following.

Various Difficulties Which Arise in the Interpretation of Preference Experiments

1. Stability of conditions is often hard to achieve but many species tend to be immobile when temperature falls and to show "distress activity" as it rises.[489] Again a short time at high temperature may cause a reversal in humidity-response due to desiccation.[747]

2. Physical factors cannot be considered in isolation. Resistance to desiccation and humidity preference vary with temperature.[191] In the house-fly a strong preference for dry air overrules temperature preference over a wide range, but given dry air, temperatures near 30°C are preferred.[153]

3. In the absence of direct observation of animals' reactions, misleading interpretations may be given, especially in a choice chamber with a sharp boundary, where great changes in activity may overshadow true choice effects.[800]

4. End effects, in which animals tend to cluster arbitrarily or at either end must be neutralized,[747] and easily overlooked effects of light and smell must be avoided.

5. Some confusion in the literature has resulted from the fact that different criteria of activity (such as speed of movement, proportion of time active, arbitrary indices of activity and respiration rate) have been used,[489] and even compared uncritically.

6. The animals themselves vary in their reactions according to the exact genetical composition of the population being studied, their particular physiological and behavioural state, and the recent history of the individuals. Acclimatization to non-optimal conditions is the rule rather than the exception, so that animals whose temperature is raised very slowly can survive higher temperatures than those taken straight from cold field conditions.[239] Further, if temperature is very slowly raised the animal's whole metabolism at a given temperature slowly decreases and approaches that under normal conditions. Krogh,[379] for instance, shows how the metabolic rate of individual animals becomes acclimatized in this way, and similar observations have been made by many later workers. The preferenda of animals frequently, but not always, change in a similar manner. For instance, those of the stable fly, *Stomoxys calcitrans*, from Germany and from South Africa, are the same, despite large climatic differences.[518] Analogous effects appear to operate between related species covering a wide geographical range. Thus[724] tropical and arctic sea-bottom animals have similar respiration rates at the temperatures which occur in their natural habitats, so that when arctic species are brought into warmer water their metabolic rates and other physiological activities are much greater than those of tropical species at the same temperatures. Ignorance of such effects as these have caused much confusion among not very physiologically-minded ecologists, and even among physiologists who should have known better.

7. Students of animal behaviour know well that the reactions of an animal are very dependent on its behavioural and physiological state. Among invertebrates little has been done on such problems where the fields of behaviour and ecology overlap. However, some examples of studies of this sort are the following—

(i) Nørgaard[523] found that the temperature preferendum of female *Pirata piraticus* (a wolf spider living in boggy places) changes from its normal level of 20° to 22°C to between 26° and 30° when it is carrying an egg cocoon. This elevated temperature (which is little short of 35°C where the animal succumbs to heat stupor) is apparently the optimum for the development of the eggs.

(ii) Beauchamp[39] showed that the reactions of the flatworm *Planaria alpina* to direction of water-flow in a stream are completely reversed according to whether eggs are being carried or not; this causes them to migrate upstream when gravid and downstream when the eggs have been shed.

(iii) Hecht[316] investigated the influence of water temperature on the egg-laying behaviour of the mosquito *Anopheles maculipennis* and found that this animal will die without laying rather than do so in water below 20°C. On the other hand Platt[579] found that mosquitoes conjugate and "dance" in the air only within a very narrow humidity range.

(iv) Hunger, sex and season have all been shown to influence the temperature preferences of a butterfly, to the extent of up to 5°C. [515]

(v) The preferred temperature and humidity and the optima for rate of development, mortality rate, egg output and rate of increase may all lie at different levels in the same species. [676]

The Limits of Autecological Methods

It is evident, therefore, that the value of the results obtained by methods such as those discussed in this chapter depends largely on the interpretation placed on them. It is obvious on reflection, too, that since many thousands of species often live side by side in any one place, early hopes of describing the habitats of all species by such methods would fail, even if the time and energy for making such experiments were available, because the physical "habitats" of the different species would overlap. Although useful modern work[520-4, 729, 747] has been done employing these techniques, especially in distinguishing between the ranges of a number of closely-related species which appear to live together, it has recently been demonstrated[48] that a more reliable and sensitive measurement of the ecological significance of physical factors is possible when their influence on the growth rate of the population is measured. This approach by Birch, which accepts the population as the working unit for ecological research, will be elaborated in Chapter 16. Briefly, he has shown that clearly-defined optima and tolerance ranges for effective population growth can be determined experimentally, that these are different for different closely-related species, and that his experimental results are consistent with the known ranges of the animals in their normal habitats.

There is, of course, much scope for further development of such work, for Birch's experiments were conducted with populations living under completely uniform conditions and could not be applied as they stand to solving problems of the distribution of field populations.

Chapter 3

MICROCLIMATES

In the last chapter the habitat was considered from the animal's point of view. In this chapter we must consider how far the factors which influence animals are related to the readings obtained by means of instruments and attempt to dispel the notion that the use of such instruments is outside the province of the biologist.

The Meteorologist's Approach

When we read in a newspaper that "Bournemouth had ten hours' sunshine yesterday" or that "the temperature on the Air Ministry roof reached a maximum of 80°F," we know that the first of these statements does not apply to the whole of Bournemouth, nor the second even to the whole of the Air Ministry roof. Everyone knows that, as you turn a corner from sun to shade, the air is colder, that the surface of objects in the sun is hotter than the air above; that cold air accumulates in hollows and valleys at night and that frost damage is often very local and depends on the contours of the land. All these effects are called "microclimatic" by the meteorologist.

Biologists are aware, however, that the climate in which animals actually live is very different from that measured in the meteorologist's "Stephenson Screens" at a height of 1·5 m above ground and, although climatic effects such as those measured here are of interest to them, it is obvious that they must inquire further in order to understand the conditions surrounding, say, a small invertebrate living among vegetation or near the surface of the soil. The word "ecoclimate" is sometimes used in this sense.

The fundamental book from the meteorologist's approach is that of Geiger[247] which in its successive editions pays more and more attention to the climates which influence plants and animals. A knowledge of this work is an essential preliminary for the ecologist working in this field, although it is concerned with effects which are, on the whole, too remote from the small terrestrial organisms.

The importance and magnitude of microclimates in the conventional sense is illustrated by Geiger, when he remarks that the daily difference of temperature between Assaba, in the Libyan desert, and Alexandria, on the shores of the Mediterranean, is frequently exceeded by that between the actual ground surface and the air a few feet above it in the same meadow anywhere in Europe.

The Ecologist's Approach

Much recent work on the ecological significance of microclimates is due to the late Professor Krogh and his followers in Denmark; the work of Nøgaard and of Haarløv discussed below belongs to this school. These workers were perhaps the first to take seriously the attempt to measure the true conditions in which animals occur and to relate their findings with laboratory experiments and with field observations.

The Measurement of Microclimates

The description of methods for making measurements of micro-climates is scattered over a very wide literature. A paper by Findlay[222] reviews methods used in mammalian physiology. In an appendix to this chapter a review of the more practical references is attempted.

The main differences between the biological and the physical approach to microclimatology result from biologists being more interested in the climate as it affects living conditions than in the mechanism of production of the climate. Thus in measuring light, for instance, we are concerned not only with intensity but also with spectral content, which may be quite different among vegetation. Unpigmented Collembola of the Onychiuridae family are killed in a few minutes when exposed to sunlight containing the ultra-violet component. Air temperature, air pressure and air movements are important factors which must be measured by instruments capable of insertion into small spaces without altering the conditions. This applies even more forcibly to air humidity.

The Relation between Biological Effects and the Readings of Instruments

The dampness of the air is usually expressed as the relative humidity (R.H.), which is the ratio of the quantity of water vapour present in the air at a given moment divided by the amount which would be present if the air were fully saturated *at the same air temperature and pressure*. The last seven words are important because relative humidity varies automatically with changing temperature and pressure, even when the quantity of water per cubic metre stays the same.

The saturation deficit, on the other hand, is the amount in grammes per cu m or in millibars vapour pressure by which the water vapour concentration or the vapour pressure is below saturation and therefore measures the drying power of the air; this does not fluctuate with temperature through the day as relative humidity does. It is generally considered to be a better measure of humidity from a biological point of view, although Dakshinamurty (see Chapter 2) was unable to distinguish between the two scales in his study of house-flies.[153]

The evaporation rate is an extremely complicated factor dependent on wind speed, saturation deficit, temperature and the nature of the surface; it is often measured directly, but no standard evaporimeter has been agreed upon.

It will be realized that the physical factors into which climatic conditions can be analysed, the quantities measured by instruments, and the influences which are significant for living organisms, do not necessarily correspond; Table 2 represents an attempt to indicate the relationships between these three sets of factors.

The lines in Table 2 link together those factors and measurements which are related. Thus in the "effects measured" column, evaporation rate results from the interaction of air movement, solar radiation and air humidity. In column 1, the temperature of the animal is determined by the interplay of humidity, solar radiation received and by air movement. It will be seen that the biologically significant factors by no means always correspond with the effects which can be measured by instruments.

Some Results of Microclimate Work

TOPOGRAPHICAL EFFECTS. Results of microclimatic investigations on the meteorological scale are fairly well known and topographic effects of this sort will not be repeated here. On a smaller scale, however, a considerable amount of work of biological interest has been done in connexion with "windbreaks" in the United States, Russia and Northern Europe.[26, 86, 248, 408, 450, 801] This work has practical implications for the yields of agricultural crops in particular.

In general, any type of barrier destroys the normal laminar flow of wind and results in the production of an area of eddies immediately behind the barrier, followed by a turbulent region. A solid barrier,

TABLE 2
Correspondence of climatic factors.

Biologically Significant	Primary Physical Factors	Effects Measured	Meteorologists' Methods	Micro-methods
Oxygen lack and other effects	AIR PRESSURE	AIR PRESSURE	Barometer	
Saturation deficit	HUMIDITY	Relative HUMIDITY	Dew-point / Hair / Wet and dry	Co salts (Solomon) / Dew-point (Köie) / Hair (Krogh) / Wet and dry (Penman) / H_2SO_4 (T-Nielsen) / Conductivity
Air temperature		Air temperature	Hg and alcohol thermometers / Bimetal	Hg thermometer / Bimetal (Krogh) / Thermocouple / Elec. resistance
Temperature of animal and surface	SOLAR RADIATION	Surface temperature	Nil	Thermocouple / Elec. resistance
		Received radiation (total)	Thermopile / Integrator (Buxton)	Nil
Light intensity		Light intensity	Sunshine recorder	Photocell
Light spectrum		Light spectrum	Spectrometer	
Dispersal	AIR MOVEMENT	Wind speed	Anemometer	Thermistor anemometer (Penman)
Damage		Wind direction	Wind vane	
Evaporation		Evaporation rate	Atmometer	Evaporimeter
Soil moisture	PRECIPITATION	Soil moisture	pF measurements, etc.	Boyoucos block
Insulation by snow		Precipitation	Rain gauge, etc.	Miniature rain gauge

such as a wall, is followed by an eddy region in which the wind speed is low and small particles, such as snowflakes, seeds, etc., are deposited, extending to ten or fifteen times the height of the wall to the leeward. This is followed by a turbulent band about fifty times the wall's height in thickness, in which turbulent winds may cause mechanical damage to crops and in which the climate tends to be colder and drier than normal. A narrow, windward belt is somewhat sheltered and more favourable to crop growth. It is evident that an impermeable barrier is not an ideal shelter for a crop, but if the barrier is made more permeable to the wind the region of turbulence is reduced at the expense of the eddy-current region. With a barrier such as that constituted by a normal hedge, in which about half the wind passes through and half rises over the hedge, there is virtually no turbulent area at all. The tendency for hedges to be more permeable at the ground than high up also enhances their value as sheltering screens. In the eddy-current region the mean temperature tends to be slightly higher than normal in the morning and colder in the afternoon; this, if anything, is beneficial as it results in the ground warming up earlier in the day. The humidity is definitely higher and, in areas such as the Russian Steppes, this effect is greatly enhanced because the greater part of the annual precipitation occurs in winter in the form of snow. Artificial planting of windbreaks has been shown to have very beneficial effects on crop yields, a number of examples being given by Wendt. American maize yields have been increased by as much as ten bushels to the acre. When the breaks are planted in parallel rows, their effect is cumulative provided the spacing is not greater than about a hundred times the height.

A very detailed study of the microclimate, including both air and soil measurements in different directions and distances from a windbreak has been made by Aslyng.[26] He showed that a slightly increased risk of late frosts in the sheltered region is usually balanced by the higher humidity which reduces the actual damage to plants. No differences in soil moisture were detected but potential evapotranspiration (see p. 46) was reduced.

SMALL-SCALE EFFECTS: TEMPERATURE. The climate of the air near the ground depends on two sets of factors: those which result from the mere presence of the ground, and those which result from the nature of the ground surface and covering. A most useful concept, formulated by Geiger, is that of the "outer active surface," which is the surface at which absorption of the sun's radiant energy mainly occurs and from which it is mainly radiated. Whether this is the true surface of the ground itself or, as in most vegetated regions, the zone of maximum leaf development, it is the level at which the highest day-time and the lowest night-time temperatures are found. In other words, it is here that the most extreme climate occurs, and just how great the variation can be will be seen from a few examples.

The temperature at the surface among the Finnish sand dunes[378] on a sunny day reaches a maximum of 47°C. At the same time, the air 30 cm above the ground was only 29°C and that of the sand at 10 cm depth was 17°C. At a depth of 40 cm the temperature was constant all day at about 21°C. Even more extreme figures[247] have been obtained for an asphalt pavement (Fig. 2), while the reverse effect occurs at night when the surface was 3°C *colder* than the air above. This is due to outward radiation from the earth, but the temperature gradient is not nearly so marked as in the day-time owing to the much lower penetrating power of the longer wave radiations from the earth and their susceptibility to reflection back towards the earth.

It has recently been shown[396] that the lowest temperatures at night occur two or three inches above the surface. Although the physical reason for this is obscure the importance from the point of view of frost damage is great.

The nature of the soil surface has a great influence on the amount of heat required to bring about a given change in temperature: colour, texture and water content are of outstanding importance, the first two governing the ratio of absorbed to reflected energy, the last, owing to the high latent heat of vaporization and high specific heat of water, governing the rate of rise of temperature.

In an experiment on the effect of colour on rate of germination of seedlings, Ludwig and Harper[422] measured maximum temperatures to 6°C higher and minima up to 2°C higher under the surface of black as compared with white soils. Yellow and brown soils gave intermediate results and the time of germination varied in proportion from twenty to thirty-one days. An extreme example of the effects of soil texture is provided by Cloudsley-Thompson's[121] study of microclimates under stones. Even within a wood the range of temperature beneath a 3-in.-thick stone was halved compared with that of the air, while on the upper surface the range was three times as great.

The effect of plants is normally to reduce the steepness of the temperature gradients above bare earth and to change the height at which the outer active surface occurs. The effects result from the distribution of the outer active "surface" in depth, the damping effect of the water produced by and contained in the plants, and a number of

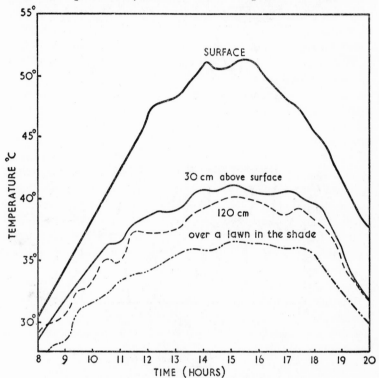

FIG. 2. TEMPERATURES ABOVE AN ASPHALT PAVEMENT

other factors. The formation of dew at night, with the resultant liberation of latent heat, is one of the factors which reduces the magnitude of the cooling effect.

Geiger made a series of temperature measurements in beds of different types of vegetation throughout the year and the results, which illustrate some of the principles just enumerated, are represented in the diagrams (Fig. 3). The coincidence of the daily maximum with the outer active surface—the upper leaf surface in the case of the antirrhinums, and distributed down the stems in the case of the rye—

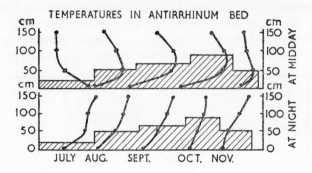

TEMPERATURES IN ANTIRRHINUM BED

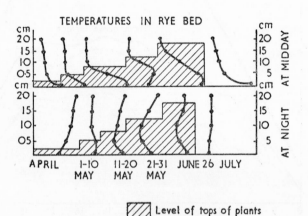

TEMPERATURES IN RYE BED

⬚ Level of tops of plants

●———● 1 °C

FIG. 3. TEMPERATURES IN BEDS OF DIFFERENT TYPES OF VEGETATION: SEASONAL CHANGES

(*top*) Antirrhinum bed; (*bottom*) rye bed.

The shading indicates the mean heights of the plants in each month. One characteristic temperature-distribution graph is given for each month, the relative temperature at the scaled height intervals being represented by displacement along the horizontal axis.

is particularly clear. The inversion occurs at night in the former, but is prevented altogether in the latter, because of the closeness of the stems which impede the free flow of air. Similar results have been obtained from mixed meadows.[783] When a definite layer of matted grass stems occurs such effects are exaggerated, Waterhouse[785] measured summer midday temperature differences of about 8°C per 10 cm depth in the grass mat compared with 1°C in the grass stems above. The blanketing effect at night was correspondingly great, causing the soil surface to remain at least 3°C above air temperatures.

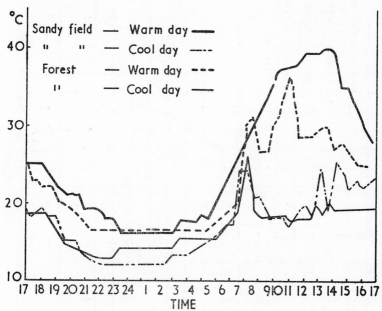

FIG. 4. COMPARISON OF SANDY FIELD AND FOREST CLIMATE ON COLD AND ON WARM DAY

Measurements[520] of daily temperature range in different habitats show the influence of different soil types (Fig. 4). A field soil is warmer and shows a greater range of temperature than that of a forest, while the soil of a bog is cooler. The effect of the forest in reducing daily fluctuations is very marked. A further figure (Fig. 5) shows the much greater daily range of temperature at the surface of a *Sphagnum* bog than 10 cm below the surface of the moss.

Haarløv and Petersen[293] made 9,000 temperature readings taken in or on sitka spruce and mountain pine trees and were able to relate the temperatures, which are important for wood-boring insects, for

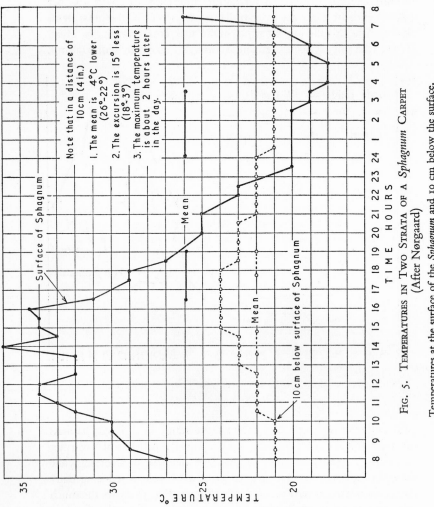

FIG. 5. TEMPERATURES IN TWO STRATA OF A *Sphagnum* CARPET
(After Norgaard)

Temperatures at the surface of the *Sphagnum* and 10 cm below the surface.

instance, to such factors as the distance within the tree, its diameter, presence of bark scales on the surface, the extent to which the forest has been thinned and the compass direction of the particular part of the tree. South-west facing parts are the warmest as the cumulative effect of the day's sun and the lower altitude of the afternoon sun make the sun's rays more nearly perpendicular to the surface. A further set of readings by Haarløv[292] show very marked differences in temperature in the north- and south-facing slopes of ant-hills in grassland.

Some readings taken near Oxford by means of the continuous recorder are illustrated in Fig. 6 (pages 32 and 33). These show the temperatures of the air, bark surface, beneath the bark and within the wood for two logs, one exposed within the wood and the other in an open clearing. The figures illustrate in particular the marked influence of shade on both the maximum and the night minimum, the high temperatures reached in the sun at the surface, the considerable delay of the daily cycle of temperature as the logs are penetrated and the higher mean temperature of the log in the open. The great variation in both the normal distribution and the chances of survival of insect larvae according to the actual position in a log, have been related to the extreme temperatures beneath the bark when fully exposed to the sun.[634]

In deep media such as soil the extent to which temperature fluctuations are smoothed out and also delayed is often surprising. In general, soil is warmer than the air throughout the winter and colder in summer, an inversion of the temperature profile occurs in early spring and autumn. In a forest in Aberdeenshire in 1952 Coutts[132, 133] measured annual excursions of weekly means at screen height, 1 in. depth, 6 in. depth and 18 in. depth of 38°C, 22°C, 15°C, and 13°C respectively. By 6 in. depth the weekly mean does not fall below freezing point and by 12 in. the diurnal fluctuations are hardly detectable. A comparable study made near Oxford under *Brachypodium* grassland[438] with a considerable mat of postrate stems shows similar results and even at 5 cm the annual cycle of temperature was delayed about a month compared with that in the air. In N. Dakota[587] frost penetrates to 4 ft depth and annual excursions were: in air, 26°C; 1 in. depth, 17°C; 1 ft depth, 15°C; 6 ft depth, 12°C.

Attempts to generalize from information of this kind have been made by several authors. Kristensen[377] estimated that, in Denmark, a temperature change at the surface travels at a rate of 18 days per metre depth and that about 5 per cent of the solar radiation incident on the soil in summer is stored in the soil as heat and liberated during the winter. A more rigorous treatment, allowing for variations in thermal properties with depth, has been published[429] and Coutts[133] considers the practical problem of predicting soil temperatures from minimum and maximum screen temperatures.

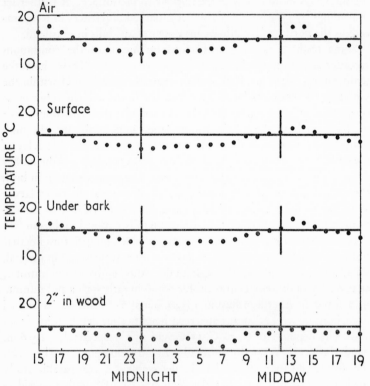

FIG. 6. (a) TEMPERATURES IN AND NEAR LOGS: DIURNAL CHANGES
Log in shade.

OTHER FACTORS. No consistent description of the effect of other microclimatic factors on the environment of animals is possible because so little work has been done in this field. Todd's and Nørgaard's work on the effect of humidity on harvestmen and spiders, which is discussed in Chapter 5, indicates how important this factor can be in limiting the habitats occupied by species in the field. Measurements have been made on the humidity in the fleece of sheep[162] and related to the development of the larvae of the sheep blowfly, *Lucilia sericata*. It was shown that conditions are rather rarely sufficiently humid and thus the sporadic occurrence of "strike" in this country and its virtual absence from many continental countries was explained.

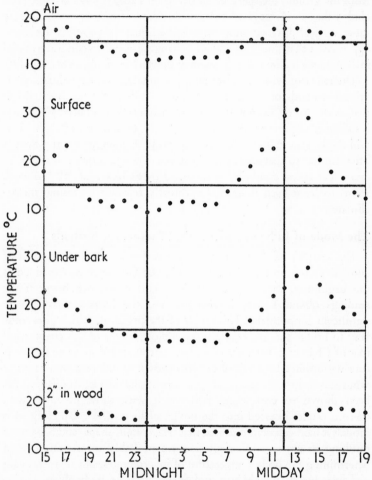

FIG. 6. (*b*) TEMPERATURES IN AND NEAR LOGS: DIURNAL CHANGES
Log in open.

In the study of microclimate in grass mentioned above, Waterhouse[785] measured humidity and wind speed as well as temperature.

He found that the grass mat and even, to a lesser extent an under-story of clover, were able to retain a layer of nearly saturated air next to the ground at a time in summer when adjacent short grass was completely withered. The wind profile was equally steep and at levels below 20 cm from the ground the speed never exceeded 1 m.p.h. Waterhouse concluded that an insect is offered a wide range of climate within a very short vertical distance under these conditions; however, it should be appreciated that under the rapidly changing weather conditions usual in Britain such climatic systems may themselves change very rapidly.

The effect of wind on plant and, presumably also on animal, metabolism depends on mean temperature. Wilson[820] has pointed out that, in the Arctic, evaporative cooling may result in a fall of 7°C which is sufficient to prevent all metabolic activity, even on sunny days. This will apply also in mountainous regions of Britain where the flora is often similar to that studied by Wilson. The question of evaporative loss under forest conditions is discussed by Selleck et al.[644] No work seems to have been done that is directly relevant to animal microclimates.

The Mode of Influence of Physical Factors on Animals

This chapter has been mainly concerned with the measurement of climatic factors in the vicinity of animals; however, as explained at the beginning, there is not an exact correspondence between the readings obtained with instruments and the influences which are significant for animals. This aspect of the problem, which goes some way to bridge the gap between the subject-matter of this chapter and that of Chapter 2, has only recently received attention. The temperature within metal models of insects exposed to different conditions of wind speed, ground temperature gradient and incident radiation, has been shown to correspond fairly well with those obtained with thermocouples inserted into the bodies of locusts.[557] By using such models it has been demonstrated that size, colour, shape, and behaviour resulting in changes of orientation are probably most important in determining the body temperature of invertebrates, but that heat gain and loss due to metabolism and evaporation of body fluids are insignificant. Measurements of the temperatures within small insect larvae and pieces of clay of the same size, in the absence of radiation, showed that passive evaporation and condensation of water when they were moved from saturated to non-saturated air caused great temperature changes in both.[784] Pubescent larvae, owing to the lesser gain and loss of water, maintain a more equable temperature.

Experimental studies reveal that the efficacy of water loss as a means of controlling temperature in Arthropods is more marked for woodlice than for insects; they have the ability to lower their temperatures over short periods by this means and this is of considerable survival value.[191]

The *effective* temperature encountered by mammals, which are capable of temperature regulation by sweating and other specialized mechanisms, is a topic of importance in the fields of medicine, air-conditioning and factory welfare. Its assessment requires that allowance be made for humidity (which reduces the efficiency of evaporative cooling), air movement and also the gain and loss of radiant heat from the surroundings. Somewhat arbitrary formulae have been devised to combine these factors and they are discussed by Bedford.[40]

The Role of Microclimate Studies in Ecology

Although the subject-matter of this chapter would be more adequately covered by a book it may have served to introduce the ecologist and the potential ecologist to the field and to make it clear that reliable observations can be made without elaborate equipment or an extensive knowledge of physical meteorology. This is important because studies involving physical measurements are often avoided by biologists, and where physical measurements are appropriate they have the advantage of being subject, as a rule, to much smaller errors than biological ones. It should be stressed, however, that the enhanced value of *continuous* records is out of all proportion to the extra trouble involved. Owing to the kind of time relationships exhibited by Fig. 6, comparisons which are based on single readings can be very misleading. Further, some general knowledge of climatology[47] is essential for those who wish to do more than copy the methods of others.

Appendix

SOME METHODS FOR MICROCLIMATE WORK

Temperature Recording and Measurement

The normal mercury thermometer has many applications even in microclimate work, but there are four important factors which restrict its field of use. These are its large size, the tendency for heat to be conducted by it from the measuring bulb along the stem, the proximity of the sensing and reading parts of the instrument, and the fact that it cannot be used to measure air temperature when exposed to any source of radiant heat, owing to direct absorption by the bulb itself. Differences of 5°C in a centimetre are commonly encountered along gradients near surfaces, and in such cases a much smaller sensitive element is essential. On the other hand, valuable information has been obtained by the use of such thermometers in shaded places. As long ago as 1873 Ebermayer demonstrated that the daily range of temperature inside logs is much less than that outside in the open air. Geiger used mercury thermometers in his classic researches described above, on the relationships between temperature and height above ground in flower beds. Mercury thermometers have also been used for the indirect measurement of leaf temperatures by calorimetry, and for measuring long-term soil temperature changes at a considerable depth, where diurnal fluctuations are eliminated. [132, 642]

The thermocouple, however, is usually a more practical instrument for microclimate work. This is simply a pair of wires of dissimilar metals joined at both ends. Copper and constantan are usually chosen, and the copper wire is interrupted to include a galvanometer. The current flowing in the galvanometer depends on the difference in temperature of the two junctions and also on the resistance of the circuit, the junctions acting as a source of about 50 microvolts per degree Centigrade difference in temperature. If it is desired to make the maximum use of the potential difference the galvanometer can be replaced by a potentiometer, but since accuracies of about $\frac{1}{10}$°C can be achieved with a good galvanometer, such as the Cambridge "Unipivot" type, the more elaborate apparatus is not usually employed in the field. The main advantages of the thermocouple are that it can be made easily and cheaply. The two wires are best joined by arc welding, the thermocouple being connected in series with a $\frac{1}{4}$-ohm resistance to the positive side of a supply of about 20 volts and low internal resistance such as an accumulator and the junction is touched against a piece of carbon rod connected to the negative terminal. (However, soldered joints, if carefully made, can be quite satisfactory. [34]) Secondly, thermocouples can be made extremely small for insertion into small cracks or even into minute animals. On the other hand, the galvanometer is an expensive, delicate instrument, and the calibration is affected by the lengths of the leads, which can only be a few feet in length when used with a galvanometer owing to the low resistance of the whole system. Further, if the wires are to be reasonably robust they will also conduct heat away from the site of measurement.

A type of thermocouple employing the very soft alloys of antimony and bismuth has recently been introduced; these produce a much greater potential difference, but have to be supported in glass capillaries and are very fragile, so they would appear to be of rather limited application. New techniques have been developed for the manufacture of very small thermocouples (e.g. in hypodermic needles) [175, 687, 691] and for their use in recording rapid temperature changes. [398]

Normal thermocouples are unsuitable for use in the field with recording instruments because amplification is necessary before any normal recording apparatus can be used and this would require a costly amplifier, usually operated by mains supplies. A fairly simple, battery-operated amplifier for continuous recording is described by Denton. [173] Platinum resistance thermometers, however, can be made to operate a continuous recorder without an amplifier. These are simply lengths of platinum wire whose resistance changes with temperature. They are of moderately high resistance, usually about 100 ohms, and therefore can be used with fairly long leads; they are widely used for industrial purposes. The recording meter is expensive because the change in resistance per degree Centigrade is only a few per cent and the elements themselves are too large for many purposes.

A greatly improved type of resistance thermometer (produced in Britain by Standard Telephones and Cables Ltd.) is the "Thermistor." This is a "semi-conductor" device related to the transistor and the germanium diode and takes the form of a small bead less than a cubic millimetre in volume. The resistance of this varies greatly with temperature and in the opposite sense from that of a metal; thus, an increase of 15°C is sufficient to halve the resistance. The bead is mounted at the end of an evacuated tube, containing connecting leads which are joined to the bead by extremely fine platinum wires, with the result that there is little heat transfer from the bead to the connecting leads. Thermistors can be used in a Wheatstone bridge circuit in conjunction with a cheap meter and torch battery for measuring spot temperatures, can be placed in almost all places where a thermocouple would have been employed previously and can be used in conjunction

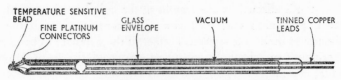

TEMPERATURE SENSITIVE BEAD

FINE PLATINUM CONNECTORS

GLASS ENVELOPE

VACUUM

TINNED COPPER LEADS

FIG. 7. SECTION THROUGH A TYPE F THERMISTOR

with very long leads because the resistance of the element is high—
10 ohms to 100,000 ohms, according to type.

Thermistors have been used in a simple bridge circuit (see Fig. 8).[474]
Measurements among potato crops provided useful information about
the environment of harmful aphids.[73, 74, 569] The possibility of using
long leads and the absence of any kind of amplifier (resulting in very

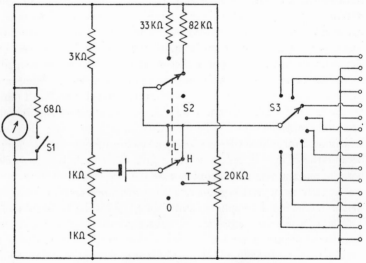

FIG. 8. A SIMPLE THERMISTOR THERMOMETER
(Based on that of Mortimer and Moore 1953)

With this instrument eight probes can be read to an accuracy of about 0·02°C
over the ranges −5°C to 25°C and 20°C to 40°C. Components—

Meter: Baldwin Bridge balance indicator, 3,000 Ω
Potentiometer: 1 KΩ Helical from P.X. Fox Ltd.
Battery: Vidor Kalium V 0106.
Thermistors: S.T.C. Type F, 2,311/300.
Switch S 1 Spring-loaded sensitivity shunt
 S 2 2-pole 4-way wave change type positions for: OFF, TEST
 BATTERY, HIGH RANGE and LOW RANGE
 S 3 Selector switch for eight thermistors.

low power demands, which can easily be satisfied by dry batteries) makes the construction of a battery-operated, continuous recorder possible.[442] This apparatus records the temperature of twelve thermistors once an hour for a week (2,304 readings) on a little over a metre of film. Some typical results are given in Fig. 6. The ratio of accuracy to maximum range is about 1 per cent, so that readings can be relied on to half a degree when a range of 40°C is used.

The thermistor can be used in conjunction with a silver voltameter in an extremely simple device for integrating mean temperatures over any desired period.[438] Information of this sort is required for interpreting metabolic-activity measurements (see Chapter 6).

Extremely small thermistors are now available and can be used to replace thermocouples—for example inside hypodermic needles.[181] At the other extreme, where reduction in physical size is unimportant, thermistors can be made at very low cost.[289] These have the advantages that much greater powers can be dissipated and that both the range and the sensitivity can be fully controlled. They consist of a solution of water-glass in a glass tube capillary with platinum electrodes at the two ends. Their use is limited to temperatures below 100°C, and they can only be used with alternating current, but they can be so made as to stand full mains voltage and are much more sensitive than the usual type.

Besides being used in many simple thermometers, the bimetallic strip (consisting of strips of two dissimilar metals joined so that they bend when heated or cooled) is the usual temperature-sensitive element in the clockwork thermograph, in which a pen moves over a revolving drum and writes a continuous temperature record. This apparatus is limited in its application to microclimate work on account of the large bimetal used, but a miniature version[381] has been extensively used in Denmark, for example, by Nørgaard[520] (see Chapter 2) and in studies on the effects of clothing and air conditioning on the climate next to the human skin. This instrument is a combined thermo-hygrograph, recording humidity as well as temperature. It is constructed from a good quality Swiss watch whose hour hand is replaced by a light turntable. On this are mounted two levers actuated respectively by the bimetallic spiral and a humidity-sensitive hair. The tips of the levers bear fine points which project upwards to touch the flat watch glass, which is smoked, and which can be easily changed. As the turntable rotates a circular line is traced by each point and the distance from the centre of the watch is proportional to the factor being measured. The glasses are read in a special holder under a microscope and accuracies of 0·1°C and 5 per cent R.H. within the range 30 per cent to 90 per cent R.H. are possible. The provision of continuous records was a great advance on anything invented previously, but the apparatus is much larger than the thermocouple or the thermistor.

The bimetal has also been used in an instrument[150a, 150b] which was left under the snow throughout the winter in Norway and provided a summarized frequency distribution diagram of the temperatures encountered during that period. This was achieved by mounting a broad pointer with a narrow radial slit on the free end of the bimetal. It was arranged to move between a radioactive source and a piece of photographic plate in such a way that the radiation was intercepted for all but a very narrow band on the plate. The fogging of the plate, as measured by a photographic densitometer, is a measure of the proportion of the time a particular temperature occurred, while the position on the plate indicates the corresponding temperature value. Such a mechanism could, of course, be used to measure other climatic factors and, if used with a moving coil meter, could be remote from the measuring position.

Plastic materials such as nylon and Dacron have considerable co-efficients of expansion and it has been suggested[581, 582] that these could be used for making "bimetals" of greatly enhanced sensitivity. Further, since the coefficient depends on the treatment to which the material has been subjected one can vary the coefficients (unstretched nylon has a large positive coefficient, while that which has been stretched to five times its original length has a large negative coefficient) and it is thus possible to make "bimetals" which are insensitive to temperature, but which can serve as hygrometers of greatly enhanced sensitivity. These suggestions have not, as yet, been tried out in microclimate work.

Humidity Measurement

Although the hair hygrometer, as used in Krogh's instrument, is capable of considerable accuracy when carefully calibrated, it is not consistent under very wet conditions—often those of greatest interest in ecological work—and is useless below 30 per cent R.H. Its long-term accuracy is poor since the hair gradually becomes stretched, especially in cheaper instruments where stronger springs are used. There has, therefore, been a constant search for greater accuracy, smaller size and for a device adaptable to continuous recording. Although all of these have been achieved separately, they have not so far been combined in a single instrument.

The most practical and widely-used method[669, 675] for very small spaces makes use of small pieces of special thin paper soaked in solutions of a cobalt salt whose colour changes with the relative humidity of the surrounding air. This property is well known to apply to cobalt chloride whose crystals change from red to blue when moved from damp to dry conditions. The change in this salt is most marked in the region of 50 per cent R.H. and for ecological purposes cobalt thiocyanate, which has its greatest colour change in the region of 75 per cent is more useful. The paper is dipped in a standard manner, dried, and then exposed to air held at a series of known humidities by means of sulphuric acid or potassium hydroxide solutions.[671] After about half an hour the papers are quickly mounted in liquid paraffin between a piece of colourless glass and a white background. Papers exposed in an environment whose humidity is to be determined are compared with the standards, and relative humidity can be estimated to about 2 per cent accuracy. Since there is almost no practical lower limit of size for the papers they can be used in very small spaces indeed.

The only disadvantage of this method is the length of time required for an exposure and the impossibility of adapting the method for continuous recording, but the accuracy is sufficient for most practical purposes.

A different method,[516] which is very accurate at high humidities and secures quicker readings, depends on the balance between evaporation and absorption of water vapour from sulphuric acid solutions of different strengths. A series of capillary tubes is made, partly filled with acid of different strengths, then sealed at both ends. To determine the humidity of a given air sample the contents of the tubes are exposed by breaking one end, and by trial and error is found that strength of acid which tends neither to increase nor decrease in volume, as indicated by the meniscus of the acid "bulging outward" or "caving inward." In fact, the method seems to have been largely replaced by the cobalt-paper method especially where many readings are to be taken.

The "Dunmore" element of the American radiosonde apparatus[186] has long attracted those interested in microclimate work and has been developed further to some extent.[192, 372] The principle of this method is that the electrical conductivity of a coating, containing usually a polyvinyl plastic and a hygroscopic salt, will vary with the humidity of the surrounding air. A double, interwound spiral of platinum wire on an insulating rod is dipped in such a mixture and dried; the resistance between the two spirals will then vary with relative humidity. The main difficulties, which do not appear to have been overcome entirely, are that the resistance is also dependent on temperature, which must therefore be read simultaneously, that the characteristics of the device change with age, necessitating frequent recalibration, and that when exposed to a saturated atmosphere the element must always be recalibrated. Earlier versions also suffered from a marked hysteresis (different readings being obtained according to whether the humidity is increasing or decreasing). Køie, who uses glass wool and no plastic nor hygroscopic salt, does not mention this difficulty and nor does Edney, so presumably it has been overcome. A similar principle has apparently been used in a very small unit claimed to have a very rapid response and to operate under saturated conditions.[767] Another variant of the Dunmore principle involves the passage of a fairly heavy current through the plastic coating until its resistance is increased and comes into equilibrium with surrounding air. The humidity is calculated from temperature measurements of a resistance thermometer built into the probe. The probes are very expensive, demand a mains-derived stabilized power supply and generate too much heat for most microclimatic purposes; however, the stability is superior to other Dunmore type methods and it is possible that the principle may be adapted for field use. A commercial version is made by Phillips.

The effects of vapour pressure on the capacity and leakage resistance of a miniature electrolytic capacitor may provide the basis of a very compact and reliable electrical humidity element.[21, 147] An anodized aluminium wire (the oxide layer acting as an insulator) is coated with a second conducting layer and the capacity and leakage resistance between the inner and outer electrodes so formed are found to vary with the vapour pressure of the surrounding air. The capacity, which is high owing to the very small distance between the electrodes, varies with vapour pressure (and hence absolute humidity) in a manner almost independent of temperature up to about 50 per cent R.H.; after that it becomes more dependent on temperature. The d.c. leakage resistance increases exponentially with humidity but is very temperature sensitive and, on the whole, appears less promising as an indicator of humidity.

The main advantage of the methods discussed so far is that they can be used in very confined spaces without appreciably altering the humidity of the air. Where this demand is less stringent the "wet and dry bulb" hygrometer can be adapted or a dew-point method can be used. [34, 372] In the latter case the appearance of condensation is indicated electrically, thus permitting the apparatus to be hidden from the operator. The need for a cooling mechanism and the considerable effect on the environment normally preclude the use of this method, but if a hygroscopic coating is used (as in the Dunmore element just descibed) the effective dew-point is raised. This principle is adopted in a hygrometer made by the Foxboro Co. (U.S.A.) and used for climate work by Aslyng [26] (see p. 25). The need for a heating coil once more limits this method to climatic rather than microclimatic work.

Wet and dry bulb "psychrometers" as they are called have been made using small bimetal elements, [699] thermistors [569] and also thermocouples. [41, 588, 349] The first two have been used with recorders in the field. A major problem with psychrometers is the provision of a reliable water supply; it is often necessary to feed a wick from a large reservoir above the probe. Alternatives are to dip the wet bulb into water mechanically before each reading [349] or to cause condensation on the junction by passing a current through it prior to reading and cooling it by the Peltier effect. [464] This can only be done at very high humidities.

Two reviews on humidity measurement should be consulted for further references and methods of calibration of hygrometers. [480, 568]

Radiation and Light Measurement

Total solar radiation is usually calculated from the rise in temperature of a black body suitably protected from cooling. Buxton's radiation integrator [85] uses a black thermometer bulb in an evacuated glass sphere; a simpler version [420] uses two unprotected thermometers placed side by side and separated only by a reflecting metal foil; one is exposed to radiation and the other is shaded. More sophisticated instruments use thermopiles (a number of thermocouples connected in series) with alternate junctions in sun and in shade. [254] Photoelectric cells are more selective in the range of radiation to which they respond, but the vacuum photocell (which must be connected to an amplifier) has a wider spectral range than the selenium type which, as in the photographic exposure meter, can operate a moving coil meter directly. Direct reading field instruments have been described for vacuum cells[535] and for the selenium type[180b] and integrators using vacuum cells have also been made.[535, 689, 689a] The selenium type have uses in rough work especially in closely similar localities but the considerable differences in spectral composition of direct and reflected light must be remembered in studies of cover density. It is difficult, when using photocells in woodland, to overcome the changes and contrasts due to the flecked light pattern; this has been partly achieved by using a special camera[214] but a further desirable stage would be the development of a recording instrument. In rough work integrated light values for periods of about one day can be obtained by suitably exposing photo-sensitive paper as described by Friend.[236a] A portable photometer for measuring very low light intensities has also been described by Evans.[214]

The spectral composition of light is important to animals because both the visual sensitivity and also the physiological damage resulting from exposure vary with wavelength. Filters (especially the modern narrow band interference filters) in conjunction with photocells[373] would appear to lend themselves to work of this kind but little appears to have been done yet.

Wind-speed Measurement

The normal wind vane and cup anemometer are hardly applicable to microclimate work, although the exponential decrease in wind speed in the air close to the ground has been demonstrated by their use. A fan type anemometer is rather more sensitive but is still too large for small spaces and low air speeds. Recording mechanical anemometers for microclimatic work have also been described.[407, 635] A thermistor anemometer[569] is useful for measuring very low wind speeds. This uses a type of thermistor in which a heating element surrounds a naked sensitive bead. Over a range of speeds up to about 5 m.p.h. the extent to which the element is heated above the ambient air temperature is found to vary inversely with the air speed in a linear manner. Thus, by measuring the ambient temperature with a separate element, wind speed can be calculated. This device has the advantage of allowing simultaneous reading of temperature, humidity and wind speed by a single measuring or recording apparatus. Thermocouple anemometers have also been described in the literature[334] but the need for sensitive amplifiers normally precludes their use in the field. This however would appear to be a particularly suitable application of transistor amplifiers since the thermocouple, the transistor, and the recorder can all have relatively low impedances.

Some delightfully simple methods of measuring low wind speeds have been described by Wilson.[820] He uses ammonium chloride smoke and soap bubbles and times their rates of movement with a stop watch. The effects of air movements on animals have so far been almost entirely neglected by biologists, but it has been shown that they have a very marked effect on the behaviour of aphids.[702a]

Evaporation-rate Measurement

Evaporation rate depends on three factors: first, the temperature of the surface from which evaporation takes place (which in turn depends on the received radiation, the nature of the surface and air movements); secondly, the movement of air over the surface, and, thirdly, the saturation deficit of that air (also depending on a number of factors as explained above). It is hardly surprising, therefore, that although a number of "evaporimeters" or "atmometers" have been devised, they do not agree in their readings. The best known of these is the Livingstone type, which incorporates a porous sphere, filled with water, and a means of measuring the quantity of water withdrawn from a reservoir to which the sphere is connected. This is a bulky instrument and a miniature version, much used in Denmark, consists of a small (1 cm diameter) sintered glass funnel connected to a capillary tube which is filled with water and graduated. The sintered surface is horizontal and it is important that the capillary should also be level. The rate at which the water is withdrawn from the capillary indicates the evaporation rate. A number of these instruments, suitably calibrated, can be used for comparing evaporation rates in different places simultaneously, but results cannot be expressed in absolute units and it is only by continuous observation that anything more than an integrated mean value can be obtained.

An even simpler version consists of a 1 cm disc of filter paper adhering by capillarity to the ground end of a capillary tube.[820]

On the topographical scale evaporation can be measured in principle by the loss of water from the surface of a large tank.[419] This changes the humidity status of the surrounding air and is not easily reconciled with conditions in the indigenous vegetation. A more useful concept to the ecologist is the "evapotranspiration," an index of the water balance of the area, including its vegetation. It is calculated from the flow of water draining from a large tank which has been built flush with the ground and planted with something approaching the surrounding vegetation. It has been shown that the potential evapotranspiration, measured by adding sufficient water to the tank, when rainfall is deficient, to keep the soil up to field capacity, provides results less influenced by local vegetational characteristics.[280] The potential evapotranspiration is the difference between the rainfall plus added water on the one hand and the loss by drainage on the other. It varies in temperate climates from negative values in winter to positive in summer. The actual evapotranspiration can be obtained by subtracting the water deficiency made good artificially. The shelter screen in Aslyng's experiments (see p. 25) reduced evaporation caused by air movement but increased that from raised temperatures; these two factors varied with overall weather conditions but the potential evapotranspiration as a whole was reduced.

Measurement of Soil Moisture

The normal method of determining the water content of soil is to compare the weight of the fresh soil with that of the same sample after drying at 105°C and to express the result as a percentage of the dry weight. Such figures are suitable for seasonal comparisons of the same soil type but they are not simply related to the availability of water to plants or animals because, for example, sand is saturated with water at a much lower percentage than loam. A biologically more informative measure of soil moisture is the "suction" in height of water or mercury required to withdraw the water from the soil. This is usually expressed on a logarithmic scale as "pF" (i.e. $pF = \log_{10}$ height in millimetres). Two values on this scale are especially important biologically, the wilting point at which plants can withdraw no further water against the capillary forces in the soil (about pF 4·2) and the "field capacity" at which the soil is virtually saturated (about pF 3·2).

Measurements can be carried out in the laboratory by measuring the column of water which can be supported from a porous plate in contact with the soil, or better, in the field with a "tensiometer" consisting of a porous pot and a manometer filled with water. The theory and construction of simple tensiometers have been discussed recently[276, 643] and now commercial types with a Bourdon gauge are also available. However, tensiometers are large in size, not suitable for recording and fail in soil drier than a tension of 0·8 atmospheres. These deficiencies are rectified in the electrical method developed by Boyoucos[63, 64, 65, 218] which uses blocks of inert material (plaster of Paris, Fibreglass or nylon) containing electrodes. The "Boyoucos blocks" are inexpensive and large numbers may be buried permanently in the soil with only their leads projecting. An alternating current Wheatstone bridge[64, 303] is used to measure the resistance between the leads. The calibration is very stable and a resistance of about 10^4 ohms corresponds to field capacity, 10^6 ohms to wilting point. All the equipment is now available commercially.

A very simple field method, not tried by the author, has been suggested by Czihak,[149] which consists in measuring the rate at which water is sucked out of pieces of filter paper, suitably protected from desiccation by the air. A correction for temperature is necessary.

Chapter 4

THE RELATIONS BETWEEN ANIMAL ECOLOGY
AND VEGETATION

THE ecology of plants is in two senses a basis for the study of animal ecology. First, because vegetation is the ultimate source of energy and of many of the most important environmental influences in any habitat and, second, because plant ecology has been the older discipline and, for better or for worse, has originated many of the ideas and concepts which govern our approach to animal ecology.

Many authors have argued that there is but one subject of ecology, that a division on the basis of the taxonomic "kingdoms" is unreal and impracticable and that ecologists should study both kingdoms simultaneously. The term "biocönose" was developed by Möbius[463] to include the members of both kingdoms in a single complex of organisms. The use of this and similar terms, which have been used especially by those concerned with the "community" concept, is discussed in Chapter 12.

Succession and the Correspondence between Flora and Fauna

In certain fields the dependence of animal communities upon vegetation is so direct and obvious that to attempt to study the one without the other would be foolish; this is so particularly in the case of areas of "open" vegetation and the early colonization of bare areas such as glaciers and landslides.

Numerous examples of this are provided by a recent study[347] of the high Alps. A succession of different species occurs as bare rock is progressively uncovered by ice and gradually colonized by plants and converted into a soil. Janetschek recognizes four main zones on the basis of the age of the soil and its flora and claims that, on the whole, these correspond well with a sequence of animals (Table 3).

The first part of the "o" zone is characterized by a number of Collembola which are extremely cold resistant and are believed to feed on Algae especially; *Isotoma saltans* is confined to this region and *Proisotoma crassicaudata* only just extends into plant zone I, as does the wolf spider *Pardosa wagleri nigra*. This zone contains further Collembola and a very

48

restricted spider called *Janetschekia lesserti*. Then a number of beetles, namely *Pemphigius similis*, which occur also in plant zone IIa, appear, the most adventurous of them followed by an *Amara* and a *Notiophilus*. In this zone, too, a centipede *Lithobius lucifugus* becomes abundant and some of the more "normal" Collembola. These carry on into plant zone IIb, where they are joined by earthworms and Nematode worms. Toward the warmer part of this zone a whole host of further animals

TABLE 3

Correspondence of animal and plant associations.

(After Janetschek)

Plant Zone	Plant Association	Animal Zone	Animal Association
o	—	Ia	*Pardosa wagleri nigra— Proisotoma crassicaudata*
I	*Poa laxa–Cerastium uniflorum*	Ib	*Plaesiocraerus helleri— Proisotoma schötti*
IIa	*Agrostis rupestris— Polyrichum juniperinum*	IIa	*Lithobius lucifugus— Notiophilus biguttatus*
IIb	*Trifolium pallescens— Polytrichum juniperinum*	IIb	*Lithobius—Meioneta gulosus—Oxypoda tirolensis*
		IIIa (glacier soils)	*Lithobius-Leptyphantes fragilis—Quedius alpestris*
III	*Festuca halleri*	IIIb (sunny slopes)	*Lithobius-Haplodrassus signifer—Oxypoda tyrolensis*
	High alpine meadow association		Much more complex association with numerous species

appears, merging into the grass-meadow fauna and including grasshoppers, many species of spiders, beetles and, almost last of all, the ants.

There are two topics to note especially from this very sketchy summary: first, even in a rather simple succession of this sort, with a steep gradient of physical factors and clear vegetation zones, the animals do not in fact correspond in a simple way with the plant zones; in fact, Janetschek recognizes a series of animal zones and the only boundary which they share in common with the plant zones is that between plant zones I and II. This incomplete dependence of animal associations on obvious plant zones seems to be a common phenomenon and in other studies of arctic[436] and sand-dune[746] animals the same is found; the mechanical structure of the soil particles, the spaces between them and the density of the vegetation, seem to be much more significant than the taxonomy of the plants.

A second point to note is that not all animals are equally restricted in their range; some, such as *Janetschekia lesserti*, come into the category of "vicariants" or "indicator organisms"; this spider, for instance, is restricted to plant zone I in the *Gepatschvorfeld*. (The use of such animals in defining communities is discussed in Chapter 13.) Others, such as the beetle *Amara quenseli*, which occurs throughout zones I and II, are much more tolerant. A disputable point, which is, however, upheld by many naturalists, is that predators very frequently make the best indicator organisms, and seem to be more restricted to one plant type than the more numerous "Saprophages." (In reality these usually feed on fungi or bacteria.) This may be because the predators are more influenced by cover and the life forms of the plants; it may also be a reflection of our complete ignorance of the basic requirements of the other groups. It is certain, as anyone who has tried to keep them alive will agree, that predators are far harder to rear in captivity.

In a somewhat similar study[284] of more advanced alpine conditions the author maintains that some groups of snails and Myriapods are strictly related to vegetation while others, including the Collembola, follow details of soil structure in their distribution.

Edge Effects in Time

An instructive example[187, 246] of a transient "community" was provided by observing glass slides which were exposed in a stream and examined every other day under the microscope for colonization by algae. The numbers of species present increased rapidly—

Day	1	3	5	7	9	26	42
Number of species	13	20	33	33	43	47	45

and then settled down to a fairly constant level. However, the species which appeared at first were those which occurred in the surrounding water while, as soon as the plates became fully occupied (at about one week), these species disappeared and were replaced by others which were apparently better adapted to the special conditions on the glass slides.

In cases such as this, interpretation of results is often complicated by the preponderating influence of chance arrivals both among plants and animals; such forms, which would be rapidly eliminated if the vegetation were closed and competition more intense, may occur very sporadically and for short periods only and it is often very difficult "to make sense" of fauna and flora lists from such places.

From the point of view of the organism concerned, however, these transient phases in succession constitute a complete system of habitats. They are exploited both by animals and by plants—ephemeral species found in disturbed places, such as the willow herb *Epilobium angustifolium*, with its well-developed, seed-dispersal mechanism, are examples. Among animals examples are the successive larvae which colonize cow-pats[397] and sheep carcases[443] and the invertebrates which are attracted to rotting food substances as they decay.[775] The mobility of animals makes them well suited to exploiting niches of this sort, even when they are widely separated in space and transient in time.

The Justification for the Separate Study of Animal Ecology

It is certainly true that very little field animal ecology can be done without a knowledge of taxonomic and ecological botany and that, just as both plants and animals modify their physical environment, so animals modify the vegetation of their surroundings—the "biotic" factors of the plant ecologist. It is also true that the taxonomic division of living things is arbitrary and unsatisfactory because the plant kingdom includes both the autotrophic forms (that is, organisms synthesizing higher organic compounds from simple inorganic substances with the energy of sunlight) and the heterotrophic forms such as the Fungi, most Bacteria and Actinomycetes which are incapable of such synthesis.

As has already been stressed, an important attribute of an animal ecologist and, I suggest, most other scientists, is to be able to sport a pair of "semi-permeable" blinkers which allow him to make use of information from adjacent fields of knowledge without thereby feeling impelled to explore those fields in detail. The doctrine, generally recognized by animal ecologists, that plant ecology should be "required reading" for all of them, and that collaboration with botanists is often essential in practice, is perfectly reconcilable with the limitations of human nature which make it impossible to be equally well acquainted with the members of both kingdoms.

In the British list there are about 1,000 species of flowering plants, 2,500 toadstools, 650 mosses, to say nothing of ferns, Algae, Bacteria and the smaller Fungi, while some figures for the number of species in some important groups of living organisms for the world[37] are—

TABLE 4

Fungi . . .	100,000	Nematoda .	80,000
Mosses and liverworts .	17,000	Annelida . .	8,000
Ferns, etc. . . .	8,000	Echinodermata .	6,000
Seed plants. . .	150,000	Mollusca . .	80,000
		Chordata .	70,000
		Insecta . .	500,000

It is estimated that there are another million insects which have not yet been named.

There is an instructive story about Sir J. D. Hooker, who, when Director of Kew Gardens, was reproved by a lady for whom he had been unable to name an exotic shrub. Hooker replied, "Madam, I am not a horticulturist; I am a botanist."

Just as the botanist has other interests in addition to "horticulture," so the ecologist's knowledge of taxonomy is only one of the tools he must wield to aid him in his main pursuit.

Apart from the above "argument from human frailty," of course, the arbitrary division of ecology into two is further justified by the difference of technique and approach demanded by the much greater mobility and searching power of animals.

Further, despite their lesser biomass, animals fulfil more different functional roles than do the holophytic plants. Because they may be herbivores, carnivores, parasites, or belong to successive classes of saprophages, there are greater possibilities for interaction, whether co-operative or harmful, between populations of different animal species. For the study of these phenomena there are no models to be found in conventional plant ecology, but they are very much to the forefront of the animal ecologist's attention.

The uncritical adoption of plant ecological technique by animal ecologists has at times proved misleading and in many respects the reverse position would be equally unsatisfactory.

In Chapter 13 the primarily botanical techniques of detection and description of communities and associations will be considered and in Chapter 12 the implications of these methods among others for animal ecology. It will be shown that botanists themselves are becoming less confident about the stability and uniformity of communities and that in both fields there are dissenters who claim that the community is such a nebulous and indefinable entity that it is of little use to practical ecologists.

Chapter 5

THE DISTRIBUTION OF ANIMALS IN SPACE
AND IN TIME

Hitherto in this book we have been concerned with the factors which determine the outer periphery, as it were, of the range of animals; the physical and floristic factors which impose limits beyond which the animal cannot extend. It has already become clear that, important as such information may be from many points of view, a detailed understanding of the distribution of animals is not possible on such a basis alone, because animals are distributed in a very patchy manner within such ranges, because they move about a great deal and because the density of their populations varies enormously from place to place. The last feature is now considered so important that the study of animal populations is tending more and more to supplement and sometimes to replace that of individuals for ecological analysis. However, before proceeding to population ecology, to which the remainder of this book is devoted, there are some features of animal distribution which are more appropriately treated in this part of the book as belonging to individual animals and not to populations.

A provisional attempt will be made in this chapter to describe and illustrate those principles, derived from autecology, which govern what animals occur where and when. The combination of suitable biological attributes with suitable spatial distribution is considered on a geographical and a local scale; this is then related to discontinuities in space and in time. Some examples of recent work provide illustrations of attempts to analyse relations between habitat factors and the occurrence of animals. Finally, the limitations of this type of approach are considered.

Habitat Selection

One set of factors which determine distribution of animals and which deserve a book to themselves, are those aspects of animal behaviour which govern how the animal selects the habitat in relation to its different biological needs, especially to feeding and reproduction. The analysis of the factors which determine the territorial limits of a stickleback, for instance, is discussed by Spurway[690] and the methods of habitat selection in birds by Lack.[388, 388a] These and many similar studies are from the behaviour point of view. Harritt,[304] on the other hand, discusses the hereditary basis of habitat selection habits in mice, while at the opposite extreme are studies of migration on the geographical scale.[285, 451, 451a]

These topics have been well reviewed and need receive only passing mention here. From an ecological point of view their main significance is that they emphasize the extremely wide range of animals' activities and that they imply that the complete description of the composition of an animal community over a long period must inevitably allow for many apparently "chance" occurrences which are only to be explained on a behavioural basis. In fact, the great differences in the material and methods of plant and animal ecology are largely attributable to differences in behaviour and movement of animals and plants.

Factors Determining the Distribution of Animals

Both on the zoogeographical and on the ecological scale, the distribution of animals is the result of interaction between two sets of factors, the past history of the distribution and the biological demands of the animal. Examples of animals hitherto excluded from an area on the geographical scale, but becoming highly successful when ultimately introduced there by man have been given in Chapter 2. The factors which decide the spatial distribution of animals are often quite mysterious to man. Thus van der Drift[744] found that ground beetles were numerous in some parts of a particular wood and rare in others, but he could detect no differences of vegetation, soil type or physical factors. Furthermore these regions of high density persisted from one year to another. Similar results have been obtained by Edwards[193] working with Symphyla.

Many cases of unsuccessful attempts to introduce animals and of extinction of existing fauna in the presence of introductions show how biological adaptation does not necessarily follow from geographical presence. A striking example[110, 111] of this is the attempted introduction in Australia of beetles which, it was hoped, would result in the biological control of St. John's wort. The beetles concerned, *Chrysomela gemellata* and *C. hyperici*, are specific herbivores for this plant in its native Europe, where they are very abundant. A combination of biological characteristics of the species—poor dispersal powers and limited rate of multiplication—limit their effectiveness in Australia to a level at which the plant can regenerate faster than the beetles can eat it down. When, however, suitable agronomic methods are used, resulting in greater competition between the St. John's wort and other plants, it is possible for the beetles to control the weed.

On the more local scale similar principles still apply; no animal has a very extensive range in all three dimensions of space and many are discontinuous also in time, at least in the form of active phases. Further, animals frequently move, in apparently erratic fashions, from one part of a habitat to another. Thus, the harvestmen in English woodland have regular diurnal rhythms of movement, moving up the trees or from the underside to the upper surface of leaves in the herb layer according to species. In addition, the seasonal periods of hatching and of greatest activity are staggered so that different species, although inhabiting the same wood, rarely encounter each other, although an oak wood may contain five or six species. A somewhat similar situation was detected among woodlice in woodland by Brerton.[70a] *Porcellio scaber* ascends the trunks of trees on summer nights and there is a tendency for other species to occupy the moss at the base while it is away. Brerton also observed that the micro-habitats of the woodlice vary with the major habitat; *Armadillidium vulgare*, for instance, is the main form living under stones in fields while *Oniscus asellus* lives there in woods, although both species are present in both woods and fields. Many beetles and other insects "commute" freely between the soil and vegetation.[172]

Interspersion

Such features of animal distribution, which Elton[203] has called "interspersion," frequently permit many animals to live in the same area in a state of dynamic equilibrium, whereas this would be impossible if the area were more uniform or smaller in size. Aphids, for instance, are preyed upon by ladybirds (see Chapter 15[177, 178]) and colonies, once found, are liable to be exterminated. Thus, although on a small scale one finds overpopulation and extinction succeeding each other, in a mixed deciduous woodland of some extent, the population of both insects per acre will be fairly constant because both herbivore and predator migrate to other localities in the area.

On the one hand, we find the extremely patchy distribution of the sycamore aphid, which seems to be able to locate its specific food literally miles from any other tree in a vast inhospitable "sea" of "useless" vegetation, while, on the other, we find the almost continuous range—in two dimensions at least—of common soil animals, such as the Collembola *Folsomia quadrioculata* or *Onychiurus armatus*, which occur in an extremely wide range of soil types in Britain and elsewhere. Evidently the animals showing both types of distribution require special biological attributes and it is by no means certain that the commonly occurring Collembola should be regarded as the more "successful."

The animal whose distribution is patchy must have highly specialized methods for detecting its selected habitat and means of dispersal and reproduction which will ensure its arrival and allow for the inevitable heavy mortality *en route*. However, such highly specialized forms, at least to begin with, may be expected to suffer less competition for food and other requirements, and are also likely to benefit from the evolutionary advantages associated with small and rapidly expanding populations discussed in Chapter 1.[198] The more uniformly distributed animal is more likely to suffer intensive competition for resources and less likely to enjoy the peculiar genetical advantages which contribute to greater racial versatility. Presumably, in the course of geological time, any species may vary from one condition to the other, although it appears that some of the very "unspecialized" long-lived species, such as the Brachiopod *Lingula*, have avoided morphological specializations for very long periods of time.

The Significance of Boundaries

By far the greater part of the world's living organic matter appears to be concentrated at the boundaries between matter in different phases, the air-land, water-land, and air-water boundaries. This rather obvious statement is worth supporting with a few examples. The distribution of the numbers and living weight or "biomass" of soil animals in relation to the surface of the soil is indicated in Fig. 9,[434] which applies to successive 5 cm deep layers in a fen in England. Similar distributions have been found by other workers[694] with soil animals, although some groups in some soils may descend to greater depths. Similar rapid diminutions of the numbers of animals are found not only from the sea surface going upward into the air, but also where water and land meet at lake and sea shores and at the bottoms of shallow bodies of water.

Evidently life tends to be concentrated where at least two phases of matter meet because photosynthetic plants demand access to sunlight and air for the elaboration of food materials and the support of a solid or a liquid medium. The density of animal life falls off rapidly as it leaves the primary food source, and it is only the remote links of the "food chains," such as the predatory fish and birds and some specialized "scavengers," which spend most of their life history far from this source. It also appears that the absence of firm anchorage in seas and lakes limits the biological exploitation of them, for shore life is proverbially rich and varied, both in numbers and in variety of species.

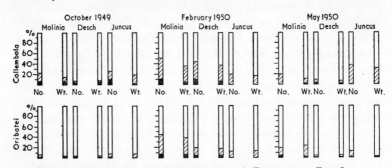

FIG. 9. DISTRIBUTION OF INVERTEBRATES IN DEPTH IN A FEN SOIL

0–5 cm, unshaded: 5–10 cm hatched: 10–15 cm black. Three vegetation types were studied, namely: *Molinia*, *Deschampsia* and *Juncus*.

Pennak[569a], for instance, gives the following description of the fauna of the lake shore sands in North America—

> If an "average" 10 cc sample be taken from the surface of a beach . . . it will be found to contain 4,000,000 Bacteria, 8,000 Protozoa, 400 Rotatotia, 40 Copepoda, 20 Tardigrada and small numbers of other microscopic Metazoa. The sample will be found to contain 2–3 cc of water. In this small volume is concentrated a great population. . . . So far as the author has been able to discover there is no other environment which is capable of supplying such a diversified and dense population of microscopic organisms.

A similar high concentration occurs at the sandy shores of Arctic islands,[436] where a square metre to a depth of 5 cm of even quite "barren" sands contained about 17,000 individuals of *Archisotoma besselsi*, while that sand in which the marine detritus was supplemented by the refuse from bird cliffs had as many as 220,000 Collembola (mainly *Xenylla humicola*), 31,000 Enchytraeid worms, and 50,000 Nematode worms.

Fringe Habitats

It is frequently contended that boundaries *within* one physical phase are also regions of high animal density. Audy[27] found that the rodent population and its parasitic mites were, when compared with those in natural Malayan rain forest, very much more diverse and abundant in the "Parang" vegetation areas—where the forest had been cleared with "parangs" (machetes) and where regenerating vegetation contains a mixture of different heights and types of plants. This greater diversity is attributed to the great increase of "fringes" (one square mile of parang vegetation may contain fifteen to twenty miles of fringe). Here "the tempo of animal and plant life is increased so that more marked population fluctuations occur. . . . Fringe habitats on the whole contain a much greater abundance of life than do the adjacent units. Also one gets the impression that there is something dynamic about the conditions at the fringe." Leopold is quoted to the effect that game birds are also more abundant in the United States under such conditions.

Unfortunately, no detailed comparison of the entire communities of fringes with surrounding vegetation has yet been made. If Audy's generalizations are applicable to the whole spectrum of life in such places they contrast forcibly with the alternative view that the greatest intensity of life is to be found in the stable climax communities. Tischler,[727] for instance, failed to find evidence for a distinct fringe community or enhanced populations of invertebrates in his study of the distribution of invertebrates at the edges of woods. Boness[59a] found that most groups of invertebrates were more numerous near the hedges of clover and lucerne fields. He attributes this mainly to microclimatic factors and to a greater growth of weeds near the hedges. In both these cases there are so many complicating factors that the results throw little light on Audy's thesis.

Diurnal and Seasonal Rhythms

If the distribution of animals in space is patchy, it is hardly less so in time. We are so familiar with the daily "scene shift" which occurs at dusk that we cease to appreciate its significance. Equally familiar, and even more significant for the lives of animals in temperate climates, is the annual cycle of the seasons influencing both the vegetational and the physical environment; this is said to be one of the most surprising features of temperate conditions to one brought up near the equator. Occasionally we are reminded of less regular fluctuations in the numbers of animals by a plague of cabbage-white caterpillars or of oak-defoliating moths or of crane flies or wasps or we read of the devastation caused by a locust plague in tropical countries.

Regular rhythms, such as the diurnal and the seasonal, have been studied to some extent by physiologists and students of behaviour, and a combination of laboratory and field study has been particularly fruitful in those cases where it has been applied. Cloudsley-Thompson,[119, 120, 120a] for instance, has studied in particular Myriapods and Crustacea from this point of view and has been able to show how a combination of innate rhythm and of reactions to quite specific combinations of physical stimuli can account for the animal's normal behaviour and also its reactions under laboratory conditions. This would appear to be a great advance on the highly abstract and artificial experiments of earlier workers in this field. A particularly important discovery is that animals kept under uniform conditions—as is frequently done in the laboratory—may behave in quite abnormal ways and may even die off rapidly, apparently for no other reason.

The innate and environmental components of rhythmical behaviour are the subject of much work by experimental biologists,[301] and will not be described here. When two sets of stimuli of different period interact as, for example, tidal and diurnal rhythms, the analysis becomes more complicated.[483] To the ecologist it is often gratifying to find that related species in the same habitat have interdigitating rhythms. This has been shown, for instance, in *Drosophila* species[188] and in ground beetles.[809, 810] In both woodland and grassland, for instance, there are species of *Notiophilus* and *Nebria* which are diurnal and nocturnal respectively. *Feronia madida*, on the other hand is diurnal in grassland and nocturnal in woodland. This study by Williams is notable for the introduction of some ingenious actographs and a clock-operated pitfall trap which helps to bridge the gap between laboratory and field studies.

The seasonal development of related species is also frequently staggered; Williams[810] reports that the larvae of his particular species of *Notiophilus* are active in the summer, of *Feronia* in the winter, and van der Drift,[744] who studied a wide range of ground beetles showed that the periods of activity as larvae and as adults tended to be staggered through the season within the same genus (Fig. 10). A similar "Cox and Box" situation was demonstrated among spiders.

Not all animals have rhythms which can be fitted to the 24-hour cycle; this is especially true of small mammals whose metabolic needs appear to necessitate a shorter rhythm. Whereas most rodents and also the shrew have rhythms which are a sub-multiple of 24 hours, the mole's rhythm of about 8 hours seems to get out of step, perhaps due to its subterranean existence. [140, 269, 457]

The more erratic variations in animal numbers, usually distinguished by American workers from "cycles" by the use of the term "fluctuations," are not to be understood from the study of autecology. They result from the interplay of factors of mortality and of reproduction and are peculiarities of populations as such. They are discussed further in Chapter 16.

Examples of Autecological Work

At this stage it is appropriate to take stock of the kind of information about the ecology of animals which can be obtained from a synthesis of all the methods open through an "autecological" approach. A few examples of good modern work will help to crystallize ideas.

First, there is the sort of information which results from an intensive study of taxonomy combined with distribution in a single group of animals. For instance, [447] of the two species of freshwater leech *Erpobdella testacea* and *E. octoculata*, the latter is the commoner form; the former, which is normally capable of surviving throughout their common range in the absence of *E. octoculata* is, in nature, found only where alkalinity or pollution are at high levels. In these circumstances *E. octoculata* is not found and *E. testacea*'s presence is attributed to lack of competition rather than any "preference" for such localities.

Macan [423, 424] has contributed much to the study of the distribution of the British Corixidae. The approach used involves an analysis of the main factors which limit the distribution of the British species based on collections combined with water analyses and field notes; in this way it is possible to relate certain species to certain types of freshwater so closely that the alternative procedure of using the water boatmen as "indicator species" can be carried out with considerable success. This kind of work appears to be particularly successful in freshwater studies.

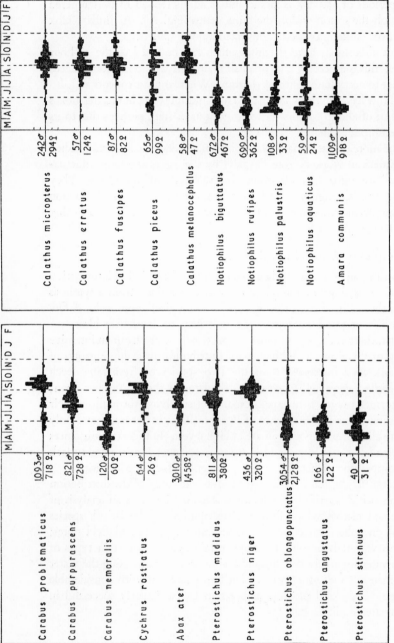

Fig. 10. Seasonal Activity of Forest Carabid Beetles
(After van der Drift)

Histograms based on pitfall trap counts show seasonal "staggering" between closely related species in the same locality.

Among recent work on terrestrial animals that of Todd[729] and Nørgaard[520, 521, 522, 523, 524] is outstanding. In both cases laboratory work on preferenda and tolerance ranges is combined with field work in which the habits and distribution of the species are related to features of the physical environment. Todd found that, among the six common species of harvestmen living in and around Wytham woods (Berkshire), there is a close correspondence between the humidity preferenda as measured in the laboratory and the relative humidity measured in their corresponding habitats in the field. The different species are active at different heights above ground and the measurements were made in these places at night when the animals were out. These results are summarized in the following table—

TABLE 5

| Species | Plant Layer | Relative Humidity as Measured— | |
		In Field (per cent)	Preferendum in Lab. (fiducial limits, per cent R.H.)
Oligolophus hanseni	Branches	50–60	46·8–54·8
Oligolophus agrestis			51·5–61·3
Leiobunum rotundum	Tree trunk	60–75	60·7–68·9
Leiobunum blackwalli			64·9–75·1
Oligolophus tridens	Field layer	70–80	63·5–72·1
Nemastoma lugubre	Ground layer	85–100	69·4–78·8

Nørgaard has studied the relationship between microclimates of the normal habitats of spiders, their temperature and humidity preferenda as measured in the laboratory, and their tolerance ranges. One of his most convincing papers applies to the two Lycosid spiders which commonly occur in *Sphagnum* bogs in Jutland. The *Sphagnum* emerges from the water with long narrow stalks which bear bushy heads some 10 cm above the water surface. This produces two horizontal surfaces, that of the water and that of the *Sphagnum* heads, rather like a miniature forest swamp. Although the two species of Lycosid usually occur together in a single bog, they can rarely meet because the one, *Lycosa pullata*, lives on the upper surface of the *Sphagnum* heads, the other, *Pirata piraticus*, on the water among the *Sphagnum* stems. In the latter zone, conditions are much damper and colder and *P. piraticus* has a temperature preferendum around 20–22°C and prefers high humidities near saturation. *L. pullata*, on the other hand, prefers temperatures around 30°C and considerably drier conditions. Correspondingly, heat stupor occurs at 35°C and 43°C in the two species respectively.

Furthermore, when the female of *P. piraticus* is carrying the egg cocoon, which apparently cannot develop at the low temperatures near the water surface, she undergoes a change of behaviour, climbs the *Sphagnum* stems and thrusts her abdomen through into the warmer region above. One result of this is that, when one approaches such a bog cautiously, one notices many white cocoons at the surface in numbers sufficient to have a very noticeable effect. If, however, one stumbles or stamps a foot, the entire appearance of the bog changes as thousands of white egg cocoons of *P. piraticus* are withdrawn into the safety of the animal's normal habitat. During this incubation period the temperature preferendum changes from 20–22°C to 26–30°C.

A study of Schaller[633a] on Collembola involves a similar combination of microclimate, preferendum and field work; it describes the effects of vegetation thickness on the microclimate of the surface soil and relates this to the laboratory behaviour of the different Collembolan species.

A rather more zoogeographical slant is provided by the work of Tischler[727a] who related the fauna of bombed sites in Kiel to the microclimate and was able to show that the constituent species belonged to Southern German faunas, corresponding with the much milder microclimate in the bombed sites.

One contribution from this school[59] describes the invertebrate fauna of the hay meadows and shows how the abundance and life histories of the animals are related to the rather catastrophic effects on the environment of the twice-yearly hay harvest. Some ground-living species are little influenced by the hay-making regimen, but other species, especially those which feed on the leaves, appear in a variety of ways to have adapted their movements within the meadows and to other habitats and also their life cycles.

It is usual in German and Austrian work of this sort to generalize about the behaviour of the species with the aid of a classification which describes the physical features of the environment. Thus, "eury" and "steno-topic" indicate respectively a broad and a narrow ecological range of tolerance, "poly-" and "oligo-" the occurrence of much and little or high and low values of the factor in question. "Therm," "hygr," and "ion" imply temperature, moisture and pH respectively. These roots are compounded in the form stenopolyhygr, euryoligotherm and so on (meaning restricted to a narrow range of moist conditions, but tolerating a wide range of colder places). Such statements are generally used to summarize a large mass of field observation and, as such, have their uses. Unfortunately, one sometimes gains the impression that they can become the only goal for certain studies, the magic of this cacophonous vocabulary apparently allowing the worker to forget that the divisions between the categories are highly arbitrary and that, even when species have been so labelled, one does not know much more about the ecology of the animals. More recently, however, work of this sort has been used as a basis for some first-rate ecological studies; an example of these is Strenzke's [694] work on North German beetle-mites.

Nørdberg, [518a] in one of the most authoritative studies on the invertebrate fauna of birds' nests, includes with the same ingredients of microclimate measurements, preferenda and distribution, a very careful study of the life histories of the birds' nest inhabitants of many groups; he shows how the life stages of the different species are related to one another and to the birds' activities and enables one to build up a conception of the nest fauna as an ecological unit. But perhaps this should be regarded as a population study rather than an autecological one, for like all distinctions between subjects this one is not always easy to make.

The Nature and Limitations of Autecology

It is now possible to consider the value and the shortcomings of the type of ecology so far discussed. First, it must have become clear that much of it is fundamental to a full analysis of the factors determining the occurrence of animals and the composition of any assemblage of organisms. Autecological work is the basis of much general ecological and economic work. However, it should also be clear that some other techniques must be developed in order to delimit the precise niche of a species; only the extremes can be indicated by a range of physical factors. Secondly, because the physical factors are but a small component of the set of forces acting on a species in nature, we need methods for analysis of the interrelations *between* species of animals, and this kind of relationship is hardly touched by autecological techniques. Thirdly, we have, as yet, been unable to suggest any answer to questions about what limits the size of populations of animals in a particular area and at a particular time, but have only been able to say that a certain species occurs, or does not occur in a region easily identified by man; we have not considered the fact that its density may be enormously variable and that criteria of presence or absence are so arbitrary and dependent on technique and skill as to be almost worthless. Finally, from the point of view of the whole assemblage of species inhabiting a given area, autecology can give us no information about the quantitative effects of one species on the rest; nor can it enable us to decide whether some species are to be regarded as of greater importance than others in such an assemblage nor provide us with criteria for judging importance.

In Parts 2 and 3 of this book, therefore, an attempt is made to show that by a study of animal populations, as distinct from individuals, answers to some of these questions can be given. We can enlarge on our conception of the meaning of the niche and the interrelations between species, we can describe and to some extent predict the factors which determine the limits of population size in time and space— a possibility of potential economic importance—and we can go some way towards singling out the more significant and important species in communities of incredible complexity in a way which will permit the limited powers of man to comprehend and eventually control what is perhaps the most elaborate form of organization he has to encounter.

Chapter 6

ECOLOGICAL ASPECTS OF ANIMAL METABOLISM

THIS chapter is concerned with ecologically important aspects of metabolism regarded from the point of view of the individual animal. Much of this work is not normally regarded as ecological at all. However, no animal can feed, excrete, defecate or die without affecting other species which it feeds on, which compete with it for food or which feed either on its body or its waste products. It is obviously important, therefore, for us to consider in a general way the main factors which change metabolic rates. As will become apparent in Chapters 14, 15 and 17 the metabolic links do in fact constitute one of the most rewarding, and at the present time most exciting, approaches to an understanding of the structure of biological communities.

The Need for a Special Approach

We shall consider first the influence of a series of factors on metabolic rate. A general indication of the methods employed is provided in the Appendix to this chapter. In work of this kind it is always possible to concern oneself with two distinct levels of organization. If, for example, one is interested in the dependence on temperature of metabolism the approach of the physiologist is to analyse the mechanisms which bring about changes in the metabolic rate chiefly by isolating the animal as far as possible from environmental influences and changing one factor at a time. This leads to equations relating metabolism to temperature, the study of acclimatization[240] and regulation under changing conditions and so on. Such work is important and necessary, but it is not the only possible approach. In nature, animals do not live under constant temperature conditions and to the ecologist, primarily concerned with the animal as a constituent of a community of interacting organisms, the *result* of the metabolic measurements is more important than the mechanism which achieves that result. (The physiologist on the other hand is more concerned with the mechanism than with the absolute level of the result.) The ecological approach, therefore, is to measure metabolic rates under conditions as close to those in the field as possible, to subject the animal to normal environmental influences such as diurnal temperature changes, a 24-hour light rhythm and so on and then to use a statistical technique (the ecologist's equivalent to the physiologist's test tube) to relate mean respiration to mean temperature and to find a relation between the magnitude and phase of excursions of the two quantities.

The difference in approach may well mean the development of new technical methods, as has indeed happened in the case of respiration measurements,[441] because methods designed for short-term experiments under constant conditions are unsuitable for ecological purposes. The need is at once apparent when one contemplates the discrepancies in the literature between different authors' figures for respiration rates. These discrepancies are not surprising in the light of the many factors listed below which influence respiration rate and most of which are ignored—quite rightly—by the physiologist concerned with only one aspect at a time.

The ecologist's requirement, then, is a synthesis, related to the conditions prevailing in his particular complex system. When more is known of the mechanisms involved it may be possible to extrapolate from one system to another, but this is the province of the physiologist and it is a very complex one.[439] Unless ecology is to suspend operations for several generations, methods of obtaining information appropriate to the ecologist's level of organization must be employed.

The Physical Meaning of Energy and Power

It is not easy to visualize by "common sense" the meanings and quantities involved in the energy exchanges of organisms and for this reason a short digression is appropriate, especially for the benefit of those to whom the word "thermodynamics" has a forbidding sound or an indefinite meaning.

"Energy," to the physicist, is an inclusive word covering both "work" and heat: all these three terms have the dimensions L^2M/T^2 (L = length, M = mass, T = time) and can be measured in the same unit, the "erg," which is the amount of work done in raising one gramme weight against the force of gravity to a height of one centimetre. This is a very small amount of work indeed and for practical purposes the joule, which is ten million ergs, is much more useful. Energy was first studied in this form of mechanical work, but it can also manifest itself as heat, which is the result of doing work within a piece of matter on a molecular scale. Independently of these studies of mechanics a unit of heat was defined which is the calorie, namely the amount of heat required to raise one gramme of water by 1°C. It was not until Joule's famous determination of the mechanical equivalent of heat that a factor was estimated by which units of work could be converted to units of heat. Joule found that $4\cdot2 \times 10^7$ ergs are equivalent to one calorie (or, as we now say, $4\cdot2$ joules $= 1$ calorie). Thus, if a piece of coal were to be burned in a bomb calorimeter (which is a device for carrying out complete combustion without loss of energy) it might produce, say, a thousand calories. If the same piece of coal were burned in a completely efficient steam engine and this were used to wind up weights against the force of gravity, the amount of work done would be 4,200 joules.

So far nothing has been said about the time taken for the work to be done or the energy liberated. However, in real life we are usually greatly interested in the time it takes to do things and the performance of one joule of work in one second is termed a watt; this is a measure of power or work $\div$ time. Thus, if the same piece of coal were burned in ten seconds and the steam engine were to drive a (100 per cent efficient) dynamo, 420 watts of electrical energy would be produced, enough to heat an electric iron for ten seconds.

The main point for the biologist to grasp from this diversion into elementary physics is that, according to the law of conservation of energy, whatever the method by which an energy source is exploited, a certain precise quantity of energy either in the form of mechanical work or of heat, will appear; neither more nor less. The "rate of exchange" between heat and work is one calorie to $4\cdot2$ joules. All practical mechanical engines are inefficient to some extent with the result that some of the energy content of their fuel is "wasted" in producing heat; this applies equally to organisms although they are often concerned, for biological reasons, to produce heat as well.

A further important point (and a rather fortunate one from the point of view of the physiologist) is that, when a certain amount of energy would result from, say, the oxidation of a given quantity of some carbohydrate, the same amount of energy would be liberated whatever the path of the chemical reactions involved. Thus, complete combustion of the gramme molecular weight of glucose always results in the liberation of 673,000 calories of heat (or $4\cdot2 \times 673,000$ joules of work or an equivalent combination of heat and work) according to the equation—

$$C_6H_{12}O_6 + 6O_2 = 6CO_2 + 6H_2O - 673,000 \text{ calories}$$

The same order of energy liberation results from the oxidation of all carbohydrates while a greater amount of energy can be obtained from fats (for instance, the complete combustion of the gramme molecular weight of palmitic acid produces 2,338,240 calories) and proteins produce rather less.

The Scale of Biological Energy Transfers

How can the biologist bring these facts of physics into relation with his experience of living creatures? How, for instance, does an insect compare with a man-made machine in its energy consumption, its efficiency, and the energy content of the "fuel" it uses?

The fuel consumption of a fruit fly (*Drosophila melanogaster*) which weighs 0·1 mg, while on the wing, is one microgramme of glucose in 6·3 minutes;[806] it carries about 20 microgrammes of glycogen which supplies it for about two hours' flight. This rate of metabolism is equivalent to about one calorie per 24-hours' flying. The fuel consumption of a desert locust (*Schistocerca gregaria*) weighing 1·8 g is 18 cu mm of oxygen per minute when resting and 300–900 cu mm per minute when flying.[382] These figures are equivalent to 0·08, 1·4 and 4·1 calories per minute respectively. In other words, the locust, which is 3,000 times the weight of the fruit fly, consumes only about 1,440 times the energy, despite its greater speed, and uses less than half the fuel. The locust is peculiar among insects for it can obtain energy directly from fats instead of carbohydrates. Some amusing comparisons of animal fuel consumptions and efficiency with those of aeroplanes have been made.[795]

Since we are all nowadays familiar with the heating power of an electric current, one means of visualizing rates of energy consumption is to use the conversion rate mentioned above. One calorie per second is equivalent to 4·2 watts. Thus, a locust burning food at the rate of 4·1 calories per *minute* is producing heat at the rate of $\dfrac{4\cdot2 \times 4\cdot1}{60} =$ 0·288 watts; and a man assimilating food containing $2\cdot7 \times 10^6$ calories per day at the rate of 131 watts.

The Components of Metabolism

In the light of the above it will be appreciated that, as a first approximation, the organism can be regarded as a "black box" which consumes high-energy matter in a discontinuous manner, rejects some of it little changed as excreta, breaks down some of it with the liberation of energy and simpler compounds and at the same time increases its own content of organic matter. When the animal dies this "packet" of high-energy materials is made available to other organisms. It is only by considering whole populations of organisms that the discontinuities due to feeding and death can be smoothed over and the idea of an energy "flow" can be justified. This idea is, therefore, discussed in Chapter 15. The metabolism of the individual black box is, however, measurable over a period of time in terms of the calorific content of its food, its faeces and its body. It is also possible to measure the energy loss due to respiration as oxygen intake, carbon dioxide output or heat production. The technical problems of measurement are treated in the Appendix; here we must discuss the relations between these quantities.

Most animals start life as eggs already endowed with a supply of organic matter. They may well draw on this to begin with but soon start to eat their own food. Some of this is lost as faeces and the rest is assimilated (through the gut). Since the efficiency of digestion is most variable and faeces are rapidly made available to the community it is often more practicable to work with assimilation rates than feeding (or ingestion) rates. Many predatory animals kill their prey but do not even eat it all. Thus, we can distinguish the following quantities—

$$\text{Food killed} = \begin{cases} \text{Food eaten} \\ \text{(or ingested)} \\ + \\ \text{Food not eaten} \end{cases} = \begin{cases} \text{Food assimilated} \\ + \\ \text{Faeces} \end{cases}.$$

The food assimilated undergoes complex chemical changes the final outcome of which is the storage of some organic matter as flesh and food reserves and the breakdown of some by respiration with the liberation of energy and lower-energy matter. The chemical pathways are complex and can hardly be traced in their entirety but the energy equation is quite rigidly defined and must balance. Thus if we consider the *calorific contents* of the food we can extend the above diagram as follows—

$$\text{Food eaten (with energy)} = \begin{cases}\text{Food} \\ \text{assimilated} \\ \text{(with energy)} \\ + \\ \text{Faeces} \\ \text{(with energy)}\end{cases} = \begin{cases}\text{Food} \\ \text{stored} \\ \text{(with energy)} \\ + \\ \text{Food} \\ \text{metabolized} \\ \text{(with energy)}\end{cases} = \begin{cases}\text{Energy} \\ \text{liberated} \\ + \\ \text{Breakdown} \\ \text{products}\end{cases}$$

When the total energy balance of an animal is to be investigated all aspects of the system must, of course, be followed. However, some aspects are quantitatively more important than others. The ratio of food stored to the total food assimilated approaches 50 per cent in adult *Daphnia* when they are laying down eggs[658] and 75 per cent in some insect hyperparasites[756] but these are both exceptional cases and figures around 5 per cent to 30 per cent are more usual.[399, 658, 659, 706] In other words when one is, for example, comparing a number of species feeding on the same food resource and requires to know to an order of magnitude which is the most important exploiter of the food it is permissible to use either energy liberated or food assimilated according to which is the more convenient, because the first amounts to about 90 per cent of the second, and is likely to be about the same proportion in both species.

On the other hand when the food stored, which may represent the potential food supply of some predator, is to be compared with food assimilated then obviously it is necessary to distinguish the latter from the food metabolized.

Examples of Food Consumption Figures

The food consumption of man and of domestic animals is of course well documented.[5,25,76,195] Figures have been obtained for fish[79,367] which indicate that their food demands are much less rigid than those of the higher vertebrates. Few estimates have been made for invertebrates and those which have are mainly for Arthropods. Slobodkin and his colleagues[654, 655, 656, 658, 659] have studied the population aspects of feeding in *Daphnia* (see p. 166) and Cushing[143, 144, 145] of

Calanus and other marine Copepods. A very labile consumption rate is indicated in both cases. Phillipson[571, 572] has measured the feeding and assimilation rates in detail for the harvestman *Mitopus morio* in relation to age, sex and other factors. He found that during successive instars there is an increase in assimilation and in proportion of food lost as faeces but a general fall in assimilation per unit of body weight. However, the latter trend was reversed by an order of magnitude at the attainment of maturity and this and other physiological factors precluded generalizations about the relations between food consumption and body weight or surface area. Gere has measured such rates in the butterfly *Hyphantria cunea*[250, 251] and has reviewed the literature up to that time.[252] He makes a sharp distinction between the herbivorous and the decomposer organisms on the grounds that while the former "waste" less than half their food in faeces the latter extract only about one quarter to one-third of its calorific value. A similar result is reported by Dunger[185] who finds that both Diplopods and Isopods assimilate a very small proportion of the food they eat. These results contrast with Phillipson's figures for *Mitopus* which range from 44 per cent $\pm$ 5·2 per cent at the sixth instar to 74 per cent at the second. It would appear that in general assimilation rates for flesh, plant food and decaying matter decrease in that order, a conclusion which might have been expected but is none the less valuable.

Efficiency

The ratios between the calorific contents of the foods and the bodies of animals are often termed efficiencies and a great many such ratios can be distinguished.[527, 558, 659] As Slobodkin has so clearly expounded, efficiency is a matter of your point of view; normally the efficiency of a locomotive is the ratio of mechanical work performed to potential energy in the coal consumed and the efficiency of a light bulb is the ratio of light output to electrical energy consumed. However, "from the standpoint of a moronic bookworm the efficiency of a locomotive might be measured as ratio of visible radiant energy from the firebox to potential energy consumption" while a "chilled illiterate in front of a draped light bulb might measure efficiency as total radiant energy output over total electrical energy input." In terms of our present problem, from the animal's point of view, its efficiency might be the ratio of the energy it extracts—and presumably puts to good use—during its lifetime over the energy assimilated in its food, a definition employed by Teal.[706] In fact, because man is often a predator concerned with exploiting the energy reserves stored up by his domestic or wild prey he usually expresses efficiency in terms of the energy in body tissues compared with the food consumption up to the time of death. Slobodkin has selected three efficiency ratios as being of major ecological importance; of these only one can be applied to the individual organism; the others are considered in Chapters 11 and 15. *Growth efficiency* is the ratio of potential energy in an animal's tissues to potential energy used in its birth and growth. This corresponds to the pig farmer's outlook with the additional—and important—qualification that one must take into account the metabolic cost to the sow of producing the piglet.

Growth efficiency inevitably declines with age and since it is usually defined in terms of potential energy of ingested food (i.e. assimilation plus faeces) it depends on all factors which influence efficiency such as wasteful feeding in the presence of a surplus and increased cost of searching when food is scarce (see above); Slobodkin quotes values from 37 per cent to 6 per cent. Figures for domestic animals, neglecting the cost to the mother lie between 5 per cent and 50 per cent according to age and Gere[252] gives around 15 per cent for terrestrial invertebrates.

Fisheries biologists use the term efficiency in rather a different way.[79] It is the ratio of food laid down as fish flesh to the food "available for growth." The food available for growth is that part of the food eaten which is not immediately used up in maintaining the metabolism of a fish, when food supply is regulated to ensure health but permit no growth in weight. To take an example Allen[8] calculated (see Chapter 11) that about 35 per cent of the food of trout is required for "maintenance" (= metabolism when the food is such that no growth takes place). Of the remaining 65 per cent he found that 24 per cent (16 per cent of the total) appears as fish flesh, the remaining 49 per cent of the total being metabolized but associated with the fish "putting on weight." This rather unfortunate complication is usual in the fisheries field and means that an unqualified "efficiency" figure from this source is greater than the growth efficiency defined above. This definition is probably justified by the great plasticity of fish metabolism which permits survival under very adverse conditions.

Metabolism in Relation to Size of Different Species

In a general way the metabolic rates of a wide range of organisms can be related to their surface areas. Useful discussions and a wide range of data are provided by Odum[527] and Hemmingsen.[317] This relationship is expressed in various ways as for example—

$$M = kW^n$$

or $$\log M = \log k + n \log W$$

where M = metabolic rate
W = weight
k and n are constants

Since the surface of a sphere is proportional to the $\frac{2}{3}$ power of its weight, n should have a value of about $\frac{2}{3}$ if M is to be proportional to area. In fact, Hemmingsen quotes a value of 0·73 as being more usual and gives a wide range of other figures. Zeuthen[829] studied a wide range of marine animals and found that within the main phyla the "law" that log metabolism was linearly related to log weight was fairly well obeyed but that progressive increases in complexity of organization (e.g. Protozoa/Metazoa, Annelida/Arthropoda, Invertebrata/Vertebrata, Poikilotherms/Homoiotherms) were associated with increases in the coefficients. Hawkins et al.[313] obtained a log/log relationship for British small mammals. Among soil Arthropods the metabolic rates of equal sized animals may cover nearly an order of magnitude (Hawkins and Jewell, 1962).

Metabolism in Relation to Size during Development

During the lifetime of animals there is also a general tendency for metabolic rate to follow a surface law but with many exceptions, as the figures of Phillipson indicate. As an example Mann[447a] found that rates for leeches which fell on a log/log curve had coefficients varying from 0·7 to 1·0. The constant C in the equation

$$C = \frac{\text{assimilation}}{\text{weight}^{\frac{2}{3}}}$$

has been termed the "van der Drift" constant by Balogh and his colleagues and the Consumption Quotient by Phillipson[572] and Dunger.[185] This accepts the approximate identity stated on p. 72 that assimilation and respiration are equal in practice. Gere concludes that, while C is approximately constant for decomposer organisms, the assimilation of herbivorous insects is more closely related to volume.

It is uncertain whether this is associated with the diet of the insects or their need to store food for metamorphosis.

Metabolism in Relation to Behaviour

Closely related species often show marked differences in locomotory activity which seem to be associated in a general way with rate of development. This is particularly true of different families of Collembola—contrast *Neanura* and *Onychiurus* with *Folsomia* and *Tomocerus* for instance and of Mites—compare *Platynothrus* with *Ceratoppia* among Oribatids and *Epicrius* with *Pergamasus* among Parasitids. In each case the first named are slow moving and have long developmental periods approaching a year;[462] the latter are active animals with short life cycles. Similar findings for Crustacea are due to Conover.[127] Some aquatic invertebrate species from running water metabolize faster than related forms from stagnant water.[447a] It seems unlikely, therefore, that metabolic rate can be strictly governed by a surface law in such cases.

In addition to contrasts between species there are also large diurnal changes in the activity of animals as revealed by actographs.[119, 120] In a few cases these have been related to metabolic rate[273] but usually this information is not available. An example of a daily rhythm of this kind was obtained by the author for the harvestman *Platybunus triangularis*,[441] an evening peak in metabolic rate probably coincides with a peak of locomotory activity detected by Phillipson[573] and with the habit of some Opilionid species of ascending trees at dusk[729] see p. 63. Phillipson has pointed out to the author that the younger instars have no such metabolic peak and may lack the habit of ascending trees.

Most Crustacea have a metabolic rhythm synchronized with eye-stalk secretion rhythms and the moulting cycle.[129] In the case of barnacles, however, where growth is continuous and moulting less demanding of resources, no rhythm was detected.[56] It follows from these few examples that short-term experiments on metabolic rate are not likely to provide reliable indications of rates in nature.

Metabolism in Relation to Temperature

An enormous amount of work has been done on animal metabolism in relation to temperature and few generalizations are possible. It is widely stated that the Q_{10} quotient of metabolic rates at two temperatures 10° apart approximates to 2, but nearly all practical values obtained by careful study seem to produce different values.[240, 194] Indeed, since more complicated relationships obtain even in the case of simple enzyme systems[30] such a relationship is hardly to be expected. An exponential law governing the metabolism/temperature relationship was suggested by Krogh[379, 380] and has frequently been quoted since. This curve was used by Bornebusch[60] in order to extrapolate from laboratory to field conditions.

Many cold-blooded animals show an ability to acclimatize their metabolic rates to new temperature regimes[80, 240] and it is commonly found that related species living at different temperatures have more similar metabolic rates than a strict dependence on temperature would imply.[240, 724] Mammals and birds are, of course, capable of temperature regulation and over a wide range metabolism is independent of temperature. At high temperatures cattle react by reducing food intake and all other aspects of metabolism.[222, 240] Under low temperature conditions the reverse is true but after a time acclimatization occurs and animals can endure cold with less metabolic strain.[240]

In normal practice respiration measurements are made at constant temperature. In simpler animals,[506] e.g. Nematoda, extrapolation from such results to temperature conditions experienced in the natural habitat is probably justifiable. In the case of Arthropods, however, diurnal changes in temperature, light and humidity are necessary triggers for normal activity[119, 120] and it has hitherto been one of the main objections to metabolic-rate measurements that it is difficult to relate them to field conditions. There is a good deal of evidence that sudden changes in temperature lead to over-compensation by certain components of metabolism, particularly respiratory rate[278, 279] and nervous activity.[362] This would appear to indicate the existence of regulatory mechanisms and perhaps acclimation over short periods but its significance has yet to be determined by long-term experiments. Kinne, in the fish experiments cited above found that temperature affected food intake, growth and assimilation independently in a complicated manner, the effect on assimilation being less than that on digestion.[367]

Metabolism in Relation to other Environmental Factors

Many environmental factors can influence metabolism through their action as triggers for behaviour patterns (see above) and hormonal mechanisms also operate in this way. In addition to transitional effects of such stimuli on blowflies, Digby[176] found that flies responded more quickly (in terms of flight activity) to a decrease in light intensity than to an increase. Very little definite information is available on the effect of such factors on metabolic rate even at the physiological level. In conclusion this rapid survey of influences of internal and external factors on metabolic rate should at least serve to stress the need for a cautious approach by the ecologist to generalizations. It should not, however, deter him from attempting a new synthesis at the ecological level on the lines indicated on p. 67 and may serve as a basis for understanding the metabolic properties of more complex systems discussed in Chapter 15.

Appendix

METHODS FOR METABOLISM STUDIES

1. Feeding Habits

In the case of some larger animals there is little difficulty in determining feeding habits by observation, although this may demand much patience and the use of special equipment—as for example Andersen's[9a] study of the food of hares with an astronomical telescope. Frequently, however, animals cannot be seen feeding and indirect methods are necessary, especially for quantitative work. In such cases, feeding studies may be technically very difficult indeed. Only a representative selection from the literature can be given here.

FAECES AND PELLETS. These may be examined for resistant remains and, where the food consists of whole organisms or organs, counts are possible. This has been done for many small invertebrates[611, 637] where it is sometimes difficult to distinguish truly digested from more resistant material, and for predatory birds such as owls which reject pellets containing bones of their prey. In the latter case Southern was able to recover magnetic leg rings from rodent prey with a magnet and link together population estimates of two separate species.[683]

GUT CONTENTS ANALYSES. These are commonly performed when sample animals can be killed without appreciably affecting the population under study. This is frequently done with carnivorous fish whose prey can be counted and related to that available in the habitat.[237, 238, 306]

MEASUREMENT BY DIFFERENCE. Where the food type is clearly known the quantity eaten can, of course, be determined by presenting the animal with an excess and finding how much is eaten in a given period. This superficially simple technique has the serious disadvantage, however, that many animals including fish,[367] planktonic[659, 144] and bottom-living[241] Crustacea ingest far more food when presented with an excess than they can digest efficiently: the greater the supply the less the proportion which is actually assimilated. Furthermore, as is known too among men who have experienced food rationing, the amount eaten is partly a matter of habit and subject to acclimatization.

CHOICE EXPERIMENTS. These are frequently used to determine the food of animals which can be cultured in the laboratory. The simplest method is to present a variety of foods and to record which disappear or, in the case of less active animals, which are most visited or surrounded with faeces. The obvious disadvantage here is that the choice is limited by the ingenuity of the experimenter and that many animals can be reared on foods which do not occur in nature. Since, however, it is not known for many invertebrates even whether they are carnivorous, fungivorous or herbivorous such work is often useful as a first approach. A variant of the choice experiment is the use of baited traps in the field. If potential food substances such as rotting vegetation, cultures of fungi, corpses and faeces are used as bait, information on food chains can be obtained.

TRACER METHODS. Radioactive tracers do not seem to have been widely used except for studying the uptake of nutrients by plants[610] in aquatic environments. The reason for this is probably the very rapid turnover of inorganic substances in the community. The use of labelled organic substances is widespread in the physiological field and appears to be applicable in ecology also.

A serological technique has been used by Dempster[171] to determine which of a number of possible predators in fact feeds on *Phytodecta olivacea*, a Chrysomelid beetle which itself feeds on broom. This involves preparing antisera from *Phytodecta* which react with traces of its own juices and Dempster was able to distinguish single animals which had consumed the beetle up to twenty-four hours beforehand. Obviously this is an extremely powerful method with a considerable future for use in the field.

2. Measurement of Size and Weight

It is often difficult to determine the body weight of small animals directly owing to uncertainty about how much water and how much inorganic matter they contain. Water can be evaporated by drying at 105°C but this often reduces small invertebrates to a size and weight which are very difficult to handle. Direct weighing is possible down to a little over a microgramme[45] with the new electrical balances and some torsion balances. Alternative procedures are firstly the measurement of the total content of nitrogen—for instance, with a micro-Kjeldahl apparatus followed by Nesslerization[829] and the use of a numerical factor to determine dry weight. Secondly, linear measurements can be substituted in a formula to determine weight, assuming a constant density.[11, 506, 743] The nitrogen method has much to recommend it especially as it is not affected by inorganic material such as calcium carbonate. The method based on linear measurements can probably never be precise and some dispute has arisen through failure to understand this. It is, on the other hand, a useful preliminary method and linear measurements have been related to weights for small Arthropods by Berthet[45] and for small Nematoda by others.[506, 743]

DETERMINATION OF CALORIFIC CONTENTS. The only satisfactory way to determine the calorific content of animals' bodies, foods or faeces is to bring about complete oxidation and liberate the energy they contain. This is quantitatively very large. For instance the 4,230 calories which result from the combustion of 1 g of starch are equivalent to 13,026 ft lb of work.[33] This is equivalent to lifting a 56-lb sack of corn a vertical distance of 233 ft. It is not surprising, therefore, that the calorific contents of quite minute quantities of organic matter can be determined. The best method is by means of a device which measures the heat of combustion, the bomb calorimeter but, unfortunately, technical problems due to the rapid liberation of heat make these very expensive. Greatest accuracy is possible with an adiabatic instrument in which the bomb is surrounded by water whose temperature is made to follow that inside the bomb because, in this way, problems of heat transfer can be avoided. One such instrument capable of 5 per cent accuracy with 6-mg samples and 1 per cent with larger quantities has now been made available in America.[660, 660a] Commercial instruments usually require much larger quantities of material. A less expensive approach is to measure the amount of oxygen absorbed by a "wet combustion" method; i.e. when the sample is oxidized by strong acids. This should be proportional to heat output but a main difficulty is the incomplete combustion of proteins especially. Ivlev[344] introduced a method in which protein estimation and wet combustion were combined; samples between 1 and 30 mg were used. He obtained figures differing little from those given by bomb calorimetry and it is not obvious why his technique has been so little used. Modern versions of carbon estimation apparatus which appear to be suitable are described by Van Slyke[747a] and by Tinsley.[726]

3. Determination of Metabolic Rate

The determination of metabolic rate is too large a subject for summary in a few pages: the interested reader is referred to the literature for conventional accounts.[76, 179, 740] Here it is proposed briefly to mention some special aspects relevant to ecological work.

Four distinct aspects of animal metabolism can be measured. The respiratory activity can be determined from oxygen uptake, carbon dioxide output or heat production or fourthly the food assimilated can be calculated and allowance made for that which is stored in the body.

CALORIMETRIC METHODS. Of the three respiratory measurements, the heat production in calories has the advantage that it permits direct comparison with the calorific content of food-stuffs, faeces and body stores. Direct measurement of heat production in a calorimeter is quite feasible for larger animals but it is complicated by the large quantities of heat used by animals in vaporizing water. (It requires 590 calories to evaporate one cubic centimetre of water at 10°C.) This and other problems have prevented the wide adoption of calorimeters for small animals and the most sensitive apparatus known to the author is Pratt's[589] which can operate with as little as 6 mg of animal tissue.

RESPIRATORY QUOTIENTS. The quantity of oxygen used and carbon dioxide produced in the oxidation of food depends on the ratios of carbohydrate, fat and protein, the Respiratory Quotient or ratio of oxygen/carbon dioxide for the pure substances being the following—

carbohydrate   1·0
fat   0·71
protein   0·79

The oxidation of carbohydrate involves equal numbers of molecules— and therefore, equal volumes—of the two gases but the amount of oxygen required is proportionately less in the case of the other foods and the amount of carbon dioxide produced is more.

From an inspection of the last four columns of Table 6 it will be seen that the relation between heat and carbon dioxide production is very dependent on the R.Q. while the oxygen consumption varies little. For this reason, where the nature of the food is uncertain, oxygen-uptake measurements are preferable to carbon-dioxide-output measurements. Conversely if any two of the three figures (R.Q., O_2 or CO_2) are known the third can be calculated.

OXYGEN-UPTAKE METHODS. Most measurements of gaseous exchange have been made with manometric apparatus such as the Warburg respirometer[179, 740] in which carbon dioxide is absorbed with alkali and the decrease in total volume of gas is measured. At the end of an experiment the carbon dioxide can be liberated again from the alkali by adding acid and the R.Q. calculated from the ratios of the two gases. More sensitive means of measuring small volume changes have been used, particularly in the Cartesian Diver[325, 410] which can detect oxygen-uptake rates down to $\frac{1}{1000}$ cu mm per hour. A very simple large-scale version of the Diver has also been described.[78]

Most respirometers of this kind are only suitable for physiological experiments because (amongst other things) readings are made manually, because oxygen is gradually depleted and because constant temperature must be maintained. A series of respirometers has appeared recently using automatic mechanical[735] and electrical replacement of oxygen as it is used up: the latter have been reviewed by the author.[441] In the latest of these, fluctuating temperature conditions can also be provided in a respirometer sensitive down to 0·1 cu mm per hour—the sort of rate at which single Collembola and large mites respire.

Because the quantity of oxygen which can be dissolved in water is very limited the oxygen uptake of aquatic organisms can be measured directly either by chemical (e.g. Winkler[230]) analysis or with a polarograph.[447a] The use of the latter permits continuous automatic readings on animals the size of leeches.

CARBON-DIOXIDE-PRODUCTION METHODS. The rate of carbon-dioxide production can be measured chemically in the Petenkoffer respirometer[346] for large organisms or the Conway microdiffusion apparatus for small ones.[128] In both cases the carbon dioxide is absorbed in alkali and this is titrated against acid. Electrometric titration allows continuous recording but this has not been widely adopted.

TABLE 6
Table of calorific constants of foods.

Food Substances	R.Q.	calories Liberated During					Oxidation of 1 mg Food Involves				Liberation of 1 calorie Involves			
		Combustion of	Oxygen uptake of		Carbon dioxide production of		Oxygen uptake of		Carbon dioxide production of		Oxygen uptake of		Carbon dioxide production of	
		1 mg	1 cc	1 mg	1 cc	1 mg	cc	mg	cc	mg	cc	mg	cc	mg
Carbohydrate	1·0	5·65	5·05*	3·57	5·05	2·56	1·12	1·59	1·12	2·21	0·198	0·280	0·198	0·390
Fat solid (oils)	0·71	9·35	4·60 (4·40)	3·22	6·5	3·06	2·04	2·91	1·44	2·84	0·218	0·310	0·154	0·327
Protein, plant	0·79	4·15	4·6	3·22	5·83	2·95	0·90	1·29	0·71	1·40	0·218	0·310	0·171	0·339
animal		3·90					0·85	1·22	0·67	1·32				
Dry plant matter and approximate human diet	0·82	4·0	4·7	3·29†	5·7	2·88	0·85	1·22	0·70	1·38	0·212	0·304	0·175	0·347

Notes: Volumes of gases are at N.T.P.

calories are small or gramme calories.

Density of Oxygen at N.T.P. is taken as 1·429 g per litre, of CO_2 as 1·977 g per litre.

* Glycogen 5·14, Starch 5·06, Sucrose 5·08.

† Ivlev's (1934) Oxycaloric equivalent is given as 3·38 cal per mg O_2.

Note that the range of oxygen-uptake figures associated with the liberation of one calorie is about 5 per cent, that for the carbon dioxide is about 18 per cent.

On the other hand a variety of physical properties of carbon dioxide are readily used for continuous measurement. In particular the thermal conductivity has been used in the katharometer[91, 692] for animals as small as bees and the strong absorption of infra-red radiation in certain bands for large-scale work[328, 465] and for animals the size of locusts[300] with an infra-red gas analyser. Carbon-dioxide output of aquatic organisms can be measured directly in closed vessels by chemical methods[456, 622] and from the change in pH.[761,762] All carbon-dioxide methods, of course, require that the R.Q. be independently determined except in the case of very approximate work.

FOOD-CONSUMPTION METHODS. The fourth approach to metabolic-rate measurement is by way of the food consumption. This requires a knowledge of the calorific coefficients of food and faeces, the measurement of their daily consumption and production on a dry weight basis and an allowance for the proportion of assimilation which is laid down in body tissues. The difficulties of obtaining calorific food analyses relating faeces to particular meals of food account for the fact that this method has rarely been used. Phillipson,[571, 572] however, has applied it to the harvestman (Opiliones) *Mitopus morio* with great success using published calorific content figures and assuming that body tissue added is negligible. By using foods of different colours he was able to distinguish the faeces due to particular meals. Slobodkin[658] has used a somewhat similar approach on the population scale in *Daphnia pulex* and other animals (see p. 166).

CHOICE OF METHODS. It is not feasible to provide general guidance on choice of methods here if only because factors such as available equipment, finance, purpose of the investigation and accuracy demanded are all likely to be important. For terrestrial animals of reasonable size the last method requires only a good balance to give results which apply *under field conditions* provided the order of accuracy of published calorific content figures is sufficient. The artificial conditions pertaining in most respirometers are often a serious disadvantage and a compromise between an approach to natural conditions, sufficient sensitivity for the organisms concerned, continuous recording of results and a minimum of guess-work on the Respiratory Quotients and calorific values of the foods are offered by the author's respirometer mentioned above.[441]

Part II

THE ECOLOGY OF SINGLE SPECIES POPULATIONS

Chapter 7

COLLECTION METHODS IN ECOLOGY

In the first part of this book was surveyed the kind of knowledge which results from ecological studies based on single animals, and it was shown that such "autecological" methods have their limitations because the most ecologically valid unit in nature is not the species or the individual but the population; it is only by studying the properties of whole populations that the necessary quantitative basis for ecological generalizations can be found. The next set of chapters is concerned with methods for first acquiring and secondly interpreting information about the ecology of populations consisting of a single species.

Since one must first catch one's animals, this chapter illustrates from examples, in the field of terrestrial ecology in particular, the kind of problems involved in doing so. Chapter 8 is concerned with how to obtain quantitative information from the catches, i.e. with sampling methods and the estimation of errors; also included here are some notes on the quantitative aspects of irregular or patchy distributions in space. Chapter 9 is concerned with the demographic properties of populations; their age structure, mortality and birth rate. In Chapter 10 the factors which determine the size of a population are discussed, both as regards the general level of abundance of the animals and also influences resulting in regular or irregular variations in size. Chapter 11 is concerned with the functional aspects of populations, in particular their metabolism, productivity, efficiency and related properties; this chapter concludes with a brief résumé of the properties of single species populations in preparation for Part III which is concerned with what happens in nature when numbers of such populations interact with each other.

Collection Methods for Community and Food-chain Studies

Ecological population studies tend to fall into two groups; first, the *community study* in which the census of a mixed population is intended for comparison with similar lists from other localities or from the same locality at different dates. This type of study is primarily concerned with the exact taxonomic position of the species present, estimates of their relative abundance and absolute numbers per unit of space are often not necessary. The demand is for a method of enumerating the different species equally fairly rather than that all counts should be absolutely correct. Even the first of these requirements is often difficult to achieve today. Thus, in the case of plankton, which is usually caught by means of nets, the larger animals tend to escape the net by swimming and the smaller ones by passing through the meshes, while in the use of heat-funnel methods for the extraction of soil animals, the more fragile animals tend to be killed by conditions of temperature and humidity which are necessary to make the more robust ones leave the soil. [435] The efficiency of such methods may vary also according to different physical conditions in the soil under study.

The second type of ecological study is limited to a single community and aims to trace the biological relationships between the different members. These are usually expressed qualitatively by means of *food chains* and quantitatively by what are often called *productivity* studies. In these cases it is necessary to know accurately the size of the populations of at least the more active species and how these vary in time and in age structure. This may demand the use of separate census methods and even different sampling techniques for each of a range of species. On the other hand, many rare or accidental species can often be neglected and the taxonomic work is usually much less exacting, while sampling techniques can sometimes be used which are only applicable to a peculiar habitat and are useless for comparing populations from a wide range of habitats. This implies that careful choice of the habitat in which investigations are to be carried on often justifies any extra preliminary labour. These points can be expressed by means of a table—

TABLE 7

	Aspects Demanding High Accuracy			
	Numerical Accuracy		Taxonomic Accuracy	
Type of analysis	Between species	Between habitats	Among species	Among habitats
Inter-community ("community studies")	Relative	Many but relative	All	High
Intra-community (food chain and "productivity" studies)	All	—	Selected	Less important

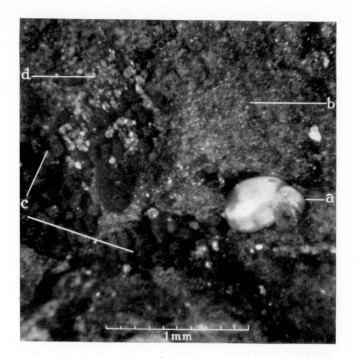

A Soil Mite *in situ*

Phthiracarus sp. (*a*) lying at the end of its tunnel in a piece of brown decayed wood (*b*). The cavity of the tunnel behind the mite is completely blocked by large faecal pellets (*c*). (*d*) is mineral soil. An example of Weis-Fogh and Haarløv's sectioning technique. (Photograph reproduced by permission of the authors.)

Obstacles to Accuracy

In so far as the methods of collection and census are technical processes peculiar to particular types of work, they have no place in this book. But, because they are the fundamental source of all information and involve difficulties which are often not anticipated, it is necessary to consider some examples of techniques and their limitations. Obviously the man who would make a census of an animal population is confronted with three main types of difficulty: the animals' mobility, their ability to conceal themselves and the unfamiliarity of the media they occupy, either because this is due to difference of physical state (solid or liquid instead of air) or of scale. These difficulties may be rather obvious, but it remains true that most of the inaccuracies of current techniques result from them. For instance, far more is known of the life history and general ecology of birds than of any other group of animals because observation, census and collection are made relatively easy for us by birds' conspicuousness, the fact that they inhabit the air, and their relatively large size. Only their mobility hinders their study and, in the case of flowering plants, which are even better known, this factor too operates in our favour. Similarly, the knowledge of butterflies is out of all proportion to their true abundance for the same reasons.

Direct Methods

The direct approach of trying to put oneself in the animal's place and studying it in the field by observation, as used by Fabre and his followers, is a fundamental and profitable one. Similar in approach are the use of the aqualung and of television[309] for studying the life of the sea-bed and a special soil microscope[383] mounted on a firm base which can be pushed into the side of a rapidly dug pit for the study of soil under nearly natural conditions. By this means features of the soil spaces inhabited by different kinds of organisms and the natural methods of growth of the bacteria and fungi were revealed.

A recent advance in this field[291, 294] is a method for preparing sections of soil and its inhabitants for microscopic examination. The soil is rapidly frozen, impregnated with agar, and cut in sections about $\frac{1}{2}$ mm thick, with all the living organisms in their natural positions. A number of photomicrographs (one of which is reproduced here as Plate 1) demonstrate how animals and micro-organisms can be preserved in this way without disturbance. Among other things the feeding habits of the animals can sometimes be deduced in this way and their very patchy distribution is given ecological meaning.

A final example of the use of direct methods in census work is provided by the estimation of bird numbers from their song. [124, 388a] It is possible to allow for the effects of relative noisiness and conspicuousness and to obtain reasonable estimates of density by means of transects.

Indirect Methods

In the greater part of terrestrial ecological work, however, indirect methods of sampling must be employed; the best way to appreciate the kinds of problems involved is to consider specific examples. In the Appendix to this chapter the main types of collecting methods are briefly reviewed. In general it will be seen that such methods can be separated into those involving mechanical separation (by means of sieves, flotation, etc.) and those in which the animals, owing to peculiarities in their behaviour, are either attracted or repelled into a place whence they can be easily removed. These we shall call *mechanical* and *behaviour* methods respectively. It will be seen that different types of method are suitable in different circumstances.

Adaptation of Methods to Problems

There is little prospect of a single universal method for the accurate sampling of terrestrial faunas being developed in the near future; methods should be adapted to the particular circumstances of the investigation and there is much room for further development in both mechanical and behaviour-type methods and also for combinations of these where animals are driven into media from which they are more readily extracted by mechanical methods. The former methods are always likely to underestimate populations to the extent that dormant stages, pupae, eggs and aestivating animals will not respond to the stimulus, while mechanical methods can cause over-estimates because recently dead animals are often difficult to distinguish from those which were alive at the time of sampling. The latter methods usually produce only dead animals, while the former can mostly be arranged to extract the animals alive.

The review of methods, mainly concerned with soil animals, provides examples of some of the kinds of difficulty which face the would-be student of animal populations. Errors due to the patchy distribution of the population (considered in the next chapter) are added to those due to the variable, and often unknown, efficiency of the extraction methods and make these harder to evaluate, especially as populations in the soil may change rapidly in time as well. Lest the reader become despondent, however, it should be mentioned that soil sampling is a notoriously difficult field when compared to sampling methods as a whole and also that, for many ecological purposes, where population sizes may range over several orders of magnitude, the accuracy obtainable by such methods is more than sufficient.

Appendix

COLLECTING METHODS

In the study of animal populations it is usually necessary to employ special methods for collecting or extracting the animals: information on population size cannot be obtained by direct observation.

Mechanical and Behaviour-type Methods

Such methods fall into two groups: those of the *mechanical* type, which employ some purely mechanical device to sweep or wash the animal from its surroundings, and those of the *behaviour* type, in which the animal is induced to move to some place from which it can be easily removed, by the use of attractive or repellent stimuli. The latter are often (and rather confusingly) called "automatic" methods by continental authors. Examples of mechanical methods are all kinds of land and water nets, sieves and various flotation devices depending on differences of surface tension or density. The practical difficulties associated with such methods are of three sorts: first, difficulties due to the non-selective nature of the catch, which often contains large quantities of unwanted material which must be further sorted; second, in the case of samples obtained by means of nets, difficulties due to the uncertainty about how much material has in fact been swept by the net and hence the true density of the organisms in nature; and third, again in the case of nets, the imperfect capture of populations whose members either escape the mouth of the net or can pass through its meshes.

Net Sampling

With regard to the last point it has been shown that freshwater larvae and nymphs, especially those of Ephemeroptera, are able to force their way through the meshes of nets usually thought much too small for this to happen while their ability to swim out of nets also varies with age and size;[425] both these effects, of course, cause a serious bias in age distribution figures.

With regard to the second point there has long been controversy about both the relative and the absolute accuracy of sweep-net collections[93, 169, 731] in terrestrial biology. The general and perhaps the most widely-accepted conclusion is that it is practically impossible to estimate the absolute densities of animals by means of sweep-nets, for they are nearly always selective and so give only a very broad idea of relative abundance of different species, and their efficiency varies in different types of vegetation rendering them rather inaccurate when the faunas of different places are to be compared.

In one comparative trial of methods[221] only 10 per cent of aphids and less than 1 per cent of thrips were caught in nets. The catch in grass also depends greatly on weather conditions because insects respond to changes of microclimate by vertical movements and a net sweeps the upper vegetation much more efficiently than the lower layers. By multiple regression analysis of microclimatic factors Hughes[331] was able to correct for this effect in the case of *Meromyza variegata* (a Chloropid fly), the most important factor reducing catching success being wind speed. This topic has also been considered in relation to large-scale weather factors by Wellington.[797] Provided the sweeping technique is well standardized, preferably with a single operator, net collections can give fairly reliable comparative figures for a succession of samples in the same area or in areas of very similar vegetation. A useful study of this sort was made by Kontkannen.[375]

Net collections are widely used to estimate the density of animals on foliages of trees, but the errors tend to be large and an alternative method[486] is available, although it does not appear to have been widely used. Adopted in the first place for sampling mites on orchard trees, this method involves collecting samples of leaves, so chosen as to be representative but to avoid bias on the part of the observer (see Chapter 8), and washing the animals off the leaves with soap solution. If large samples are taken, surprisingly consistent results can be obtained, but normally this would involve an impracticable amount of counting and sorting. However, by the use of a simple apparatus, aliquot samples can be drawn from the soap solution in such a way that their proportion to the whole is known. It would appear that this type of method could be used more extensively in sampling populations from heterogeneous habitats, and by examining larger aliquots for the less-abundant species it should be possible to obtain counts for species of very different densities.

Even where simple sampling and catching methods are employed, sound planning can produce clear-cut results with a minimum of effort, as is stressed by Hairston et al.[298] in relation to sampling the snail vectors of Bilharzia. In all ecological census work and especially in the applied field a definite appraisal of the accuracy required in relation to available manpower is essential for success. Various applications of sieving techniques are discussed in this and other papers in the bibliography.[352, 366, 818]

When it is not possible to relate density of animals to area or volume of habitat and provided the amount of cover does not vary appreciably it is often useful to express results in terms of numbers per unit of collecting *time*. In a useful discussion of principles Reynoldson[603] has shown how populations of increasing density are counted with progressively less efficiency—

Number collected per hour	3	6	56	226	367	529	720	947
True population	3	6	60	300	600	1,200	2,400	4,800
Proportion per cent	100	100	93	75	61	45	30	20

Other problems of this kind are treated by Hairston et al.[298]

Where animals themselves are difficult to find it is sometimes possible to use their traces. The use of pellet counts for estimating vole populations by Elton et al.[205] has been extended to other mammals. In one study Taylor and Williams[704] estimated the daily number of pellets produced by rabbits at 820 and the rate of disappearance of pellets at from 2 per cent to 4 per cent per day according to circumstances; from these figures they were able to obtain reliable estimates of the total rabbit population, as checked by independent counts.

Flotation Methods

Flotation methods, for the extraction of soil organisms, were first used before 1890 by the great Italian zoologist Antonio Berlese (who was also the inventor of the Berlese funnel, Berlese's mountant, the author of an excellent textbook of entomology and the founder of the modern study of "Myriapods" and of Acari). Berlese's flotation apparatus[32] (Fig. 11) was simple: a large boiling tube with a slightly-constricted neck was fitted with a plunger made from a bung at the end of a glass rod; the bung was the same diameter as the constricted neck. The material to be examined was placed in the tube and water was added; the suspension was agitated by moving the plunger up and down and then left for a short while to settle. The plunger was then drawn up into the constriction thus separating roughly the floating

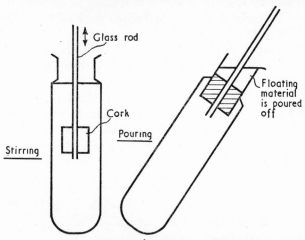

Glass rod

Cork

Pouring

Stirring

Floating material is poured off

FIG. 11.   BERLESE'S FLOTATION DEVICE

from the non-floating matter. The former was then poured off. The device was, of course, only intended for obtaining specimens for taxonomic study and was not intended to extract all the animals; however, Dr. F. A. Turk, who used it with Berlese, states that it was most effective.

As a result of extension of corn growing during war-time, the need was felt for an accurate method of estimating wireworms (larvae of Elaterid beetles). It was soon found that the usual method of washing soil through a set of sieves of progressively decreasing mesh is tedious and inefficient, as many young larvae are lost. The Ladell[395] apparatus was designed as an improvement on sieving for wireworms and produced much higher counts of the young stages. A full description of this large machine is unnecessary; soil is stirred in a tank with a strong magnesium sulphate solution in which all organic matter floats. Bubbles of air are simultaneously passed through the solution and carry plant and animal matter in a froth to the surface. The froth flows over a tank, in which heavy particles sink, and is then collected on a filter. Animal and vegetable particles are separated by hand. The main faults of this apparatus are that it causes damage to more delicate organisms and that the manual separation of plant and animal matter is inefficient, the magnesium sulphate solution is messy and the whole apparatus bulky and expensive. Some of these difficulties are overcome in Salt and Hollick's apparatus[625] in which soil samples are first frozen and thawed, to make them disintegrate more readily, and are then broken up on sieves with jets of water before being added to the magnesium sulphate flotation tank. Filtration follows flotation and the problem of separating plant and animal matter is overcome by the ingenious method of shaking the mixture in water and benzene; these two liquids do not mix, but come to rest one on top of the other and, since insect chitin is wetted by benzene and plant cellulose is not, the insects collect on the top and the plants underneath the "interface" between the two liquids. The task of removing the animals from the interface is rather unpleasant owing to the benzene fumes (paraffin is sometimes used instead). It has recently been greatly simplified by Raw,[596] who freezes the benzene and removes it as a block. This method is efficient and relatively simple for larger animals such as beetle larvae. Although the authors have claimed[626] that the method is good for small Arthropods as well, this is disputed by others who have tried to use it and have been concerned at low yields and the bad state of the resulting animals for taxonomic purposes.[215, 435, 479] It is generally believed that many animals which get tangled in the plant matter are lost or can only be separated, if at all, by very rough treatment. In soils where there is little organic matter and with the help of Raw's modification including the use of chemical treatments to break up clay soils, the method seems more promising for microfauna, even if tedious and unpleasant.

Further modifications are discussed by Davis[164] and simpler flotation methods have been used by Laurence[397] for separating the fauna of cow-pats and by Edwards for removing Symphyla from soil.[193]

A physically simple method for separating aquatic Nematodes from mud by repeated decantation is of interest because Capstick[92] introduced a mathematical theory for analysis of aliquot samples of the

Nematodes suspended in water. His method for detecting significant differences between aliquots from different samples with a minimum of labour should provide a useful tool in other fields where reliable aliquots can be obtained.

A variety of other washing and floating methods have been used at different times, [366] one of the more promising principles which still awaits full development being the use of an upward stream of water in a long narrow funnel to sort objects according to their rates of sinking.

Behaviour-type Methods

Many well-known devices in everyday use depend on the principle of attracting or driving an animal to a place where it is easier to catch or examine. Occasionally no specific lure or repellent is used, but the animal's random wanderings are relied on to bring it to a place from which it cannot escape. This is the idea behind pitfall traps, which are much used on the continent and often consist of a simple glass jar with some preservative at the bottom, either an organic mercurial substance such as phenyl mercuric acetate or formaldehyde which is cheaper but preserves animals less well. (Very dilute solutions of the former rapidly erode aluminium vessels—a practical point worth bearing in mind.) [319, 320, 652]

A development of the pitfall trap is Williams' [809] clock-operated trap which automatically changes the collecting vessel at known intervals. By baiting pitfall traps with attractant substances, in this case decaying foods such as fish, melon and cornflower, Walker [775] demonstrated that, in a forest litter, there is a wide range of highly selective species which will come readily to each of these baits but will not visit others; unbaited traps mainly collect carnivorous forms. Another trap which relies on no specific attractant or repellent is the emergence trap, variations on which have long been used by entomologists for collecting insects emerging from pupae. [351] Mundie [478] gives a useful review of types suitable for forms with aquatic larvae.

Repellents are used for bringing earthworms to the surface of the soil, a solution of $\frac{1}{4}$ oz potassium permanganate in a gallon of water per square yard being usual. [213] This method does not give a very representative sample of the earthworm fauna as the deeper-living larger species often do not react, nor do aestivating worms, and the efficiency depends on the dampness of the soil. [288] Recent innovations described by Raw[597] include the use of dilute formalin which is more effective in stimulating the worms, and a combination of sieving, hand sorting and flotation, each of which processes has advantages in different types of soil. Electric currents have been used as a stimulus but the current consumption is very high and there are many difficulties of interpretation.[629]

The live trap is an example of a method using an attractive stimulus; it is widely used by mammal workers, who are responsible for many recent improvements, especially in the use of "pre-baiting"[106] (arranging that the trap can be entered and food taken for a period without the animal being caught, so that natural suspicions of a new object are overcome and the habit of visiting traps becomes established in the population). Various difficulties in the use of these traps are now recognized. By placing smoked paper beneath the traps it has been shown[641] that less than 50 per cent of approaches result in captures and the liability of animals to be caught has been related to their position in the social hierarchy in the case of voles.[685] Poisoned bait has been used for slug sampling.[36]

In soil work the most widely-used method is that employing a combination of heat and desiccation as a repellent.[435] The Berlese funnel[44] and its successor the Tullgren funnel[736] are examples. The soil or other medium is suspended in a sieve over a funnel and heated; the animals drop into the funnel and are collected at the bottom in preservative. The avoidance of condensation at the sides of the funnels, resulting in the trapping and loss of delicate animals, is an important step introduced by Haarløv[290] and the establishment of steep temperature and humidity gradients in undisturbed blocks of soil are now known to be preferable to uncontrolled heating of broken up material. Thus a combination of repellent and attractant conditions is applied in the same apparatus (Plate II).[435, 437, 440] Although the precise mode of operation varies both with the medium being treated and the animals to be extracted, techniques have now been devised for most species which achieve very high yields approaching complete extraction. In addition to heat, other repellents, including the vapour of substances such as dimethyl phthalate can extract certain groups in a highly selective manner; this is a principle not yet fully exploited.[435] A principle related to that of the Tullgren funnel has been used by Williams,[811] who extracts almost all groups of mud-dwelling invertebrates by placing a sample beneath a layer of sand and flooding both with water. The animals leave the mud (because of lack of oxygen?) and can easily be floated out of the sand.

Rather similar principles are used in a funnel filled with water;[29, 504] this type of funnel, in which the aquatic component of the soil fauna swims out into the water and then sinks as a result of the high temperature, is used for collecting Nematoda, Enchytraeidae, Rotifera and similar groups and is often highly efficient.

An improved method for extracting Enchytraeidae[507] is of interest because it promises to be useful for extracting other groups of animals also and because it effectively combines a funnel-type method with a mechanical one. The soil sample is placed in a vertical cylinder which is open at both ends; the lower end is blocked by washed pebbles and the upper end by clean sand and these are separated from the soil by wire gauze. The pebbles stand in a warm water bath and the sand is kept cool by circulating cold water through lead tubes buried in it. The Enchytraeidae have a natural tendency to move upwards, and they are driven into the sand by the heat. They are removed from the sand by a simple flotation process and the whole procedure is very quick and efficient. In a trial of the wet funnel against Nielsen's method Peachey[561] found that each had advantages in certain kinds of soil and with different age groups and species of Enchytraeidae.

Only a brief résumé, with emphasis on principles, of extraction methods has been possible in this chapter; further details are given in special reviews of the subject.[366, 441a]

The funnel-type methods have advantages on expeditions and in other conditions where only simple methods are possible.[435, 624] The resulting sample is clean and requires no further treatment. The disadvantages are evident: the efficiency of extraction varies with different groups of animals and with the type of soil being investigated and it is essential to make independent estimates of efficiency if quantitative work is being undertaken.

Chapter 8

THE ESTIMATION OF ANIMAL NUMBERS

THE last chapter was concerned with the physical process of obtaining collections of animals and counting them, regardless of whether the collections constitute the entire population under study or, as is usually the case, a small sample, coming from a known area or constituting a known proportion of the whole. Before proceeding with the application of this information about the population, it is necessary, in this chapter, to consider the experimental design of such counting procedures and the interpretation of the figures which are obtained.

Statistics in Ecology

From the point of view of the practising ecologist one of his most characteristic (and some would say the most monotonous) activities is the estimation of the sizes of populations. In certain types of work the estimates may be based on complete counts of whole populations; this is often done in studies of conspicuous animals such as birds. In most cases, however, the count is incomplete first because more or less arbitrary limits have to be imposed on the area of study and second because it is only possible to study a small sample of the population instead of the whole. Much of the art of conducting an ecological inquiry lies in being able to obtain the required degree of accuracy of estimation with a minimum of labour and it is here that statistical methods come into their own.

The use of statistical methods in biology is sometimes objected to on the ground that they do not lead to new ideas and discoveries which could not be made by a good observer with much less time and effort. However, in fields such as population ecology, where hypotheses mainly concern quantitative data, it is not possible by mere observation to prove or disprove them, nor to decide by intuition how much difference there must be between two sets of figures before they can be regarded as describing different populations.

The Nature of Biological Errors

Furthermore, apart from observational errors of measurement such as are encountered in the more "exact" sciences of physics and chemistry, biological measurements are usually subject to additional errors of a different type. For instance, whereas the physicist can usually isolate phenomena and relate changes of one factor at a time to a set of measurements, most biological experiments cannot be isolated in this way because throughout a number of factors are usually operating simultaneously; thus the results are liable to a type of "error" which is due to many uncontrolled but often *measurable* influences.

In most biological experiments errors due to uncontrolled factors are so great as completely to outweigh observational errors, and without some means of measuring, allowing for, and discounting their effects only inconclusive results can be obtained. A method for sorting out the effects of such factors was invented by Professor R. A. Fisher[222a] and is called the "analysis of variance." Probably this method has produced as great a revolution in biological technique as the appreciation of the significance of population studies has in biological theory.

Excellent texts exist explaining the use of statistical methods,[29b,315,592] that of Snedecor[668a] being the author's favourite, and it would be neither possible nor useful to attempt to condense instructions for carrying them out here. It is quite possible for the biologist with a minimum of mathematical training to learn to operate such methods intelligently and to know when to turn for help to the statistician.

Planning a Sampling Routine

In order that a sampling programme can be planned and it can be decided how many, how frequent and of what size the samples should be, it is well worth while to go to the trouble of making some preliminary investigations. A rough programme for beginning such a study which the author has learned "the hard way" is the following.

1. TYPES OF PROBLEM TO BE STUDIED. One must come to a clear decision about whether one is attempting an inter-community or an intra-community analysis, as outlined at the beginning of Chapter 7. This means deciding whether one is aiming to cover a wide range of species or habitats, whether the proposed techniques are suitable for the animals and communities to be sampled and whether comparative or absolute densities are to be estimated. This is important because it is, at the present time, usually impossible to make a complete and accurate census of all the animal groups in one habitat, and to do so over a range of habitats is beyond the powers of one man; therefore

something has to be sacrificed. The first sacrifice, of course, should be preconceptions about a particular sampling area which has been selected on purely irrelevant grounds. So a list of minimum requirements and another of maximum assets in the form of man-hours and effective counting and sorting power, are probably a good starting-off point.

2. PRELIMINARY SAMPLING. In order to obtain a general idea of the nature of the sampling problems involved it is wise at this stage to make a field visit and, using any available means and not committing oneself to a programme of construction of elaborate sampling apparatus, to take a set of preliminary samples in order to get an idea of the range of species and numbers of animals involved. If it is a soil study, this is the stage for some rude shocks and for a further perusal of item 1. Elaborate plans for the preliminary survey are a waste of time because seasonal change, crude methods, and lack of experience will usually have the effect of reducing the accuracy of any results to no better than an order of magnitude. It is sufficient at this stage to take samples along a transect line which runs parallel to some obvious ecological gradient, such as one of moisture content in the case of soil work; a most reprehensible practice for the more accurate main investigation as we shall see. If it is probable that knowledge of absolute abundance and detailed distribution will be needed it is advisable to take the samples in pairs and to perform an analysis of variance comparing variance between and within pairs (see below).

3. TYPES OF DISTRIBUTION. This is a further stage of thinking and decision. A choice has been made between an inter-community investigation involving comparative census methods and a wide range of animals, and an intra-community investigation (such as a "food-chain" or "productivity" study) involving an absolute census probably confined to a few groups of animals at a time. A further decision must now be reached and there is only space here to review the problem[315] briefly. If one were to make a thorough and complete count of a square metre of English meadow soil using a microscope (a process which would require at least three years and would leave one in no fit state for further scientific work) one would find that the different groups of animals varied enormously in the patchiness of their distribution. One species, such as the Oribatid mite *Ceratoppia bipilis*, for example, would show a rather uniform distribution which would probably conform fairly closely to that which would result

from scattering grains of sand by some random process on a metre square tablecloth. Such a "random" distribution is described mathematically by the Poisson series in which the numbers of uniform samples selected at random containing 1, 2, 3, 4, . . . individuals conform to successive terms of the series

$$Ne^{-m} \left(1, m, \frac{m^2}{2!}, \frac{m^3}{3!}, \cdots \right)$$

where m is the mean number of occurrences, N is the total number of observations, e is the root of Napierian logarithms.

The special property of the Poisson series is that if one determines the variance of the figures for the number of animals per sample, this will be equal to the average number. (The variance is the mean of the squares of the deviations of the separate counts from their mean.) Now this situation in which the variance is equal to the mean and the Poisson distribution applies is unusual in practical sampling of animal communities; it is more usual to find that the variance is much greater than the mean. That is to say, the range of number classes is greater than would be expected by chance or, in other words, the population is "patchy" or "clumped." It is not surprising that this should be so, for there are many biological influences which lead to the members of a species being grouped together in clumps: food, water, or air may be unevenly distributed, there may be patches where the animals simply cannot exist as in stony soil or tussocky areas of vegetation, eggs may be laid in batches and the young may be rather inactive as with most fly larvae in soil, or they may show a positive tendency to congregate in a social way, e.g. ants, and, perhaps, some Staphilinid beetles. (Figs. 12 and 13.)

Thus, at the other extreme to *Ceratoppia bipilis*, we have animals like the larvae of the crane fly, *Tipula*, which, even when quite large, tend to remain in batches of thirty or so individuals, the batches being, perhaps, ten to the square metre and occupying an area of one or two square centimetres each.

Obviously the technique of sampling should be different for the crane-fly larvae and for the Oribatid despite the fact that both may easily occur at a density of 300 per square metre in the soil.

If the results of a preliminary sample are used to plot the number of samples containing x individuals (vertically) and the number x of individuals per sample horizontally (Fig. 12) the histogram which results will not be symmetrical in the case of data derived from a Poisson distribution but will be skew with an s-shaped rising limb and a more gradual concave falling limb. In most natural populations the bulk of the samples will be more spread out than this, owing to the larger proportion of samples containing larger and smaller numbers.

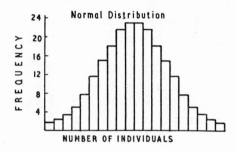

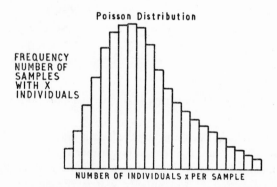

Fig. 12. Normal and Poisson Distributions: Frequency Histograms

Ordinate: Frequency, i.e. number of samples containing *x* individuals.
Abscissa: Number of individuals *x* per sample.

One distribution which frequently seems to fit such populations is the *negative binomial*. This is derived from the Poisson but is based on the hypothesis that the mean, instead of being fixed, varies in a random manner.[22, 57] This would apply, for instance, to a population grouped in patches, with the patches distributed at random and the individuals within the patches distributed logarithmically.

To specify such a distribution naturally requires two parameters, the mean m and a measure of the variability of m, k; k is defined by $s^2 = m + k\,m^2$ where s^2 is the variance of the observations. When k approaches infinity the negative binomial distribution becomes the same as the Poisson; when it approaches zero this indicates a population becoming more and more clumped or *"under dispersed"* to use the conventional jargon (Fig. 13).

A special case of the negative binomial distribution arises when those units containing no individuals are disregarded; in this case we have a

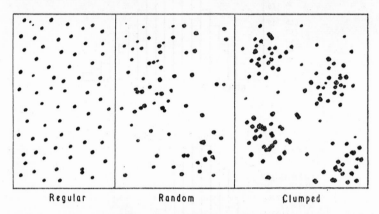

Regular   Random   Clumped

FIG. 13. TYPES OF DISTRIBUTION (REGULAR, RANDOM, AND CLUMPED)

set of figures which is described by the logarithmic series of Fisher and Williams,[808, 808a] and is discussed in Chapter 13.

The methods for testing a set of data to find out what distribution they fit are discussed by Anscombe[22] Waters[786] and Quenouille.[592] Since both the above distributions have a variance which increases with the mean, and since methods for detecting valid differences in size between sets of samples assume a stable variance, it is necessary to "transform" raw data if such tests of significance are to be applied.

If the variance and the mean are approximately equal (Poisson) the square roots of the values should be used.[668a] When the counts in the groups 0–1, 1–2, 2–4, 4–8, 8–16 and so on are symmetrically distributed, a logarithmic transformation is appropriate.[592] The correct transformation for the negative binomial can be obtained from a preliminary sampling by plotting the standard deviation s (vertically) against the mean (horizontally) and drawing a line through the points. Where this

PLATE II (a)

Multiple Tullgren funnel apparatus designed to ensure hot dry conditions above the samples and cool moist conditions below. Samples in trays are suspended between heaters (now raised on pulleys) and airconditioned cabinet containing funnels into which the animals fall.
(Samples are $4\frac{1}{2}$ in. diameter = 100 cm² area.)

PLATE II (*b*)

Multiple extraction apparatus for soils which can be sampled with a core sampler (*left*). Samples in plastic rings are fitted over aluminium cans which dip into cold water, thus ensuring a steep gradient of temperature and humidity. (Samples are $2\frac{1}{4}$ in. diameter = 25 cm² area.)

cuts the horizontal axis is the value for k and the raw data are then transformed by log $(x + k)$.[315]

A further distribution which, according to Taylor[703] frequently fits biological data better than the negative binomial is the Power Series. This is based on the equation $s^2 = am^b$ where—

s^2 = variance
m = mean
a = constant depending on sample size
b = constant indicating extent of aggregation.

Taylor provides a number of examples in which b varies from 0·7 to 3·08 and also tests of significance of fit. It should be remembered, of course, that the type of distribution followed by living populations is not an immutable property of the species of the habitat. Naylor,[482] for instance, showed that, as density in *Tribolium confusum* populations increases the distribution changes from aggregated to random and then uniform. Also females tended to be less aggregated than males at a given density. Useful examples of practical experience in this field include Hartenstein's[305] with forest soil Arthropods and Jones and Mollinson's[354] with patchy distributions of bacterial colonies. Both these papers provide worked examples.

One of the least satisfactory features of attempts to apply a distribution analysis of this kind to a practical situation is that one is assuming that the sample unit is considerably smaller than the population pattern, otherwise results obtained are dependent on the size of the sample unit.[274, 283] The obvious solution of employing very small, very numerous sample units is often not practicable.

Morisita[471] describes a distribution in which this effect is overcome over a considerable range of quadrat size. His index is—

$$I_\delta = q \frac{\left(\sum_{t=1}^{q} fn_i{}^2 - N \right)}{N(N-1)}$$

q = number of quadrats taken at random
N = total number of individuals from all quadrats
n_i = number of individuals in each size group
i = size group classes, 0, 1, 2, 3. . .
f = number of quadrats belonging to the appropriate size group

$$N = \sum_{i=1}^{q} n_i$$

This index is less than, equal to or greater than unity in a uniform, random or clumped population respectively. It is independent of population size when the population is randomly distributed because the part of the equation in brackets equals $\frac{1}{q}$ when the observations fit a Poisson series. When the distribution is uniform it increases and when patchy it decreases towards unity as sample size is increased. The index is thus independent of sample size provided this is not too large. In practice it seems that "too large" a quadrat will be one containing more than about five or a whole patch of individuals, but the original work should be consulted before attempting to use this technique in practice.

The effect of sample size on index of dispersion does not apply to a different method of studying density and distribution pattern which is now used by plant ecologists but is unfortunately restricted to static populations. This involves measuring distances from one individual to another and thus obtaining samples of distance measurements. [469, 470] The literature is covered in a recent review by Pielou[575] who advocates the use of measurements from a random point to the nearest plants rather than from plant to plant. He calculates, from a sample of distance measurements and an independent measure of density, a statistic α which equals $\pi D \omega$

where $D =$ density

$\omega =$ the mean of the squares of the point-to-plant distances.

α is less than, equal to or greater than unity as the population changes from regular to random and patchy.

A somewhat similar approach is due to Hughes[333] (also tested for Enchytraeids in soil by Peachey[561]), who set out to determine from the densities of paired samples at the two ends of a sample number of "*tie-lines*" of fixed length, the magnitude of pattern and range of densities which would in fact be found if a complete system of density contours could be drawn. Although based on a somewhat restrictive model Hughes' approach appears to constitute a distinct advance in this field.

4. RANDOMIZATION. A further decision has now to be made, again with the aid of literature, [223a, 282a, 827a] namely on what principle to decide the exact position of each sample on the ground. To estimate the size of a population by means of a sample is to indulge in statistics. One of the first rules is that the samples themselves should be distributed

without bias. This is not always as simple as it sounds and by far the best way is to use a method which depends on a table of random numbers.

The samples themselves may be distributed along a straight line or transect, the points at which to sample being determined by their distance from one end. This method, which is very widely used, is not free from error, especially where it is used to relate animal distribution to a known or suspected physical gradient. The exact procedure adopted should be related to the uniformity of the material,[442a] quadrats being more efficient for uniform and transects for non-uniform distributions. Combinations of the two are useful in certain cases.

In a uniform environment undoubtedly the most reliable method for obtaining a representative sample is to lay down a two-dimensional physical grid on the ground, to number the squares of the grid, and to select the squares in which samples are to be taken by means of a table of random numbers. Those numbers which are drawn for a second time are rejected. Usually the samples themselves are smaller than the squares of the grid and, in this case, of course, it is necessary to determine the exact position of sampling as being at some particular point in the square, usually the exact centre or one of the corners. The essential point is that there must be no room for personal choice in determining the sampling point. When a very extensive investigation is planned the process of selecting squares by a table of random numbers becomes very tedious, especially towards the end of an experiment in which a high proportion of the numbers have been "used" because the proportion of already-used numbers increases. In this case it is best to have all the possible numbers written on cards or counters and to mix these in some machine such as is used for gambling. Numbers once drawn are not returned to the machine and, provided all counters are the same in weight and size, there can be no objection to this method.

Random sampling has an annoying property of resulting in a number of sample units aggregated in one portion of the study area. A practice which apparently involves no bias and overcomes this difficulty is that of *stratified random sampling* in which the area is divided first into a number of sub-areas and these are then sampled at random. The results from the sub-areas represent replicates and differences between them can be detected by analysis of variance (see below). When absolute mean densities are not required but only comparative figures for density *within* an area, random sampling is not, of course, necessary and regular samples on a grid or transect will give better coverage, although there is a possibility of their "resonating" with any regular pattern in line samples.[812] Finally it must be remembered that the existence and extent of patchiness is not an immutable characteristic of the species. It varies with age and season and also, as is discussed in Chapter 13, with density.

The above applies to those cases where one wishes to sample truly at random and where the area of medium studied is superficially uniform. In many cases, however, this is not so: a very common type of terrestrial plant community contains a number of species of plant interspersed with one another in an irregular pattern. In such a case one may be interested in restricting one's samples to one or more of the plant types. Strictly, the thing to do in this case is to map the area and consider for selection of sampling points only those squares in the map which fall within the vegetation type, or types, selected. Sometimes, when a very large area is involved and the vegetation pattern is small, this becomes practically impossible and here an alternative is to use a coarse grid and table of random numbers to select sampling "centres" and to choose the nearest example of the required vegetation types to these, but even here, a serious difficulty is that the exact placing of the samples remains at the discretion of the experimenter. The use of a dart or similar device, to be thrown from the point selected on the grid is one way out of the difficulty. In preliminary work a simpler and frequently used technique involves throwing some object, that will not roll into the area, choosing the nearest patches of the required vegetation to the place where the object falls. The process is then repeated. Sources of error, which can be reduced by intelligent application of the method, are that a too even distance of throw may lead to a more even distribution of samples than random and that, if the area is large, one is almost bound to make a "circular tour" which will tend to have the same effect.

In both the latter techniques, which do away with detailed mapping, a further difficulty is that, when the samples are much smaller than the patches of vegetation, one is faced with the decision as to whether to sample only in the centres of the patches or whether to attempt to sample the edge area as well. In most cases it is best to face the problem squarely and take separate sets of samples for centres and edges of vegetation types.

These practical points have been treated in some detail because they frequently occur and are not usually treated in the statistical textbooks. There is nothing theoretically wrong in attempting to confine the samples to certain vegetation types provided that the fact is recognized in the analysis. In fact, the demonstration by Watt[787] of the "micro-succession" of different species of plants in the same vegetation type shows that an area containing a constant proportion of plant species may in fact be undergoing continuous replacement of one species by another. This makes it almost imperative for the animal ecologist to take the plant pattern into account. However, two conclusions which the author has reached from soil work of this nature are (1) that, except for a few very specific herbivores, the relative proportions of the different species do not vary much in the different plant types in the same plant community; however (2), the *total numbers* of all species frequently have a strong tendency to vary in unison locally, in a way which is usually more easy to relate to physical and micro-topographical factors, such as moisture, shelter from desiccation and extremes of heat, accumulation of vegetable debris in hollows and other features which are associated more with the life forms of the plants than with their taxonomy.

In a *Molinia* fen at Cothill, which is almost certainly an example of a "Watt" community pattern, it was found[434] that the density of soil animals in the dominant plant types, *Molinia coerulea*, *Deschampsia caespitosa* and *Juncus subnodulosus*, varied greatly, being approximately in the ratio 3–3–1 for Collembola and 9–6–1 for Oribatid mites. However, no single example of the 20 dominant Collembola and 36 dominant Oribatid mite species was wholly confined to one plant type and the proportions of the different species in the three plant types at any one time was surprisingly constant.

5. NUMBER AND SIZE OF SAMPLES. The sampling programme should now be falling into some sort of shape. Decisions should be possible about the relative or absolute accuracy of the samples, about the numbers of groups of organisms to be sampled and hence whether more than one set of samples, to be treated by different techniques, is necessary, about the type of distribution hypothesis that will be made in order to assess errors and the method of determining the exact positions where the samples are to be taken. By reference to the balance sheet suggested earlier it should be possible to decide the quantity of material to be sorted in each sampling period and it only

remains, therefore, to decide how frequently to sample and whether to take many small or few large samples, in order to obtain the maximum sampling efficiency.

In temperate climates, at least, the influence of the annual cycle is usually an overriding one and it is usual to find evidence of some sort of an annual cycle in animal numbers. The main factor controlling how frequently one should sample within the year is the number of subsidiary cycles within the annual one, and this, in turn, usually depends on the number of generations the animal has per annum. If this information is not available it should be obtained as early as possible. On the whole, all but the smallest invertebrates, such as Protozoa, Nematoda, and Collembola, have only one or a few generations per annum, and it is surprising what a high proportion of vertebrates have only a single reproductive period per season.

To determine on weekly sampling rather than monthly is not such an irrevocably serious decision to make as might at first appear unless there is great weekly variation in numbers. By use of the analysis of variance technique one can considerably reduce the numbers of samples taken on each occasion. However, on the whole, monthly samplings are usually adequate if only one or two large cycles of numbers can be anticipated and one does not require knowledge of the exact timing of the maximum and minimum population periods.

The final set of decisions concerns the question of size versus number of samples. [95, 223a, 322a, 617a, 827a] If it has been decided to make use of the negative binomial distribution method a trial preliminary experiment should be made to determine for each species whether the Poisson or the negative binomial distribution fits best. (A model experiment is given in Barnes and Stanbury's paper. [35a]) In the latter case, of course, the size of the samples is determined by the abundance of the species of greatest interest because it should be of the order of size of the mean distance apart of the clumps. The error can be calculated using the formula given by Thomas [712] and thence the number of samples necessary for a given degree of accuracy can be computed.

In the more conventional case, where random distribution is assumed, one is usually trying to sample a considerable number of different species having a great range of densities and one may be content with a less accurate abundance determination. A number of factors should then be considered. Arguments for few large samples are the smaller handling labour (in some techniques such as flotation techniques for soil this is important), while ambiguities about the exact size of the sample and difficulties due to "edge effects," which in very small samples lead to inaccuracy, are reduced. As arguments for many small samples we have the fact that they cover a wider range of the habitat and so are more representative. The statistical error (in conjunction with analysis by several factors) tends to be reduced because one has more degrees of freedom. It is possible to group the samples in such a way as to allow for many visible sources of variation (see below). It is desirable that the number of animals in a sample should be a convenient number for a "counting session," say the order of one hundred or so.

It is quite impossible in this more widely-ranging type of sampling to lay down hard-and-fast rules. All these factors should be considered. In a very general way it may be said that a desirable sampling layout for about 30 per cent accuracy in soil sampling where distribution is patchy is one which involves about 30 samples which are big enough to contain tens rather than hundreds or units of the more abundant organisms. For English meadow and woodland soils 10 sq cm area ($\frac{1}{1000}$ sq m) is satisfactory for Acari, Collembola, etc., about 1 sq cm ($\frac{1}{10000}$ sq m) for Nematoda, about 1 sq dm ($\frac{1}{100}$ sq m) for abundant woodlice, Staphilinid beetles, Enchytraeid worms, and about 1 sq m for earthworms and larger insects. It cannot be too strongly emphasized, however, that these sizes are only approximate and that they will vary with habitat, season and the focus of attention of the investigation.

Line Transects

Clearly visible or audible species can be sampled by means of counts along a transect and this technique has been used for estimating bird numbers in particular. A model based on random encounters such as would apply to molecules has been used by Yapp[827] to obtain the formula—

$$D = z/(2RV)$$

where D = density of population studied

z = number of encounters per unit time

R = radial range required to effect an encounter

V = mean velocity of organisms relative to that of the observer.

The use and limitations of the formula have been further discussed by Skellam.[651]

Sequential Sampling

Under certain circumstances it is unnecessary to make a detailed enumeration or even to obtain an accurate estimate of the numbers of

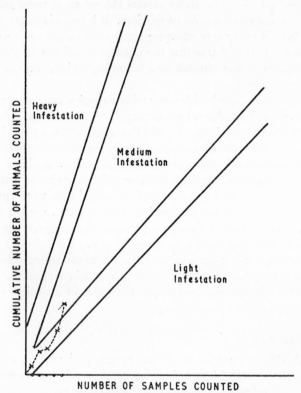

FIG. 14. A SEQUENTIAL ANALYSIS GRAPH

The crosses represent the numbers present in a series of sample units. To begin with the classification is uncertain but by the fifth sample unit the sample is shown to come from a medium infestation.

individuals on an area basis; one wishes, on the other hand, to survey a considerable area and to locate accurately those parts of it where a given species is absent, rare, moderately abundant or very numerous. Such are often the requirements of surveys in crops or semi-natural vegetation of pest insects, for instance, and it would obviously be unprofitable, if not impossible, to carry out complete and satisfactory sample surveys of large and extensive areas by conventional methods of investigation.

In such cases, it is possible to compare the numbers of the particular animal found in each of a succession of samples with those to be expected if one of several alternative hypotheses are true. For instance, the hypotheses might all assume a Poisson distribution (in which the variance is equal to the mean) and one that the mean density lies between 0 and 1 animal per sq m, the second that it lies between 1 and 10 per sq m, and the third that it is more dense than 10 per sq m. The figures actually obtained, as successive square metres are examined, are then compared with those to be expected on the three hypotheses (Fig. 14). As soon as the criteria of density and error have been satisfied, counting is stopped, and that area is recorded as being heavily, lightly or insignificantly infested. Evidently the details of determining the parameters of the hypotheses require some care, but the advantage of such a method is obvious: the precision of the counting is controlled by the stringency of the hypotheses used but no time is wasted counting large numbers of animals in densely inhabited areas or searching large areas where animals are scarce. An example of the biological application of sequential sampling, which was originally developed for use in controlling the tolerances of manufactured products, is the Canadian spruce budworm surveys in which egg masses are counted by this method.[472a, 473] Practical details including calculations and how to allow for non-random distributions are given by Waters.[786]

A Method for Sparsely-distributed and Fast-moving Animals: the "Lincoln" Index

Hitherto, we have been concerned with the estimation of numbers by the relatively direct method of taking samples which are a known proportion of the total area under examination. This type of method is possible with media such as soil, bottom mud and some types of rather uniform vegetation; it is not suitable for very active animals or those which are very sparsely distributed. Aerial, water-living active forms such as fish and wide-ranging terrestrial animals such as mammals, as well as the inhabitants of trees and similar difficult habitats demand an alternative method. For this purpose the *Lincoln Index* or *marking-and-recapture* method is normally used.

There is an extensive literature[29a, 180a, 345a, 345b, 402a, 404a, 405] on the practical application of this method which was probably first used in his studies on benthos by Petersen,[569b] and it is not proposed to give details here since these vary with the animals and habitats concerned. The outstanding feature of the method is that a number (say a) animals are captured alive, marked with an identification mark and released. Trapping (in the case of small mammals, birds and fish) or capture by means of nets or by other means (for fish and insects) is then repeated and, from the proportion of previously-marked animals (r) to the total of animals in the catch (b), an estimate is made of the whole population (x) which might have been caught in the traps. (In the simplest case $x = \dfrac{ab}{r}$.) This estimate depends, of course, on the assumption that (1) the marked animals will have mixed at random among the population as a whole; (2) there is no immigration to or emigration from the population; (3) there is no tendency for animals which have already been trapped to avoid or seek out the traps. None of these assumptions is always correct and various devices are used to avoid or measure these effects.

If a continuous series of such capture and release operations is performed it is possible to follow trends in the population and to estimate some of those factors, such as births and deaths, immigration and emigration, which tend to alter the population size. When the method is combined with the recording of age, weight, or size it can provide information for the construction of life tables and other demographic data.

The method is the only possible one for large sparse populations of which a fairly high proportion is involved in the sampling (for example, small mammals) and in which the removal of large numbers by normal sampling methods would radically alter the population being studied. However, there are many sources of error involved which it is extremely difficult to estimate and the literature should be studied with care before such methods are tried on a field scale. A critical study[405] has recently shown that many of the assumptions normally made in applying the method can be false.

A useful paper in language which is easily understood by the non-mathematician is Bailey's,[29a] in which means of improving the accuracy of estimates and of estimating their errors are discussed.

Useful practical exercises and worked examples are provided in a book by Andrewartha.[15a]

Further papers on the application of the Lincoln Index to particular problems include Macleod's[444] on mobile insects which provide few recaptures and where one massive release is preferred to serial release, Welch's[796] which is concerned with estimates of error in similar populations, Turner's[738] which compares the Lincoln Index with a nearest-neighbour method and Orians' and Leslie's[537] which describes the failure of the method in a population of birds whose liability to capture varies with age. A similar effect in which risk of capture is related to "social status" in small mammals has also been detected by Southern.[685]

Methods of Marking

Marking methods depend on the animals; clipping pieces from the ears of mammals or fins of fish is not highly satisfactory; depilatories have been used to mark mammals.[106a] Numbered plastic discs, held with a silver wire passed through a dorsal fin or the body, are often used for fish and subcutaneous plastic markers have also been used. The legs of birds are ringed with aluminium and of mammals with Monel bands.[106a] Rapid drying cellulose paints or nail varnish which can be coded by colour and position on the body are much used for invertebrates such as insects.[180a] The advantage of these methods is that individuals or at least groups caught on the same day can be recognized again.

The whole field of marking methods has been surveyed in a symposium reported in *Ecology*.[698] In addition Skuhravy describes a special wing-clipping forceps for marking beetles[652] and the use of radio isotopes as markers are discussed for insects by Lindquist *et al.*[411, 827b] and by Odum *et al.*[528] and for small mammals by Godfrey.[268, 269]

Variance and its Analysis

A number of indirect references have been made to the way in which the effects of variation of vegetation or soil type or other superficially apparent factors can be allowed for in designing a sampling system. It is not possible here to go into a subject which should be part of the equipment of every practising ecologist, and the reader must be referred to the statistical textbooks.[222a, 668a] However, it is worth considering briefly the implications of these techniques for ecology. First, it should be realized that by use of the analysis of variance we can not only "allow for" variations in position and time of sampling, which may at first appear to be unfortunate complications in the situation, but can measure their contribution to the general variability of the result. Thus, both the relative effect of the different factors is assessed and the variability of the results is reduced. This has enormous advantages which are perhaps best appreciated from an example.

In statistical jargon the whole batch of lumps of soil constitute a (monthly) *sample* and the individual "lumps" are called *sampling units*. Biologists frequently use variants of this nomenclature but it is generally agreed that we should observe the statisticians' convention. In the main series of the fen study carried out by the author[434] a total of 390 sampling units were involved. These were divided between thirteen months (30 units each), three plant types (130 units each), five sampling positions (78 units each), and were always placed in pairs. If two sampling units were taken at random from the 390 they would probably appear to be very different and indeed the total "error" is very large (that is to say, the square root of the average of the squares of the deviations of the individual figures from the average figure is high; this parameter is usually called the *standard error*). However, by the analysis of variance technique (*variance* is the square of the *standard error*), this large variance is split up between all the different factors which the experimenter can recognize as being likely to influence the figures. In this case these factors (see Table 8) were—

(i) the time factor (a large annual "cycle" was demonstrated);

(ii) the plant type factor (there was a large and consistent difference between the fauna of different plant types);

(iii) the position factor (this was never appreciable; in other words the initial supposition that the fen as a whole could be treated as a single unit was justified);

(iv) the variance between members of pairs of samples placed adjacent to one another on the ground. This was as large as the position factor; thus the chances of two adjacent sampling units being exactly the same were no greater than those for two units in the same vegetation type from opposite sides of the fen;

(v) residual errors: this is a "dumping ground" for all the errors which were not apparent to the experimenter at the time and included the "experimental error" in the normal sense, i.e. that due to imperfections of technique. An additional subdivision of residual errors can be made, in which errors due to "interaction" between the different factors can be separated out, that is to say, one can measure the extent to which variation due to plant types is linked with seasonal variation for instance.

All these errors can be determined by analysis of variance technique and it is possible to decide whether they are *significant*, that is to say, whether the differences due to plant types are so large in comparison with the total error for one to be justified in saying that plant types have a real effect on the fauna. The results are obtained by a calculation of this sort. As in all such work decisions can only be made on a probability basis. Thus, most of the results obtained above are based on a probability of greater than 20–1 that the samples were so taken that the decision is justified; some of them are "true" with a probability of greater than 100–1 (these are marked * and ** respectively, in papers).

TABLE 8

An example of the analysis of variance of the distribution of Arthropods due to habitat factors. Collections from Cothill fen, August, 1949.

Degrees of Freedom	Mean Square Variation due to—			
	Plants	Positions	Interaction	Pairs
	2	4	8	15
Species				
Minuthozetes semirufus .	141·7**	49·8	11·8	42·4
Oppia neerlandica . .	8·4*	6·3	3·3	3·3
Folsomia quadrioculata .	11·3	14·8*	9·1	6·8
Nanhermannia elegantula .	13·9*	14·7*	2·8	2·4

* 5 per cent significance level.
** 1 per cent significance level.

It will be seen that this kind of technique (and there is a simpler method called the "*t* test" for assessing the significance of two sets of figures only) is a very powerful tool for the ecologist who frequently cannot isolate physically the factors in a field experiment but can appreciate that they exist. Intending experimenters should not be deterred by symbols such as Σ which only means "the sum of" and at least learn something of the capabilities of statistical analysis and when to call on the help of a statistician.

On the other hand, of course, one should make use of any isolation of factors done by nature. The more factors that are involved in the experiment the more complicated does the experimental design and the analysis become, and also the number of samples has to be increased for a given degree of accuracy to be achieved.

An attempt has been made in this chapter to indicate the impact of certain statistical methods on an ecologist who has used them. The reader who would apply such methods must inevitably consult a statistician or his works. The purpose of this chapter has been to show what can be expected of statistical methods and the way in which they can make results more precise and provide new information.

The remaining chapters in this part of the book do not demand a knowledge of statistics, but are concerned with the strictly biological approach to determining the power of growth of a population and the methods of describing its functional importance and contributions to the community.

Chapter 9

DEMOGRAPHY

WHEN describing methods of sampling and measuring populations in the last two chapters, all the individuals of a given species population have been regarded as equivalent. In at least one important respect this supposition is unjustified, because a population nearly always contains a wide range of individuals of different ages and sizes. Furthermore, it was pointed out in the first part of the book that populations are seldom of a constant size for long and it is therefore important to be able to measure the potentialities for growth or decline of populations in different conditions.

Age Structure and Rate of Increase

A census provides a numerical description of a population as it exists at a given time; such a population, however, is usually continually changing under the impact of environmental factors which tend to favour or discourage its increase and as a result of its own tendency to increase. It is well known, for instance, that the human population of Britain has grown less rapidly in recent years and that this is associated with a high proportion of elderly people in the population; the people of India, on the other hand, are multiplying by about 2 per cent per annum, despite a rate of mortality which results in few people living to "middle age."[43] Evidently if we are to understand the factors influencing the size of animal populations we must not only study the interactions between different species, but also need to be able to describe in quantitative terms two characteristics: the age structure and the rate of growth or decline of the population. As might be expected these are not independent. For instance, individuals do not usually reproduce in infancy nor in old age and the age structure will obviously be reflected in the growth rate; one of the objects of demography is to relate these two factors.

Life Tables

The methods mainly used in this analysis have been developed by actuaries, since many of them are employed by life assurance companies, which have a direct commercial interest in information about how long people can be expected to live, or the probability of their dying before they reach a certain age. One of the tools of analysis is the "life table," a table relating the probability at birth of reaching any given age to each age value in turn.[299a]

Related to this are the number of deaths within each age group, the survivors remaining, the rate of mortality and the expectation of further life. These are all interrelated and the most usual form in which the information is summarized for biological purposes is the

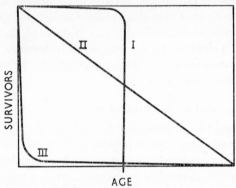

FIG. 15. SCHEMATIC REPRESENTATION OF THREE
TYPES OF SURVIVORSHIP CURVE
(From Deevey, 1942)

"survivorship curve," which relates the number of survivors from an imaginary batch of 100 or 1,000 individuals (ordinate) to age (abscissa). The raw data would provide a histogram, but the curve is usually smoothed. This curve is often called the l_x curve in the literature. If the few known animal survivorship curves are compared, as was done by Deevey,[168a] three main types, shown diagrammatically in Fig. 15, can be recognized.

If the number of survivors is plotted logarithmically and the age arithmetically a straight line (II) results. This implies a constant rate of mortality throughout life or no greater probability of dying at one age than another. This rather unlikely-sounding hypothesis appears to apply to many species of birds after the end of their first summer. (Juvenile mortality, which is not included, would almost certainly be higher.) The convex curve, No. I, indicating a very low mortality before old age and then the death of most of the population in a short time, is not met in such an extreme form, but an intermediate between curves I and II appears to apply to most of the known cases. These include the laboratory populations of the fruit fly *Drosophila*, *Hydra*, the Vole,[405b] wild populations of the Dall mountain sheep, and the rotifer *Floscularia conifera* and also man. Since improvements in public health and medicine have mainly resulted in more men reaching old age, but have done nothing to increase the maximum life span, the survivorship curves of the more "civilized" races approach curve I more closely than the curves of other races.

No cases of curve III have in fact been measured, but there seems little doubt that the many fish populations which suffer a very heavy larval and egg mortality would have curves of this shape, although for the adult stages only curve I is more applicable.

Deevey[168a] was able to compare the life tables of different species by using a time scale based on the mean expectation of life instead of on absolute time. Comfort[125] has published life tables for eight species of mammal in captivity and a useful comparison with those of wild and domestic species.

Rates of Population Increase

The rate of growth or decline of a population is measured in a number of different ways. A parameter much used in earlier work was the "net reproductive rate per generation" which is the ratio of births of one sex, say females, in two successive generations. The fertility and mortality in the population is assumed to be constant during the period studied—a manifestly improbable assumption in many cases—and the value R_0 is then given by $\int_0^\infty p(x)m(x)dx$, where $p(x)$ is the probability of the occurrence of a given age group (x), $m(x)$ is the annual rate at which females of age x give birth to daughters, dx is the interval between successive age groups.

This index is simple to calculate but is defective in that the time basis is the length of a generation and not absolute time (in most natural populations the limits of generations are obscured and the length of a generation varies with time); also it is not simple to relate R_0 to other units in population mathematics as a whole.

These objections do not apply to the measure of population increase rate which is usually employed today, namely the "intrinsic rate of natural increase" r. This is the exponent* r in the equation describing the relationship between the number of individuals in a population and its rate of increase on the assumption that the increase is unchecked—

$$N_t = N_0 e^{rT} \quad \text{or} \quad dN/dT = rN$$

where N_0 is the number of individuals at time zero

N_t is that at time T

e is the root of natural logarithms.

The intrinsic rate of natural increase is measured in terms of absolute time, not the length of a generation. It is independent of the prevailing age distribution of the population, being applicable to a population which is expanding at an exponential rate without density-dependent checks and to this extent being the potential or "intrinsic" rate of increase, a measure of the potential power of increase of the population under the particular regime of mortality and birth rate within which the measurements are made.

When a population is kept under such conditions that it is able to expand freely and there are no factors operating whose magnitude depends on the size of the population so as to increase mortality or reduce fecundity, in other words when there are no density-dependent† factors operating, the net reproductive rate expressed on a time basis will then become equal to the intrinsic rate of natural increase; for under these conditions the age structure of the population reaches a "stable age distribution" which is described by the equation

$$c(x) = b_0 e^{-rx} p(x)$$

b_0 being the constant birth rate corresponding to the particular r_x. The death rate, $d_0 = b_0 - r_0$, and is, therefore, easy to calculate.

Lotka[415, 415a] has amply justified the practical use of r instead of R_0 by showing how the latter has given quite illusory impressions of the trend of birth rate in human populations owing to the effect of the age distribution.

Age Distributions

The investigation of the age distribution of a population is usually carried out in one of three ways: in the case of the human census, as

* See appendix to this chapter for an explanation of exponentials.
† See end of Chapter 10 for a discussion of density-dependent factors.

is well known, the entire population is enumerated on a fixed day once in ten years or so. By an analysis of the ages given in the census, and of the proportions of people dying in each age group (obtained from the returns of the registrar of deaths) the age-specific mortality rate can be obtained. Similarly, the census information of the numbers and ages of children, supplemented by data from the registration of births, provides the basis for calculating the age-specific fecundity rate. The main sources of error in these calculations are the effects of emigration and immigration and the fact that the calculations strictly apply only to the time of the census.

In the case of other animal populations, it is rarely possible to investigate the entire population and only rarely can the ages of the animals be determined with certainty. The age structure and age-specific mortality rate can be obtained for birds by marking with rings and similar means when they are newly born (and therefore easier to find and to handle). Among fishes only the adults can be marked in this way, but in the case of fish and molluscs and some other groups the data for young stages can be derived from an analysis of growth rings on scales, opercula and similar structures. In all these cases only a sample of the population can be followed, although of course (see Chapter 7) information from samples can be very accurate when suitable precautions are taken.

The time at which census data can be obtained from animal populations is often strictly limited: in the case of birds most leg banding is done in the nest and many returns are not obtained until death, so it is hardly surprising, therefore, that the age distributions of such populations involve many assumptions and are only approximate. In few cases have sufficient data been collected by this method for precise ecological parameters such as r to have been calculated for field populations, although much valuable information, of importance to fisheries management for instance, has been amassed.

The Determination of r

By confining studies to laboratory populations, however, the age distribution and even r have been calculated in a number of cases. This has been done for *Microtus agrestis*,[405b] for the rat,[405c] the rice weevil *Calandra oryzae*,[47a] the flour beetle *Tribolium castaneum*,[405a] the multimammate mouse *Rattus (Mastomys) natalensis*,[536] *Daphnia pulex*[234] and the human louse *Pediculus humanus*.[213b] The only example for a field population so far is that of the brown rat (*Rattus norvegicus*) in corn ricks. [405c]

In all these papers detailed descriptions of the methods used are given and it is not, therefore, necessary to repeat them here. Since *r* is independent of the age distribution in the expanding population to which it applies, the actual age distribution under the experimental conditions is irrelevant and the stable age distribution can be calculated.

The method usually adopted is to observe a large number of females throughout their life spans, to record the age and frequency of reproduction and the age of death in each case and thus to calculate the age-specific fecundity and mortality rates. Provided, as can usually be

TABLE 9

Summary of results from laboratory populations of measurements of increase rates.

Species	R_0 Net Reproductive Rate	r Intrinsic Rate per Day	λ Finite Rate to Double
Tribolium castaneum .	275·0	0·101	6·86
Calandra oryzae .	113·6	0·109	6·36
Pediculus humanus .	30·9	0·111	6·24
Microtus agrestis .	5·9	0·0125	55·44
Rattus norvegicus .	25·7	0·0147	47·14

arranged, the animal is not subject to unusual influences which will change the mortality or fecundity rates, the assumption that conditions approach those of an ideal environment devoid of density-dependent factors, is justifiable. The effect of artificial conditions on fecundity and the extent to which laboratory populations are selected to have high rates of increase have not been investigated and to this extent the results are approximate. The fecundity table, expressing the age-specific fecundity rate, and the survivorship table, relating the probability of a female being alive in each age group, give m_x and l_x for each age group. The sum of the products $(l_x m_x)$ for all ages gives the net reproductive rate R_0, which, as has already been seen, is the ratio of female-births in successive generations. The method of deriving *r* from R_0 is given by Birch. [47a] The methods used [405c] for a field population of brown rats resemble those used for human population except that large samples were investigated and not the whole population. Some values of *r* so far calculated are summarized in Table 9.

The last column shows the "finite rate of increase" (λ), which is the Napierian antilogarithm of r and measures the number of times the population will multiply per unit of time. The superiority of r, as an index which permits comparison of such diverse animals, is evident.

The Use of r

At this stage the reader may feel inclined to ask, "Having obtained r with so much expenditure of time and money, what good does it do?" In reply it should be pointed out that this is a neglected field of ecology for which the fundamental information is still only now being assembled; however, from a theoretical point of view we now have, for the first time, a true measure of the power of increase of a population, independent of incidental factors, which permits the comparison of powers of increase of different species and of the same species under different conditions. From a practical point of view the situation in which a population is able to increase without checks is not so remote from reality as might at first appear. Violently fluctuating populations are common enough, especially as the result of human interference and human cultural operations, and the increase of species to pest status must frequently occur almost without check. The outcome of situations in which competing species or predators and their prey are rapidly expanding can only be predicted from an analysis of this sort and we are thus provided with an analytical method of potential importance for economic entomology and similar lines of investigation.

The value of this approach has recently been vindicated by a study of experimental populations. Birch[49] (see also Chapter 10) has been able to relate the maximum population level reached by three species of grain beetles to their respective intrinsic rates of natural increase. He found that the population in the initial stages of colonization of an empty environment followed the predictions of a logistic curve which was calculated independently from the life table and the age schedule of fecundity.

Also from the practical point of view, the use of r provides a simple analytical method for the analysis of the *components* of the power to increase. For instance, in the rice weevil[47a] and the flour beetle[405a] the contribution to r made by females of the different age groups was not at all the same. In the rice weevil, although this insect lives, and continues to produce eggs for up to 19 weeks, and although the eggs laid at different ages are in all respects similar, over half (56 per cent) of the contribution to r is made by females during the first week of adult life, while 85 per cent and 94 per cent respectively are contributed by the end of the second and third weeks. Factors affecting oviposition in the first weeks are therefore overwhelmingly important, or, as Birch expressed it, 2·1 times as many eggs are required to make the same contribution in the second week as in the first and $(2·1)^{n-1}$ in the nth week. A similar disproportionate effect on the power of increase of the population would result from changes in the infant mortality rate. These points of course have special significance for applied biologists concerned with biological control who have hitherto assumed that all eggs laid are equally important as contributions to an expanding population. From the point of view of the species concerned this may be an important factor in evolution; factors tending to bring forward the reproductive period of a species might be favoured by selection even when coupled with otherwise harmful effects, and, conversely, factors adversely affecting the reproductive rate in old age would have little influence on the power of increase of the population.[453a] The relatively greater contributions of younger members of a population to growth rates have been substantiated by experimental studies of Anderson[10] on salamanders, by Frank[233] on *Daphnia pulex*, and Park and Leslie on *Tribolium*.[555]

A demonstration[48, 49, 50] of one way in which r can be of practical use has recently been provided by studies on grain-feeding insects. The value of r was measured under constant conditions in the laboratory for three species of graminivorous beetles over a wide range of temperatures and humidities. It was found that for each species there was an optimal zone of certain combinations of conditions at which r reached its highest value, and that, as each of the factors under study departed from the optimum, r fell off until the population first could not balance mortality by reproduction, and then could not reproduce at all. It may be objected that constant laboratory conditions are remote from those in the natural environment. However, these particular animals are highly successful colonizers of grain stores, the conditions in which are extremely uniform, and further, the approach is justified in practice because it has permitted the prediction not only of the climatic conditions under which each species would best thrive, but also the outcome of competition situations in which two or more species live together and one of them survives at the expense of its competitors.

An introduction to the use of matrix algebra in the analysis of the relative contributions of different age groups is provided by Leslie.[401] This technique can be used to predict the fate of populations (whether or not they follow a stable age distribution) introduced to a new environment. It was also used to analyse the case of a chafer beetle with a three-year larval life and to show how a stable three-year cycle in abundance was built up. (The use of matrices is discussed in simple language by Smith.[662])

Until recently the study of demography was somewhat isolated from the other aspects of ecology; this is no longer true. In addition to the examples already mentioned the analysis of age-dependent birth and death rates has been used to bring simple models of population very much closer to reality. The long-term history of experimental populations has been successfully described by models incorporating demographic constants, even when oscillations in numbers occur.[233] They have also been used in the analysis of experiments on biomass and metabolism of populations.[233, 658] The operation of selection on the rate of increase, reviewed by Birch[53] throws light on conditions under which the rate of increase may be reduced. These topics are discussed further in the next two chapters.

Appendix

THE MEANING OF EXPONENTIALS

A. A great many phenomena in everyday life depend on the principle that the rate at which something changes is proportional to the size of that "something" at the period of time under consideration. Thus, the amount of interest owing under a system of compound interest is related to the capital held by the borrower at the beginning of each period and increases as the capital increases. Again, the rate at which a cup of tea cools depends on how much the tea is hotter than the surrounding air; the cooler the tea the more slowly the cup will cool; the first degrees of temperature being lost in a few seconds while the loss of the infinitely small last fraction of a degree will theoretically

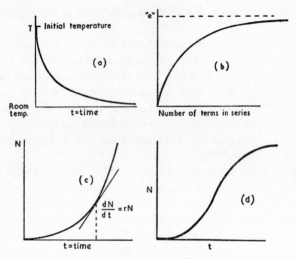

FIG. 16. EXPONENTIAL CURVES
(a) Newton's Law of Cooling.
(b) The Exponential Curve.
(c) Growth Curve of a Population.
(d) "Logistic" Curve (see p. 132 et seq.).
(N = number of individuals; r = natural rate of increase; t = time)

take an infinite time. This is expressed by Newton's law of cooling (see Fig. 16 (a))—

$$dT/dt = -kT$$

where T = temperature
    T_0 = temperature difference to start with
    k = a constant
        d/dt is the calculus way of saying "rate of change per unit of time"

as we shall see below this can also be written $T = T_0 e^{-kt}$.

B. It will be remembered from elementary algebra lessons that, in order to multiply x^3 by x^2, one simply adds the indices and arrives at x^5. If a table is constructed relating the powers of 2 to the equivalent numbers, it begins like this—

power (logarithm) .	. 1	2	3	4	5	6	7	8 . . .
number (antilogarithm) .	2	4	8	16	32	64	128	256 . . .

(the mathematician calls the power used in this sense the logarithm).

Then if one wishes to *multiply* together two of the numbers in the lower row one can do so by finding their equivalent logarithms, *adding* these and then, again using the table, finding the antilogarithm of the sum. Thus, $4 \times 32 = \log 4 + \log 32$. Then $2 + 5 = 7$ and antilog $7 = 128$.

Because this table is based on the powers of 2 the logarithms are called logarithms to the base 2 or "$\log_2$."

A system of logarithms provides, therefore, a method of substituting addition for multiplication, by relating together a geometrical (or multiplying) series of numbers and an arithmetical (or adding) series. The table provided is not, of course, a very practical one because there are a great many gaps in the series of numbers. Filling gaps by means of fractional powers is tedious.

C. If we consider the infinite series of numbers—

$$1, \frac{1}{1}, \frac{1}{2!}, \frac{1}{3!}, \frac{1}{4!}, \frac{1}{5!}, \cdots$$

in which ! (called "shriek" or "factorial") means "multiply together all numbers up to this one," i.e. $3! = 1 \times 2 \times 3 = 6$.

On working out the terms of this series we have—

$$1, 1, \frac{1}{2}, \frac{1}{6}, \frac{1}{24}, \frac{1}{120} \cdots$$

It will be seen that the successive terms of this series become very rapidly smaller.

If the series is now added together successively, taking first term 1, then term 1 + 2, then term 1 + term 2 + term 3 and so on, we have the following set of sums—

1
2
2·5
2·666
2·7083
2·7168

In fact, the successive sums get closer and closer together and if the process were continued to an infinite number of terms it would get no larger than a certain special number which is called e and is equal to 2·718281825 . . . which, like π, goes on without repeating.

One of the special properties of e is that e raised to any power, say x, thus e^x, can be very easily calculated to any desired accuracy, because the answer is given by the exponential series—

$$e^x = 1 + x + \frac{x^2}{2!} + \frac{x^3}{3!} + \frac{x^4}{4!} \cdots$$

This explains why the first table of logarithms was calculated by Napier with e as a base and why e is so often referred to as "the base of Napierian or natural logarithms."

If a graph of the successive terms of an exponential series of this sort is made (Fig. 16 (b)) it will be seen that the line starts off at a steep angle but rapidly approaches a horizontal equal to the value of e; this is called an asymptote. If, on the other hand, the terms are turned upside down, i.e. their reciprocals are plotted (Fig. 16 (c)), the line gets progressively steeper until it approaches the vertical.

Now, going back to the beginning of this diversion from ecology, it will be remembered that the special property of a system of natural growth is that the rate of growth is related to the size of the thing growing at any instant; in other words the growth curve fits the reciprocal exponential curve we have just discussed. This is because of the special property of powers of e which very simply relates the rate of growth to the corresponding value; the successive powers which are equivalent to successive equal additions on the abscissa when worked out give one the appropriate intervals in the ordinates of Fig. 16 (b). It will now be evident why the alternative forms of Newton's law of cooling are

$$\frac{dT}{dt} = -kT \quad \text{and} \quad T = T_0 e^{-kt}$$

or why (getting back to biology) the natural growth of a population (Fig. 16 (c)) can be written—

$$\frac{dN}{dt} = rN \quad \text{or} \quad N_t = N_0 e^{-rt}$$

Taking this formula as an example, it will be seen from Table 9 that a common value for r in invertebrate populations is about 0·1 per day. We can now see precisely what this means when applied to an expanding population.

Thus, if the value for r is taken as 0·1 per day, the growth of a population of 1,000 individuals to begin with can be calculated—

Given that $N_0 = 1,000$ and that $r = 0·1$ and using the series

$$e^x = 1 + x + \frac{x^2}{2!} + \frac{x^3}{3!} + \frac{x^4}{4!}$$

Day	x	e^x	N
0			1,000
1	0·1	$1 + 0·1 + 0·005 + 0·00016 + 0·000004 = 1·10516$	1,105
2	0·2	$1 + 0·2 + 0·02 + 0·0013 + 0·00006 = 1·2214$	1,221
3	0·3	$1 + 0·3 + 0·045 + 0·0045 + 0·00089 = 1·3504$	1,350
4	0·4	$1 + 0·4 + 0·08 + 0·0106 + 0·0011 = 1·4978$	1,498

Note particularly how the later terms, in this case that with the fourth power, make only a very small contribution and can be ignored, at least to begin with. Note also the steady growth of the population, the increment between successive days being 105, 116, 129, 148. These results could have been obtained less laboriously of course, by looking in a table of natural logarithms for the antilog of 0·1. The value 1·1056 is the ratio by which the successive daily total can be seen to increase. Thus, r is a measure, not of the slope of the growth curve because that changes with population size, but of the rate at which the slope increases as the population increases.

Chapter 10

FACTORS DETERMINING POPULATION SIZE

THE description and analysis of single species populations, in terms of age, size and growth rate has been considered in Chapter 9. We now have to consider the properties of single species populations as discovered by such techniques, with special reference to factors determining population size and to those which concern the behaviour of populations as components of a community.

Population Growth and Its Limitation

Malthus[446] first appreciated that the successive numbers of the offspring from a single pair of parents can be fitted to an exponential series* such that if any increase at all occurs in successive generations this will be on a proportionate basis. That is to say that, given a constant rate of increase, the population size mounts according to an "exponential"* curve. It was this unlimited potential increase which led Malthus to realize that the only logical end to such a process is through a factor such as starvation or disease, and that in the case of human populations, some consciously applied birth-control method would be preferable. As far as practical application of his ideas is concerned his lesson is more insistent and applicable today than ever before. As is well known this idea was an important component of Darwin's outlook and led to Verhulst's analysis of the problem.

The Logistic Curve

Verhulst[764, 765] derived an equation for the rate of growth of a population in a limited environment which is so constituted that only a certain maximum density could be supported by the resources available. To allow for this factor, the intensity of whose operation evidently increases as the population size increases, he introduced a term whose value depends on the extent to which the population at any given time is short of the maximum attainable population. Thus,

* See Appendix to Chapter 9 for an explanation of these terms.

if the simple exponential increase envisaged by Malthus is expressed by—

$$N_t = N_0 e^{rt} \quad \text{or} \quad \frac{dN}{dt} = rN \text{ (these two expressions are equivalent)}$$

where N_0 = initial number of organisms at time $t = 0$
  N_t = number of organisms at time = t
  e = the base of natural logarithms
  t = time since t_0
  r = a constant, the intrinsic rate of natural increase already
      discussed (Chapter 9)

the Verhulst-Pearl "logistic" equation states that

$$N_t = N_0 e^{r\left(\frac{K-N}{K}\right)t} \quad \text{or} \quad \frac{dN}{dt} = rN\left(\frac{K-N}{K}\right)$$

where K = the maximum possible attainable population under the given conditions. The two curves are given in Figs. 16 (c) and 16 (d), where it will be seen that the first is a simple exponential curve whose characteristic is that its slope increases at a constant rate; the second begins like the first but reaches a point of maximum slope (point of inflexion) and then the slope falls off progressively until the curve approaches more and more slowly the "upper asymptote" or level of maximum attainable population under the given conditions.

It was shown by Pearl that a number of natural populations in a limited environment do, in fact, follow a curve which approximates closely to the "logistic equation." His *Drosophila* (Fruit Fly) populations living in bottles and fed only a fixed amount of food each day did this and so, too, has the human population of the North American continent.[562, 563]

For a number of reasons the uncritical application of the logistic curve to all examples of population growth appears to be misleading. From a theoretical point of view it is somewhat unsatisfactory that populations frequently do exceed the upper "asymptote" level of the curve and tend to oscillate above and below it; this is a feature which was not apparent from the earlier experiments because the experiments were usually stopped as soon as a fairly level higher density was reached. Thus, the "upper asymptote" is not an absolute limit which is never quite reached, as it theoretically should be. Again, many newly-started populations in a limited environment tend to increase initially to a high density and then, after a period of oscillation, to settle down to a lower level. This may be of the order of half the maximum level, as pointed out for *Tribolium* (grain beetle) cultures by Kennington.[361] The curve of many of these cultures[549] often resembles more closely that of a pendulum coming slowly to rest or other examples of "simple harmonic motion" than the logistic curve.

This subject has recently been investigated by Birch[49] who compared the population history of three species of grain beetles and related it to the intrinsic rate of increase (*r*), calculated independently. The early history of the population numbers followed closely a logistic curve calculated from *r*, and it was shown that the peak density reached at the end of this initial period was related to *r*, being higher for species in which *r* was greater. Departures from the predicted shape of the curve were attributed to non-stable age distributions, variation of population size with density and a lag in the operation of the density-dependent factors which reduce the rate of increase. In fact, a great variety of complicated processes take place within a "simple" population experiment of this sort: in *Tribolium* cultures different life stages compete with and prey upon one another, while in the *Drosophila* bottle,[627] not only is this happening, but also competition and succession phenomena occur among the yeasts which provide the food. In other words, it is only possible to fit the logistic curve at all to such populations which are increasing from a low to a high density; one must ignore what happens after the high density is reached. The subsequent history of even such simple populations will depend on the magnitude and phase relations of a considerable number of density-dependent factors and takes us well beyond the simple predictions of the logistic curve. This topic will be reverted to later in this chapter.

Lotka[415] followed up Pearl's analysis and considered the various ways in which the rate of increase of a population may be measured; this has already been reviewed in Chapter 9, and it is, therefore, possible to continue here with a consideration of other internal factors which affect population size.

Co-operation

First, it should be mentioned that the effect of population increase is not always negative; a considerable number of cases of "co-operation" are known. On the experimental level, Pearl showed that

Drosophila cultures with very few individuals do not reproduce as fast as those with a certain optimum number. Park[545] showed the same thing with *Tribolium*; at densities less than two pairs per 32 g of flour, fewer offspring per head were produced. This was tentatively attributed to insufficient contacts occurring between individuals of opposite sexes for an optimal rate of mating. Many other experimental results of this sort have been reported.[6, 7, 672]

Similar results have been obtained for field populations: the breeding success of birds which have communal mating behaviour is reduced,[154] while small seal colonies around British coasts are only maintained by immigration from larger ones.[161] In a certain small colony the numbers of young produced were one and five respectively by 20 cows in two successive years; this compares with 190 calves from 440 cows in a nearby large colony.

Examples of this sort, although by no means scarce, have perhaps been given undue prominence by some writers who have implied that natural selection and "nature red in tooth and claw" are out-dated conceptions.[802]

FLUCTUATION IN POPULATION SIZE

Theoretical Considerations

The distinction between factors associated with the production of fluctuations in population size and those associated with its control over long periods is an arbitrary one and to some extent begs the question as to whether the two are related. Nevertheless the interest of most ecologists working in this field has been focused on one or other of the two types of phenomenon and a clearer presentation is possible by describing first the main features of population fluctuations and then considering these amongst others as candidates for the determinants of long-term population size.

Firstly, it is necessary to propose some definitions. The terms *fluctuation*, *oscillation* and *cycle* have been used loosely in the past. Some agreement is now fairly general, however, and in what follows a *fluctuation* is any type of numerical variation whether or not a mathematically detectable consistency or trend can be discerned. *Cycle* and *oscillation* are less easy to discriminate but since the verb and adjective associated with the latter are less embarrassing to use, *cycle* will be relegated to cases where field observation indicates some regularity but no rigorous definition has been achieved. *Oscillations* are widely thought by biologists to be chiefly typified by a definite and fixed time period. However, it is not difficult on the basis of this definition to show that a moving average suitably derived from a purely random set of values can show "oscillatory" properties.[123] For this reason it is preferable to follow Moran[468] and define oscillations in the terms of their more general attribute that a departure from the mean implies a tendency for the value subsequently to "overshoot" the mean. "Thus if at some time *t*, *n*, the size of the population is greater than its mean value, there will be a tendency at some later time for *n* to be less than its mean value . . . This, when applied to random processes is equivalent to asserting that there is at least some serial correlation, of some order, which is negative." It will be appreciated that such a definition could be applied equally to a simple mechanical oscillatory system such as a pendulum or to a complicated time series containing both random and oscillatory components. The analysis of these more complex series cannot, however, be carried out by eye: that it is a matter for the expert is shown by two papers[466,467] containing analyses of lynx cycles in Canada which are, and game bird figures from Scotland which are not truly oscillatory.

OVERSIMPLIFICATIONS OF THE LOGISTIC EQUATION. From the simple approach to population growth illustrated by the logistic equation it would not be expected that population numbers would fluctuate. However, the simplifications inherent in this equation cause serious distortions in at least two respects.

Firstly it is assumed that adverse effects of density are instantaneously followed by the appropriate response by the population. In other words, as $\dfrac{K - N}{K}$ decreases from 1 to 0 with rising density, the rate of population increase dN/dt falls correspondingly. This is manifestly untrue of the response of a population when this takes the form of reduced birth rate and probably also in the case of increased mortality.

A physical analogy is perhaps relevant at this point. In simple mechanical control systems, such as the steam-engine governor, the thermostat which controls a constant temperature bath or the power-assisted mechanism by which a ship is steered, a device which measures the extent by which the output of the system differs from the desired output is made to alter the input in such a way as to reduce the disparity from the desired state; the governor, for instance, shuts off the steam when the engine is going too fast. The control pathway in such a system is termed a "feedback loop" and, where it operates in the way described, the feedback is said to be negative.

When a time lag occurs between the application of negative feedback and the occurrence of the appropriate correction in the output, it is quite usual for the whole system to "oscillate" or "hunt" about the desired condition because the correction is not effective until the output has already overshot the desired condition. The conditions under which (a) a steady approach to the desired state occurs without oscillation, and those in which (b) oscillations occur but die down, and those in which (c) oscillations build up from a small displacement, can be calculated in mechanical systems from a knowledge of the "transfer function" of each link in the causal chain (error detector, amplifier, input control, power unit and output, for instance). The transfer function expresses the relation of amplitude and of phase of the input and the output for each stage, and therefore takes into account any amplification or damping and any phase changes which occur. Transfer functions of successive stages can be multiplied to give a transfer function for the whole system.[445]

In those mechanical systems in which delays cannot be avoided oscillation can be eliminated by one of three methods: (i) damping the output, e.g. making it operate under conditions of greater friction. This is wasteful of power and reduces precision; (ii) using "velocity feedback," i.e. feedback proportional to the rate of change of the output. This results in steady state errors, but in a dynamic system this may not matter; (iii) using an error-modifying network so as to achieve a phase advance in the error signal fed back and thus to compensate for the lag introduced elsewhere.

An interesting example of the application of this type of analysis to a biological system has recently been provided by measurements on an insect sense hair.[591] The hair was subjected to a mechanical stimulus which varied in intensity in a sinusoidal manner (i.e. was subjected to a pull derived from a spring oscillating in simple harmonic motion like a pendulum). The electrical nervous output from the sense hair also varied sinusoidally, but was 45° *in advance* of the stimulus. The phase lead is due to the sense organ responding to the rate of change of the stimulus and not to its instantaneous value. As Pringle had pointed out earlier[590] such a phase lead is required in a proprioceptor if oscillation of muscular movements is to be prevented because the slow speed of nervous conduction in sensory and motor pathways and in the central nervous system result in a considerable lag in response and this would cause "oscillation" or "hunting."

Returning now to the question of oscillation in animal population systems, it is evident that a system in which a tendency to geometric increase is balanced by a density-dependent controlling factor incorporates a "negative feedback" loop; the population enlarges, the intensity of the controlling factor increases and ultimately the population is reduced. The application of servo-mechanism analysis involving the use of transfer functions has not so far been made to such a system, presumably on account of the difficulty of breaking the system down into its component parts.

The only attempt to apply an analysis of this sort was made by Hutchinson[337] who refers to the "logistic curve" formula

$$\frac{dN}{dt} = Nb\frac{K-N}{K}$$

the term $\frac{K-N}{K}$ applies to the self-regulatory mechanism and if the operation of the population-reducing force were instantaneous no oscillation would occur. However, if there is a time lag T between the increase in the population and the appropriate response by the population size, and if $N/K = y$, then

$$\frac{dyt}{dt} = y_t(1 - y_{t-T})$$

It can then be shown that—

if $T < \frac{\pi}{2}$ oscillations will die out,

if $T > \frac{\pi}{2}$ oscillations will increase in magnitude until the above identities no longer hold, for the value of y must lie between 0 and eT.

The second serious defect of the logistic equation is that it ignores the complexity of the age structure of a natural population and the dependence of birth and death rates on age. In a general approach Leslie[401] provided a method for analysing the effects of age structure and illustrated a rather special case where it can lead to oscillations in itself. In a later study,[404] a more generally applicable example is given in which population oscillations are generated simply by the interactions inherent in a particular type of age distribution and the lag in response of mortality and natality to density.

In other words it can be shown that as soon as we take into account two almost universal features of the simplest population systems, oscillatory tendencies are revealed and it is quite legitimate to ask with Hutchinson[338] why are such oscillations not more frequently encountered in real life. Two possible answers which will be considered after the study of some actual examples of natural and experimental populations, are, firstly, that under natural conditions interactions between populations result in damping of natural resonances and, secondly, that since violent oscillations might be thought potentially harmful to the chances of perpetuation of the species, positive biological mechanisms which reduce the lags in response to high density have been favoured by selection. A third possible answer is suggested by the analysis which we now consider.

ALTERNATIVE MODELS INCORPORATING THE INFLUENCE OF EXTERNAL MORTALITY FACTORS. Nicholson was the first to offer an alternative to the logistic curve as a mathematical model.[493] A graph of the numbers of adults which emerge against numbers of larvae in the cages is found to take the form shown in Fig. 17. As the number of larvae increase from zero the curve at first is tangential to the dotted "no mortality line"; however, as the effects of crowding are felt, the number of adults is steadily reduced to the point "×2." Thereafter there is a rapid, almost exponential, *fall* in number of adults until at about 200 larvae per cage no adults at all succeed in emerging from the pupae. The points marked ×1, ×2, ×3, etc., represent the reproductive rates corresponding to the number of larvae along the abscissa, and it will be seen that up to a reproductive rate of ×2 the left-hand (ascending leg) of the curve is followed; at greater rates the right-hand (descending) leg is followed. Now, if the population conditions are described by a point on the descending leg of the curve it is evident that the greater the number of larvae the fewer the adults and vice versa. It is this condition—analagous, perhaps, to the negative resistance condition of a radio valve oscillator—which inevitably results in oscillation. Although the actual figures apply only to Nicholson's experiments, it can be seen how in general any Metazoan animal with a high rate of reproduction, and a delay between reproduction and the application of the appropriate density-dependent check, can be expected to show oscillation when in an isolated state.

Ricker[608, 609] developed the use of a very similar curve in his model for measuring the effects of exploitation of fish stocks, which will be referred to again in Chapter 11. His treatment differs from the assumptions of the logistic curve chiefly because he considers external mortality factors. These he recognizes to be of two kinds, *compensatory* and

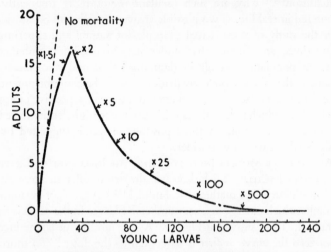

FIG. 17. THE RELATIONSHIP BETWEEN LARVAL DENSITY AND ADULT EMERGENCE WITH REGARD TO MORTALITY IN *Lucilia cuprina* (BLOWFLY)
(From Nicholson, 1950)

random (see below). In Ricker's model mortality is assumed to operate only up to the time the fish attain maturity and he also makes the simplifying assumption that fishing is confined to mature fish.

In examining the curves in Fig. 18 let us assume firstly that the young breed after one year and do not breed again. The horizontal axis represents the number of eggs produced by the parent fish stock in a particular year and the vertical axis the number which will, in their turn, be produced by the fish hatched from those eggs. The curves represent the relations between the two so that, for example in curve *a*, using arbitrary egg units, one unit of eggs produces 2·5 after one year. These in turn produce 4·5 and so on until the population reaches equilibrium at six egg units per year. In curve *e* on the other hand equilibrium from one egg unit is only reached after a series of damped oscillations and in curve *f* an unstable situation with increasing oscillations will occur.

If the assumptions are now changed, it is found that the overlap of egg laying between the generations results in a damping of oscillatory tendencies while a delay in attainment of maturity increases them.

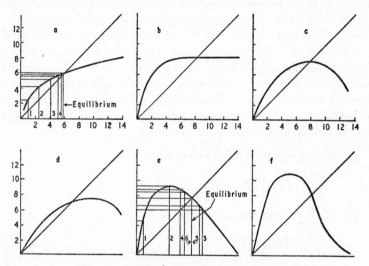

FIG. 18. RICKER'S REPRODUCTION CURVES

Abscissa: number of egg units produced by parent stock in a given year.
Ordinate: number of egg units produced by the progeny of that year.
Curves (*a*) (*b*) and (*c*) represent stable, non-oscillatory situations; (*d*) and (*e*) show damped oscillations while (*f*) is unstable. The lines parallel to the axes indicate the number of egg units produced in successive years (for full explanation, see text).

The shapes of Ricker's curves are considered to be determined by factors whose effect on the numbers of eggs laid varies with density; otherwise the curves would simply be straight lines. In other words we have been considering up to now what Ricker terms *compensatory mortality*. This corresponds closely to density-dependent mortality, an expression to be discussed further below (p. 153). Not all mortality factors act in this manner however; many act in an arbitrary manner which is independent of density and constitutes Ricker's *random mortality*. This, he finds can obscure the effects of the oscillations generated by density-dependent factors at rather a low level of intensity. In other words, under natural conditions where non-compensatory mortality is usually important the overt effects of oscillatory tendencies are likely to be suppressed.

A very similar relationship between density and effective reproduction has been obtained from quite another direction by Watt.[792] Dissatisfied with the arbitrary approach of the classical equations due to Lotka, Volterra and Nicholson, and especially the oversimplifications implicit in such assumptions as that reproduction rate is independent of density, he set up a model which incorporates a number of biological features typical of insect populations. Given that k = constant, ε = intrinsic rate of oviposition, N = population density, P = effect of probability of contact on fecundity (e.g. through copulation) and $(1-aE)$ = effect of competition for oviposition sites on fecundity, (a being the area required for an egg to develop and E the number of eggs laid in time t), he gives three equations—

(a) relating egg production rate to time,

$$\frac{dE}{dt} = K\varepsilon NPI(1 - a\,E)$$

(b) relating copulation rate to density

$$\frac{dP}{dN} = bP(1 - P)$$

(c) relating density to interference

$$\frac{dI}{dN} = -f\,(I - I_{\min}) \text{ or } \log_e(I - I_{\min}) = d - fN$$

these are then combined into a single equation relating mean fecundity to density. When plotted with density on a log scale, curves are obtained which strongly resemble Nicholson's (Fig. 17) in which the ordinate, of course, is number of larvae rather than fecundity.

In a further paper[793] Watt discusses the philosophy of constructing mathematical models for use in ecology, and certainly to judge by the success with which the above formula fits many practical examples this approach would seem to have a great future. This subject of model building is also discussed by Beverton and Holt.[46]

EFFECTS OF "QUALITATIVE" VARIATIONS IN THE POPULATION. It must not, of course, be forgotten that animal populations are genetically heterogeneous. It is unlikely that conditions will be equally favourable in any population for all the genotypes present over the full range of density, and many examples to the contrary have been given by Birch.[53] When population oscillations have become a well established feature of the biology of a species it is even probable that a balanced polymorphism will arise, as has been suggested by Chitty[102, 104] and Andrewartha,[14] which favours the expression of different genotypes at high and at low density. Furthermore the properties of these genotypes are likely to influence the population characteristics of the species: as so often in biology the concept of cause and effect gives way to the development of a system with several interrelated attributes.

Since it is arguable that very high densities, leading to the over-exploitation of food supplies, the destruction of cover, or the decimating influences of disease will reduce the chances of the survival of the population as a whole, it might be postulated that those populations in which high density is associated with a genotype or a physiological condition which reduces the rate of increase would be favoured by selection in comparison with other populations which pursue the consequences of overpopulation to their Malthusian bitter end. A hypothesis based on a genetical switch of this kind has the attraction that such mechanisms are already widely known, as are polymorphic populations in which sometimes one and sometimes another form is favoured. It has been argued that natural selection operates only on individuals and cannot favour altruism,[391] but this would not apply to a polymorphic system. It is, nevertheless, true that the above argument is at present speculative and cannot be applied to particular situations until many more details of its mechanism have been worked out.[210a]

Experimental Evidence

Early experiments[96a] made on flour beetles,[96, 324] on Drosophila[627] and on Protozoa and Yeasts,[243, 244] in which populations were maintained on a limited daily ration of food, had all tended to give the impression that single species populations in a limited environment increase according to the logistic curve, reach the "upper asymptote" level and there maintain a steady density which results from the balance between the animals' reproductive potential and starvation due to the limited food supply, or other density-dependent factors. In the case of the *Tribolium* work, Chapman believed that the sole density-dependent factor of importance was the cannibalistic activities of the beetles in eating their own young; the greater the density the more would young tend to be eaten. Park[547] reported a reduction in fecundity when the flour became "conditioned" by some unspecified excretory product of the beetles. Boyce[62] showed that neither cannibalism nor conditioning can act in this way, cannibalism being independent of density over a very wide range and conditioning quite insignificant. She also showed that interference with copulation in crowded colonies and reduction of feeding due to interference are unimportant, and attributed the decline in population size to a reduction in egg laying, probably due to reduced opportunity for oviposition. A similar theory was given by Crombie.[135, 136] However, it certainly appears that, whatever the factor limiting population size may be in *Tribolium* cultures, it is not lack of food, since the amount available is more than enough to support the populations. It is also noticeable in the reports[550] of the very long-term experiments that single species populations are far from uniform over a considerable period; evidently the situation even in these apparently simple experiments is much less simple than was thought at first. Some of the unexpected complications in *Calandra oryzae* are discussed by Voûte,[771, 772] who found that emigration is dependent on density, but "lags behind" when density changes. Thus, the extent of emigration at a given level is higher with a falling population than with an increasing one. Effects of this sort would tend to cause fluctuations by themselves, as discussed above.

Nicholson[488, 493, 494] in connexion with another investigation, set up experiments in which blowflies were kept in cages with a regular but limited supply of meat. A daily census was made of each cage. It was decided to investigate the relationships between larval and adult densities of a single species of blowfly (*Lucilia cuprina*) and it was discovered that the numbers of flies oscillated violently. The particular explanation offered by Nicholson is that, because their food requirements are much less, the adult flies easily obtain sufficient food in competition with the larvae. When the flies become crowded the adults lay an almost normal number of eggs. The result is that at high densities of flies there is gross overcrowding of the larvae. The effect is accentuated because the flies to some extent accommodate themselves to poor food supply by producing smaller larvae; as competition increases, larvae, and hence the pupae, diminish in size until a critical size is reached at which no metamorphosis can occur. It is found in Nicholson's experiments using 50 g of meat per day that no pupae hatch whenever the adult population is greater than 300, but the adult numbers rise to almost 2,000 at the peaks of the oscillations, and these flies continue to lay a hundred or more eggs each. It is, therefore, obvious that the larvae grossly overcrowd their environment in the "crash" phase of the oscillation. The point to notice in particular in this example is the considerable lag between the attainment of a high

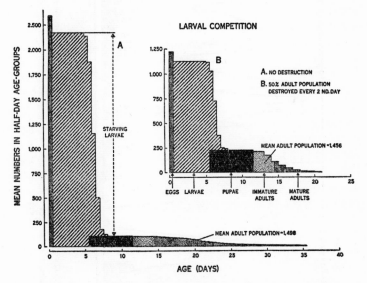

FIG. 19. (a) COMPENSATORY REACTIONS IN BLOWFLY CULTURES
(After NICHOLSON)

Age structure in (A) control culture and (B) culture in which 50 per cent of larvae are destroyed on every second day. Note compensatory increase in remaining stages.

density and the operation of the controlling factor, namely starvation. This lag is of the order of three or four weeks.

Further experiments by Nicholson[496, 500] have analysed the effects of competition and imposed mortality at different stages in the life cycle. If adults are killed or prevented from feeding adequately the population adjusts itself so that the recruitment rate to the adult stage is increased. Similarly heavy larval competition results in more eggs being laid and more larval recruitment (Fig. 19a). Nicholson terms these *compensatory reactions* and points out that this population property

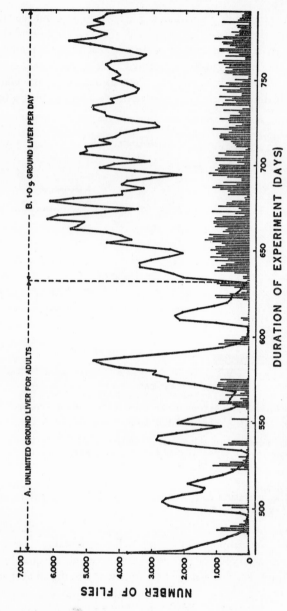

FIG. 19. (b) EFFECT ON A CULTURE OF RESTRICTING ADULT FOOD SUPPLY

Continuous line = numbers of adults, vertical lines = number of adults eventually emerging from eggs laid on the date shown on the abscissa.

may result in man's efforts to kill insects having an opposite effect to the one intended.

Since in cultures governed by larval competition so many eggs were laid that larval crowding prevented any adults hatching, whereas in those governed by adult competition no eggs were laid, Nicholson argued that it should be possible to find a rate of feeding to both larval and adult stages which would prevent oscillation. The dramatic effect of *reducing* the adult food supply to the correct value can be seen in Fig. 19*b* where a ration of 1 g liver per day instead of unlimited quantities leads to consistently *higher* populations of both adults and larvae.

Evidence from Field Populations

SMALL MAMMAL CYCLES. Elton's account[197] of striking fluctuations in numbers of small mammals, followed by Lotka's[415] demonstrations and Volterra's[768, 769] that simple predator-prey situations could, in theory, lead to oscillations (see Chapter 15) were naturally followed by attempts to link these two sets of phenomena. The impetus to much work in the 1930s and 1940s was undoubtedly the search for "classical" oscillation-promoting relationships such as predation, parasitism disease and over-eating of food supplies in fluctuating populations of birds and mammals.

While many cases were discovered of predator cycles following those of their prey (see Chapter 16), it gradually became clear that variations in numbers of herbivorous mammals were not usually related to such factors because no consistent relationships between the classical factors and population cycles could be demonstrated. At the same time other features were discovered. Green and colleagues[281, 282] noticed pronounced variations in the tendency for snowshoe hares to die from a condition associated with physiological derangements, involving low blood-sugar and glycogen levels which they called "*shock disease*." Christian[108] associated this condition with Seyle's concept[19, 645] of the *General Adaptation Syndrome* and these authors favoured the hypothesis that population cycles could be explained by the incidence of the disease. A similar view has been expressed for voles by Louch.[416, 417] It has been demonstrated by Chitty, however,[103] that Green's data do not in fact support his hypothesis because the incidence of shock disease is not synchronized with the effects it is supposed to cause. In the meanwhile Chitty's studies of the vole

Microtus agrestis[99] had demonstrated somewhat similar features in a number of neighbouring populations near Lake Vyrnwy in Wales. The main features revealed by Chitty and his colleagues were the following.[99, 100, 101, 105, 115, 116, 640]

Fluctuations occurred every three or four years which periodically drifted out of phase but tended to be synchronized in general.

None of the "classical" mortality factors appeared to be important because their incidence was not synchronized with the cycles. There was no evidence of food shortage.

Even after density had returned to low levels the population continued to decline. "Shock disease" symptoms were repeatedly detected at the time of the crash phase as were increased juvenile mortality, reduction in breeding season and fertility of females.

A similar condition was produced in the laboratory when the animals were crowded. This was associated with "stress" resulting from fighting consequent on "territorial" behaviour. The condition included changes in the adrenals, thymus and spleen[115] and even features similar to the "slipped disc" condition of man (which is also associated with stress).[105, 640]

Larger-scale experiments confirmed these findings and showed that in crowded populations the female reproductive season is reduced, fertility is lowered and juvenile mortality increased.[116] Similar observations have been made on large experimental populations of house mice[141, 142] and natural populations of two American species of *Microtus*.[323]

However, Chitty also found[102] that descendants of animals which had been crowded have enlarged spleens even after several generations at low density and when compared with suitable controls Dawson[166] related the spleen enlargement to a non-infectious form of haemolytic anaemia.

Chitty therefore put forward the hypothesis[104] that this condition is inherited and that the crowding experiments had selected a genotype which had some advantage either in itself or for the population as a whole under high-density conditions. However, the same factor is associated with reduced viability and is not at an advantage at a low density. He then put forward the further hypothesis about the advantage to the population as a whole in having an anti-crowding mechanism which has been mentioned on p. 143.

Small mammal fluctuations are not, of course, always associated with a mechanism of this kind. Pitelka, for instance,[578] has described a situation in the Alaskan lemming where the rodent periodically eats practically all the vegetation which is both its food and its cover and then falls victim to a series of predators. The primary factor appears to be over-grazing by the lemming and, although the predators ultimately cause most of the deaths of lemmings these are animals which would die of starvation in any case.

CYCLES IN OTHER ANIMALS. On the other hand there is some evidence that the vole situation is not unique. Wellington[799] has described a hereditary condition in spruce tent caterpillars involving a lethargic, apparently less viable genotype which becomes more common under crowded conditions.

This appears to be closely analogous to the vole example. Birch[53] has also suggested that some rather remarkable long-term changes in the performance of Park's *Tribolium* cultures and Nicholson's blowflies may have a genetic explanation of a similar kind. Marked physiological and behavioural changes in the locust associated with crowding have of course been known for a long time, but it has recently been shown by Gardiner[242] that the offspring of gregarious-phase locusts have a higher metabolic rate at the time of hatching. Again, a condition reminiscent of the locusts' has been described by Long[413] in the lesser tortoise-shell butterfly (*Vanessa urticae*) on nettles. The mechanism involved is not known. Other examples of changes of "quality" of populations according to density are provided by Kawanabe[358] who demonstrated a switch in the social relationships in a Salmonid fish which was associated with major differences of growth rate, and Rose's[618] and Savage's[633] studies of the mechanisms of social dominance in tadpoles. One can only conclude that changes in "quality" of population with density are very widespread in the animal kingdom, that the mechanisms involved are many and various and that no study of population cycles can afford to neglect them. Chitty[104] goes on to argue, as is mentioned on p. 143, that such a widespread phenomenon argues strongly for some general selective advantage associated with any mechanism which restricts excessive expansion of a population.

SYNCHRONIZATION OF CYCLES. One point raised by the Vyrnwy vole study remains to be taken up. It will be remembered that oscillations in adjacent populations were nearly synchronous but not quite. Similar features are common in the cycles of Canadian mammals.[200]

Leslie[404] has demonstrated that a set of separate self-oscillating populations based on his model discussed on p. 138 can be brought into step rather easily by chance factors which change the rate of increase. It seems likely that a similar principle may apply in nature: oscillating populations with a characteristic period which is determined by their generation length, rate of increase and so on will gradually get out of step until some exceptionally favourable or, more probably unfavourable erratic influence brings all populations towards their upper or lower size limit. From here, they will begin to oscillate in step once more. A relevant experimental demonstration is provided by Nicholson[500] who set up several oscillating blowfly cultures and then varied their food supply in a cyclical manner and at different periods for different cultures (Fig. 20). The blowfly oscillations "pulled into phase" with either the feeding cycle or a multiple of its frequency. Among other lessons which are to be drawn from this example is the fact that coincidence between two such cycles is no proof of a causal relationship.

CONCLUSIONS CONCERNING POPULATION FLUCTUATIONS. In the earlier experiments with Protozoa and Yeasts,[243, 244] with *Tribolium confusum*[324] and with *Drosophila*,[562] Nicholson[494, 497] maintains that the steady density achieved is due to factors which cannot normally be expected in Metazoan populations. He considers that the delay which intervenes between the crowded condition of the blowflies and the reaction by reduction in the number of offspring is a much more normal occurrence. In Protozoa and Yeasts which reproduce asexually the crowded condition is immediately reflected in a reduction in the number of offspring, and, because no delay occurs, the violent oscillations do not follow. In *Drosophila* it is suggested that two separate competition phenomena, one in the adults and the other in the larvae, tend to oppose one another and damp down oscillations; by separating the larvae and adults from each other oscillations can be produced. This criticism of Pearl's work is also made by Sang,[627] who shows that the situation in the *Drosophila* culture bottle is really a very complicated one involving interactions not only between the life stages of the *Drosophila* but also between these and the different Yeasts on which they feed. In the case of the flour beetle, according to Nicholson, the adults and larvae eat any pupae and eggs they happen to come across, and the importance of this "cannibalism" increases with the density of the beetles in the flour. (This is not, however, given much support by

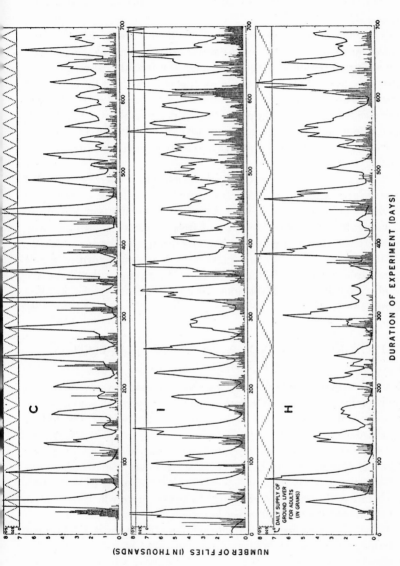

NUMBER OF FLIES (IN THOUSANDS)

DURATION OF EXPERIMENT (DAYS)

FIG. 20. EFFECTS ON BLOWFLY CULTURES OF RHYTHMICAL CHANGE IN AN ENVIRONMENTAL FACTOR
(FOOD SUPPLY)

I represents a control culture, *C* and *H* cultures in which food supply cycles of 20 and 80 days respectively were imposed. Note synchronization of population cycles with food cycles. *I* also shows a change in population history probably associated with acquisition of an ability to tolerate low-protein diet.

the figures quoted by Park and Leslie[555] for the relation between cannibalism and crowding.)

The immediately operative effect of cannibalism serves to damp down fluctuations which would normally occur owing to the delayed reproduction response to overcrowding. It can hardly be maintained that these points have been proved by Nicholson without the necessary statistical data, but it is a very useful reminder that so often in ecology the rare example of a "simple" situation is the result of a balance of many opposing forces and the simplicity is, in fact, deceptive. Perhaps the "simple reflex" of the nerve physiologists may be cited as an analogy.[190]

There can no longer be any doubt that many properties of single species populations are capable of promoting oscillations. Perhaps, even, we began by asking ourselves the wrong question and instead of wanting to know why populations (relatively rarely) oscillate we should have wondered why they (most frequently) do not do so. Some of the answers to the second question have been suggested in these paragraphs but before further reasons can be given we shall have to study the nature of interactions between different species in the community in Part III.

FACTORS CONCERNED WITH THE GENERAL LEVEL OF POPULATION DENSITY

It is a matter of dispute whether the above heading has any meaning and, if it has, whether such factors operate in the case of all populations. It is also a matter of dispute how such factors, if they exist, should be classified and named.

Disagreement is due partly to inconsistent use of words, partly to the fact that different authors have generalized from very different models of what they conceive typical populations to be and partly to a genuine difference in the operation of control factors in nature which will only be clarified in the light of further knowledge.

In what follows no original contribution will be made to current arguments, but since an unbiased review would be contrary to the spirit of this book—and also exceedingly lengthy—a definite viewpoint will be expressed. The reader is urged that personal acquaintance with the original literature is essential to the understanding of a field where opinions are many and evidence is sparse.

Semantic Difficulties

Some verbal inconsistencies must first be resolved. The word *density* should strictly be used only to relate population numbers to area or volume of substratum. However, physical measurements of this kind usually have little relation to the "carrying capacity" of an environment as is illustrated by the many studies of bird territory and also by Southwick's[686] demonstration that house mice in corn ricks can reach fantastic absolute densities without becoming crowded in any biological sense. It is therefore reasonable to use density in a relative sense in this context and to mean no more than population numbers.

The term *"density-dependent"* was introduced by Smith[663] and a useful history of its meanings and associations is provided by Solomon.[678] The same idea has been expressed by Howard and Fiske[327] who wrote of *facultative factors* and by Nicholson[487] who (at p. 83) refers to "parasites and predators which become more and more effective in their action as the numbers of their hosts increase." Howard and Fiske define facultative factors as those which, "by exercising a restraining influence which is relatively more effective when other conditions favour undue increase, serves to prevent it" and contrast such factors with *inverse* factors such as vertebrate predators which, by destroying approximately equal numbers each year consume *proportionately* more prey when they are scarce than when common. Thirdly they recognize *catastrophic* factors whose action—most climatic influences are quoted as examples—is independent of density.

Smith took over the same concepts, renaming facultative factors *density-dependent* and catastrophic factors *density-independent*. He accepted the existence of inverse factors and considered that competition for favourable living space could interact with climate in a non-uniform environment so that climate effectively becomes a density-dependent factor under certain circumstances.

A large number of variations and even reversals of the meanings of these terms have been made by subsequent authors, which are listed by Solomon.[679-81] The best attitude to this unfortunate state of affairs seems to be to ignore these aberrations and hope that they will not be widely adopted. Three points however cannot be ignored.

Varley[751, 754] has argued that when Smith defined density-dependence he was thinking in terms of the logistic equation and its implications of instantaneous response to mortality factors, whereas we now recognize as more realistic Lotka's model in which time lags effect both the numbers of predators (and parasites) corresponding to a given prey density and also the mortality of prey in response to predation (Chapter 15). It follows that the instantaneous magnitude of a mortality factor in such cases is not likely to be obviously related to the population density (of the prey) as Smith's definition would imply. Varley therefore proposes that a fourth category, *delayed density-dependent mortality* factor, should be recognized.

It seems somewhat doubtful however whether Smith (who defined the term very loosely and could hardly have been unaware in 1935 of the work of his own countryman, Lotka published in 1927), intended deliberately to restrict his term to one particular model especially as predatory insects, etc., were named as typical density-dependent mortality factors. If, with Varley, we were to restrict the expression *density-dependent* to cases where reactions to density were demonstrably immediate not only would this represent a departure from general practice since 1935 but also there would be many occasions when the ecologist, quite uncertain whether his data fitted a logistic or Lotka model would be unable to use either *density-dependent* or *delayed density-dependent* and might even be tempted to invent yet another new term.

Normally it is perfectly clear from the context whether a distinction is possible and in this case if ambiguity is likely an adjective can be appended. Otherwise Lack's[390a] practice of regarding delayed density-dependent factors as a sub-class of density-dependent seems to be the soundest.

Milne[458, 459, 460, 461] has distinguished two types of density-dependent factors, intra-specific competition for food and living space on the one hand, which he calls *"perfectly" density-dependent* on the grounds (he is not always consistent in this) (*a*) that there is a strict relationship between numbers and intensity of the effect, or (*b*) the intensity of the effect is *solely* dependent on the density of the species, or (*c*) only these mortality factors can be relied upon to operate on all occasions. On the other hand inter-specific relationships such as parasitism and disease are classed as *"imperfectly" density-dependent* because their effect on the population is proportional to additional factors besides the density of the prey population. He claims that only perfectly density-dependent factors (hereinafter called p.d.d.f.) can unfailingly control population size and, therefore, imperfectly density-dependent factors (i.d.d.f.) should be classed with density-independent factors as incapable of population control. It is evident that this argument is a *non-sequitur* and also that (*a*), (*b*), and (*c*) are not necessarily the same thing.

Since Milne is obliged to accept that the intra-specific (p.d.d.f.) factors are not always effective in depressing population size (because food supply for instance is influenced by many things besides the density of one particular species which exploits it), he relegates their "imperfect" features to a set of influences called "environmental capacity" (undefined), and thus by a circular argument preserves their "perfection." One is not permitted to qualify the operation of i.d.d.f. by means of "environmental capacity."

Milne's arguments are very difficult to relate to actual populations in the field and biological properties other than a very limited range of rates of increase do not enter into his calculations. When faced with arguments based on real life, including of course the manifest fact that many economic pests have been controlled by predators and parasites, his rebuttals are based, not on field examples but take the form of protestations that observations inconsistent with his logic must be false. However, since Varley has demonstrated that the establishment of p.d.d. rests on proving a negative hypothesis, Milne's theory is as hard to test as that of the Vitalists—but equally unhelpful.

Finally the confusing practice must be mentioned of using the terms density-dependent and density-independent in a generic sense to include not so much the influences which can be shown to operate on a particular population in such a manner but those which have been shown to do so in other situations. In particular the generalizations that weather *is* a density-dependent, predators *are* density-dependent factors prejudge the issue and are invalid generalizations for an inductive science. A particular kind of influence, for example predation or factors reducing food supply may operate in a density-dependent manner on one occasion on one population and independently of density on another. The restriction of these words to known instances would avoid needless polemics and it is perfectly possible, as Varley has shown,[755] to apply statistical tests to determine whether a mortality factor is dependent on density or not.

It is, therefore, proposed in this book to apply the epithet density-dependent to a proven or suspected factor which is so influenced by the density of the population concerned that it opposes its tendencies to increase to a greater extent at higher densities than at lower densities.

The term may be qualified with additional adjectives if delayed or immediate operation can be demonstrated.

Practical Application

Having, it is hoped, disposed of these largely semantic problems it remains to consider how far density-dependent influences have any importance in nature (see also Solomon[680]). Obviously within the conceptual framework which envisages a relatively isolated population persisting for an indefinite period, discussed by Nicholson,[488, 490, 492, 496, 497, 498, 499, 500, 501, 502] only factors conforming to the above definition can prevent population density from increasing until, for instance, all available food supplies are exhausted as happened in some of Gause's experiments (see p. 143) or else dwindling to zero. What is disputed by Andrewartha and Birch[13, 14, 15, 15a, 16, 17, 52] is whether populations in nature really work like this. They claim that most populations are doomed to extinction sooner or later, that they are highly patchy in distribution and that their survival in a particular region depends on their dispersal behaviour and on the relative frequency and persistence of localities in which their rate of increase is sufficient to maintain nuclei of active expansion.

They accept that in well established populations Nicholson's views may be correct but insist that such situations are far from universal. Thompson[716, 717, 718] adopts a somewhat similar stand except that he will not accept that the "population" is anything but a purely abstract concept without relevance to natural conditions: he considers that density-dependent influences operate only under optimum conditions.

Clearly the conclusions of different protagonists in this argument result partly from different assumptions and models which they have in mind and rest on matters of judgment about the relative frequency of such models in nature.

In this connexion it is instructive to consider two examples which help one to achieve a broader view of the range of magnitudes of different types of mortality factors in nature. The first concerns the effects of competition in plants as described by Harper[302] who shows that the plasticity of genetic and physiological variation is such that seed production in the same species and the same field may vary from four to nearly one million seeds. Under such conditions the ground is virtually saturated with seed, density is independent of parental seed production and the factors which determine survival are almost entirely those which influence superiority in competition. The second example is Reynoldson's[602] comparision of mortality factors in Oligochaet worms and a Peritrich Protozoan, *Urceolaria mitra*. The latter, living as commensals on flatworms appear to enjoy very favourable physical conditions; *Enchytraeus albidus*, which lives in sewage beds, and Lumbricid earthworms in sand dunes, on the other hand are in marginal conditions physically. *Urceolaria* is readily shown to suffer density-dependent mortality whilst the two other examples appeared not to. Reynoldson argues that marginal populations of this kind may well be more comparable to those studied by Andrewartha and Birch. As Solomon[678] has written in a broad survey of this field, it would be most unwise to condemn any of the main models of population control as impossible, especially since so few natural populations have yet been studied sufficiently well. For the same reason further discussion of this question will be resumed after, in Chapter 16, we have considered some further accounts of what appears to happen in field populations.

Chapter 11

BIOMASS AND METABOLISM OF POPULATIONS

THE animal population is not only an aggregation of potentially interbreeding individuals of characteristic age structure; it is also a quantity of living protoplasm which is simultaneously mediating chemical changes in an ecosystem and retaining to itself materials and energy at the expense of other species populations. These latter characteristics are, of course, important at the community level of organization at which their relative values for different species must be compared (Chapters 14–16). In addition both the biomass (or quantity of material retained at any one instant) and metabolism (or rate of chemical activity) are population characteristics in their own right. Both the theoretical and the practical ecologist require to know which age groups are retaining most of the available materials in their bodies, which are most effectively laying down new flesh, which are most actively processing the foods available to the population and the relative metabolic cost of rearing animals to particular ages.

When one is concerned with the *standing crop* or *stock* of a population it is purely a matter of convenience whether biomass is expressed in terms of weight or its energetic equivalent in calories; there is nothing to be gained therefore by separating those approaches in which authors happen to have thought and written in terms of calories from those where weights have been quoted. In both cases the standing crop means simply the quantity of organic matter present at a particular moment of time.

The productivity or production rate of a population is determined by its metabolic activity in unit time multiplied by a factor proportional to the ratio of the food laid down as body tissue or stores to the total assimilated food. Since there has been much confusion over the use of these and related terms a short digression on the synonymy is in order.

Production and Related Terminology

The terms "production" and "productivity" (which are synonyms) are usually used to denote the biomass of an organism produced in a community over a period of time and therefore measure the bulk of matter contributed to the succeeding stages of the food chain (scavengers included); in the case of fisheries work, man is usually one of the "predators." This concept of production is a most valuable one, although confusion of terminology has lead to some misunderstandings in this, as in other fields of biology.[8, 431, 433, 609a, 708]

It is generally agreed that the total quantity of biomass of a population at any one time is the "stock" or "standing crop," that the amount of material produced in excess of the initial stock in a fixed period of time is the production or productivity, and the proportion of the production removed by man is the yield. The equivalents of these three terms in German are *Bestand*, *Produktion* (*Produktivität*) and *Ertrag*. The difficulty about production, however, is that if one simply compares the standing crop at two intervals a year apart, the difference may well be negative, or at least will not be comparable with the total amount of matter, regardless of what has happened to it, produced by the population during the course of a year. The word production is usually kept for the latter meaning, but the wisest course[117a] is to call the annual difference the "net production," the sum total produced the "gross production." The difference between these two is the "crop" or material eaten by predators, including man's "yield" in commercial fisheries and that consumed by organisms responsible for decay. The nomenclature used here is not universal, however; the synonyms as used by the authors stated are given in Table 10, where $Q =$ instantaneous quantity, $A =$ annual rate of accumulation and $I =$ instantaneous rate of increment.

The vertical columns in the table are some of the terms used in connexion with biological productivity; the horizontal rows represent the ideas which the terms have been used to describe. Where a term has been used for a given idea there is an entry consisting of a number and a letter; the number refers to the list of references below and the letter indicates that the term has been applied in the following way—

C to apply to a whole community or natural area.
T to apply to a single trophic level.
S to apply to a single species population.
H to apply to the herbivore populations only.

The authors cited in the table will be found in the bibliography.

1. Thienemann (1931),[708] definition 2.[431]
2. Thienemann (1931),[708] definition 3.[431]

T

Showing the ways in which terms connected

TERMS USED		PRODUCTION [Produktion]								
		Unqualified	Gross Production Rate	Net Production Rate	Total Production	Specific Production	Actual Production	Potential Production	Possible Production	Utilized Production
THE PROCESS OF PRODUCTION **WEIGHT OF ORGANIC MATTER**										
GROSS INTAKE (i.e. food including faeces)	A	14 C 3 T	11 S, T, C 12 S, T 13 S, T 15 S, T							
INTAKE REQUIRED TO MAINTAIN BODY WEIGHT										
NET INTAKE (i.e. food less faeces, i.e. body weight plus secretions plus inorganic deposits)	A	6 T 7 H								
BODY WEIGHT OR BIOMASS (i) (i.e. instantaneous total of intake, less secretions and allowing for predation, respiration and decomposition)	Q	4 T								
(ii) integral of above, *not* allowing for loss by predation, etc.	A	5 S 10 S 20 S				11 S	11 S			
(iii) maximum if natural balance is not to be upset	A							11 S		
(iv) maximum if community were managed otherwise	A								11 S	
(v) maximum if there were unlimited light	A									
(vi) maximum if there were unlimited nutrients	A									
(vii) as above but confined to one species							11 S			
Difference between biomass on two occasions, e.g. one year apart. This may be negative	Q				12 S 13 S					
BIOMASS REMOVED BY MAN	Q	1 C								
(or by a given Predator)	A	18 S 21 S 22 S								11 S,
ENERGY IN CALORIES										
GROSS INTAKE (i.e. in food plus faeces)	A I									
NET INTAKE (i.e. less losses by faeces, excreta, predation, decomposition and respiration)	A I									
ENERGY CONTENT at one instant at end of a year	Q Q									
LIBERATION (by respiration, i.e. intake less accumulation in body and less losses by predation and decomposition)	A									

ductivity have been used by different authors.

| Unqualified | PRODUCTIVITY [Produktivität] | | | | Standing Crop [Bestand] | Crop | Yield [Ertrag] | Stock | Maintenance Ration | Biological Turnover [Umsatz] | Activity | Biomass | Metabolism |
	Corrected Productivity	Uncorrected Productivity	Actual Productivity	Potential Productivity									
1 C S, T, C										15 C			15 S
									13 S				
					11 S 12 S, T 13 S, T 15 S, T 19 S, T			20 S				5 S	
2 C 4 C 5 S													
			14 C	14 C									
8 H 10 S						20 S	12 S, T 13 S, T 15 S, T						
9 T 9 T	9 T 9 T	9 T	9 T 9 T										
		22 S					9 T						
S, T, C											17 S, T, C		

3. Thienemann (1931),[708] definition 4.[431]
4. Tansley (1929).[700a]
5. Borutzky (1939).[61a]
6. Windberg and Iarovitzina (1939).[821]
7. Harvey (1942).[308]
8. Palmgren (1942).[544]
9. Lindeman (1942).[409]
10. Ivlev (1945).[345]
11. Clemens, Ricker and Barnaby (1948).[117a]
12. Clarke (1946).[113]
13. Ricker and Foerster (1948).[609a]
14. Strøm (1932).[697]
15. Elster (1944).[196]
16. Kalle (1948).[357]
17. Bornebusch (1930).[60]
18. Demoll (1938).[170]
19. Riley (1941).[612]
20. Allen (1951).[8]
21. Needham (1940).[484]
22. Birch and Clark (1953).[53a]

It should be particularly noticed that "production" has been used by various authors to mean the food intake, stock, the food output to particular organisms and the yield, while the "stock" has also been called the "standing crop," "biomass," and "production."

It will have been noticed that this terminology makes no distinction between the production by plant photosynthesis, which is the new creation of high-energy organic compounds, and the production by animals, bacteria, fungi and so on, which is really the inefficient transfer of high-energy materials to other bodies. Grim[286] made the useful distinction between production and "destruction," in which the latter term is confined to the holozoic processes of breakdown of organic matter with the liberation of energy. When one is concerned with distinguishing the synthetic from the anabolic processes which take place in the community as a whole, especially in discussing the balance of energy transfer in the community (see Chapters 14 and 15), the distinction is a most useful one. From the point of view of measuring the dynamics of the populations involved, however, it is of little moment whether high-energy organic materials are obtained *de novo* by photosynthesis, or are obtained by robbing a previous trophic level. In both cases the intake is balanced by two components in the output, namely that which is decomposed with the liberation of energy, and that which is handed on to predators and scavenging or decomposing organisms.

Odum[527] has suggested that production by heterotrophic organisms should be distinguished from that by plants by the use of the word "assimilation." Unfortunately the term production is now widely accepted in this sense and assimilation is accepted to mean that proportion of ingested food which is not rejected as faeces (see Chapter 6). Although there is little agreement on the use of terms and the most important principle is that each author should define his uses, it seems inadvisable to adopt a practice which both conflicts with prior usage and also changes the meaning of a precisely defined term.

Fisheries biologists are greatly concerned with measuring permissible yields and relating them to production in order to be able to estimate the loss going to other predators and at what stage overcropping is likely to upset the existing system in a given body of water. It is not surprising, therefore, that they should have developed methods for measuring production; it *is* perhaps surprising that attempts to do so have not been made in other fields of applied biology, such as game management.

The Calculation of Fish Production in Cultus Lake and the Horokiwi Stream

Perhaps the most fundamental treatment of production measurement is that due to Ricker and Foerster,[609a] who quote figures which enable one to appreciate the orders of magnitude involved. It is at once evident that, contrary to frequent assumptions, there is little relation between stock and production; in other words, a census of the stock of a lake will give one little idea of how large a fishery it will support. Ricker and Foerster show how the three basic measurements of growth rate, mortality and stock can be made: growth rate from age determinations on a series of catches, mortality from the depletion of age classes in the same catches and stock from the weight of the age groups present or by the use of the Lincoln index method (Chapter 8). The difference between growth rate k and mortality rate i gives the instantaneous rate of increase. If P is the stock, this can be expressed—

$$\frac{dP}{dt} = (k - i)P \qquad P = P_0 e^{(k-i)t}$$

The mean stock $\bar{P}$ present during the year is given by—

$$\bar{P} = \int_0^1 P_0 e^{(k-i)t}\, dt = P_0 \frac{(e^{k-i} - 1)}{k - i}$$

This must be summed for all age groups and then gives the gross production. This apparently simple procedure is attended with many difficulties; it assumes that the sampling method for the fish is non-selective and complete, that the ratio of k to i is constant throughout the year and that all age groups are known. In the particular population worked on by Ricker and Foerster the first difficulty was overcome because the fry enter a lake by a stream in which the adults spawn, the vast majority stay there one year and then pass out as yearlings; it was therefore possible to count the incoming and outgoing populations. The growth rate : mortality ratio must usually be assumed constant, although some attempts have been made to calculate its seasonal distribution. In almost no case has it been possible to follow the population throughout its life history and compute production for all age classes.

A very complete account of the production of the brown trout and its relation to stock, fishing intensity and food supply is given by Allen,[8] who also describes a practical and ingenious graphical method of estimating production. This important study included the estimation of the stock of bottom-living invertebrate animals on which the trout feeds and showed that the trout eat from forty to 150 times the stock present at any one time, an astonishing proportion. Egg production was estimated from known fecundity and population counts and also from counts of the young fry. Stock, mortality, growth and food consumption were obtained by fishing with nets every three months, combined with Lincoln index estimates; growth was obtained from size-distribution curves and age determinations by means of scale growth rings. The stock, which averaged 1,100 kg, consumed 14,620 kg per year, and had an annual production of 2,280 kg.

By means of a voluntary census of anglers' diaries the yield to anglers was estimated; it amounted to between 0·9 per cent and

6·5 per cent in different years. By far the greater part of production occurs in the first year and a half of the trouts' life; about 95 per cent by the end of the second year. For this reason between 80 per cent and 93 per cent of production had already been removed by the time the fish were of a size taken by anglers (eels were suspected as an important predator). On the grounds of this information it is not surprising that Allen recommended that anglers should be allowed to take fish of a smaller size in order to increase the yield of the stream.

In Ricker's analysis[608] (mentioned in Chapter 10) the measurement of the effects of different types of predation on the production of populations already subject to density-dependent mortality is discussed. Three models are examined: (a) when the predator takes a fixed *number* of prey (this applies only where prey numbers have no effect on predator density, as when the predator is nutritionally independent of the prey), (b) when predators take a fixed fraction of the prey population (as might happen when predation rate is governed by random encounters; this case can result in a stable equilibrium), (c) when predators take all those prey in excess of a basic population which is protected by some system of refuges; (this situation has been described for the Bob-White Quail by Errington[211]). If predation were to operate in a density-dependent manner and if the ratio of actual density to that at which maximum reproduction occurred were ω, the actual reproduction rate would be $\omega e^{1-\omega}$. From this formula Ricker calculates the predicted relationship between stock and recruitment.

The Calculation of Production in Insects

When production is to be measured in rapidly changing populations of fast growing species such as insects, the fisheries biologists' approach must be modified because animals which die during the time between successive censuses will have contributed to gross production and should be accounted for. This is the approach of Teal[706] and of Ness and Dudale[485] both of whom use a modified version of Ricker's formula—

$$P_t = P_0\, e^{(k-i)t} \quad \text{where}$$

P_t and P_0 are the populations at the end and the beginning of the sample period respectively,

k and i are the rates of growth and mortality respectively. The later authors extrapolate from the instantaneous data applying to single

size cohorts of larvae and in practice they determined a log/log relation
between larval weight and cohort size.

Population Efficiency

The absolute values of population metabolic rates, of little interest in
the present context, are important in three distinct fields—

1. In the determination of population efficiency.
2. When they are compared with population numbers and biomass
especially over a period of time, and
3. When different species from the same community are compared
with regard to their partitioning of resources and energy. The first
aspect will be considered here; the second and third in Chapter 15.

The outstanding example to date of a laboratory study of population
energetics is that of Slobodkin and colleagues[607, 654, 656, 658, 659]
on *Daphnia pulex* and, latterly, on other species. The emphasis in
this study is on different aspects of efficiency from the point of view of a
potential exploiter of the population (see p. 72). The energy intake
measured is that associated with the food ingested, not that assimilated,
because assimilation is technically difficult to measure in this species.
Because the assimilation/ingestion ratio varies with the availability ratio
of food, both sparse and dense algal populations being under-exploited,
the efficiencies vary in this way also. A similar situation has been shown
by Cushing[144, 145] to obtain in the marine plankton, where *Calanus*
may ingest up to five or ten times as much food as it assimilates and
also with benthic Amphipods and Isopods as shown by Gajevskaya.[241]
Where it is possible to calculate efficiency from true assimilation
figures, this may be rather constant, as found by Phillipson.[571]

Two measures of efficiency are recognized in this context, first
ecological efficiency which is the ratio of yield to a predator ÷ ingested
food. The predator in these experiments is the experimenter who crops
the *Daphnia* at a series of different rates. Secondly *population efficiency*
is defined as the yield to the predator ÷ (increased ingestion by *Daphnia*
in the presence of predation less that in the absence of predation).

Under the conditions of the experiment—in which food is added at a
controlled rate, population efficiency depends very much on the age
structure of the harvested population. Richmond shows that the
proportion of food assimilated to food incorporated in growth falls
from 60 per cent in the young *Daphnia* to 4 per cent in the 34-day-old
one. A high proportion is later used by the female in producing eggs.

An optimal fishing regime for obtaining maximal calorific output from the *Daphnia* population in relation to the food supply is calculated and equated with that which involves least metabolic cost for replacement. Under natural conditions of course, this relationship might be complicated by any reciprocal effect of the *Daphnia* on its food supply, affecting the rate of increase of the latter. Thus if, as usually happens, the food supply were not strictly limited, and if, as in some of the examples discussed by Ricker (Chapter 10), the relationship between numbers and rate of increase were non-linear, increased cropping would *increase* the permissible rate of harvesting.

The *ecological efficiency* or energy contained in the yields/ingested energy is shown by Slobodkin to be fairly constant over a wide range of conditions between 5 per cent and 15 per cent. Although the optimal feeding rate effect mentioned above results in a peak value of predation which is associated with maximal population efficiency, the same effect operates to make ecological efficiency relatively independent of food supply. Slobodkin[659] gives reasons for supposing that these values around 10 per cent for ecological efficiency are typical for natural populations. It should be noted that they are higher than the values for food-chain efficiency discussed on page 74.

The Synthesis of Numerical and Metabolic Measurement of Single Species Populations

The relationship between population parameters (birth and death rates and age structure) on the one hand and characteristics of the pattern of predation (cropping rate, yield and age structure of the catch) on the other constitutes an important practical field which is the subject of a vast literature. This is also an example of a field of ecology in which concepts, initially applied to sets of data and with different objectives are now being united in a single theoretical system. The field has recently been surveyed by Watt[789] who examines the use of mathematical models as a means of maximizing the output of a fishery. The originators of perhaps the best known of these models, Beverton and Holt[46] have also provided an extensive review of the literature. Watt's original method[788] was to compare the advantages of three separate approaches to the solution of the optimum yield problem by applying them to actual population data obtained from *Tribolium confusum* cultures subjected to twelve (and later four more) cropping treatments over a period of nearly two years. Both numerical (total and adult) and biomass productivity were determined and the data subjected to (1) a statistical analysis of temporal trends, (2) a graphical regression analysis and (3) comparison with a mathematical model. The first approach was particularly interesting in showing the tendency for harvested populations like those studied by Nicholson[496, 500] to behave in a homoeostatic manner—e.g. removal of adults leads to an increase of recruitment to the adult stage; and also in demonstrating that the harvested populations are more stable when removal is close to optimal yield conditions. When harvesting is more or less severe than this the homoeostatic mechanisms break down and oscillations in numbers are likely to occur (cf. p. 140). The second analysis provided further strong evidence of homoeostasis which in the crowded population appears to result in a preponderance of adult animals. The mathematical model is claimed to allow a more precise prediction of the outcome of particular harvesting regimes; it was capable of accounting for two-thirds of the variability of the system. Watt's analysis demonstrates the complete lack of correspondence between standing crop levels and actual or potential productivity; nor are standing crop figures capable of predicting a crash in population size or yield. Another important point demonstrated by Watt is the unsoundness of the logistic curve as a model for the growth of a population: the assumptions implicit in logistic curve ignore the changes in age structure of the population and in fact the point of inflexion of the curve, corresponding to the most rapid rate of increase of the population, does not lie at a midway point to the maximum in the *Tribolium* cultures. This is contrary to many previous models used in this field. In a further study Watt went on to test this approach in practice, by analysing the population history of a sport fish population of Smallmouth Bass.[791]

Another example of a productivity and population study of this kind is due to Frank,[233] who measured age-specific mortality and natality rates of *Daphnia* over a wide range of conditions and also translated the numerical data in terms of biomass. He was able to make allowances for lag effects (see p. 138) and thus to predict the history of experimental populations (including situations leading to instability), to a surprising degree of accuracy.

In a rather different way observations on seasonal interrelations between numbers, biomass and productivity of a species population in the field can provide generalizations which also permit comparison with other parts of the ecosystem.

Odum and Smalley[529] provide one example of this approach in a preliminary study of the numbers, biomass and metabolic activity of the grasshopper *Orchelimum* feeding on a *Spartina* marsh. Over the three months during which the grasshopper was active numbers fell and biomass increased but the total metabolism remained within the rather narrow range of 0·2 and 0·4 kilocalories per sq m per day. The period of activity coincided with that during which fresh greenstuff was available, but in the case of the snail *Littorina irrorata* which feeds on detritus both the availability of food and activity of the snail persist through the year. The metabolic rate was similarly restricted in range despite changes in population structure.

Balogh[33] has also pointed out the inverse seasonal relationships between numbers and biomass in many terrestrial invertebrates. He has suggested a synthesis of information on this topic with data on seasonal variation in the demands of predators—both as regards numbers and also the size range which the predator can handle.

Although this is a relatively new field of ecology it seems clear that combinations of demographic and metabolic measurements, using the newer and more realistic population models, are already leading to a very useful synthesis of population properties. Such studies of population size stability and productivity may be claimed to contribute to what Slobodkin has called a system of population metatheory.[657]

Part III

THE ECOLOGY OF ANIMAL COMMUNITIES

Chapter 12

INTRODUCTION TO COMMUNITY ECOLOGY

THE study of communities is necessarily based on that of their constituent populations and many of the ideas introduced in Part II are essential to an understanding of what follows. This chapter contains a simple classification of the approaches to community studies followed by a short historical survey which may help to bring together the contents and explain the arrangement of the subsequent chapters. These are followed by an examination of the meaning of the community concept as the main theme and working hypothesis dominating the field of ecology.

Classification of Factors Which Determine Population Size

Population-determining factors fall naturally into three groups: first, those concerning the single species population in isolation, already considered in Part II, second, those concerning *food-chain* relationships, that is to say *vertical* relationships between different trophic levels, between predator and prey and between host and parasite and, third, the relationships between the different species populations in the same trophic level, which decide the results of competition for food and space and other factors, and of "helpful" interactions whereby one species benefits from the presence of another. Both these types of *horizontal* interaction are termed *coactions* in America.[7, 96]

Methods of Investigating Populations

Relationships between the populations within a community have been investigated in what we may briefly term the *mathematical*, the *experimental* and the *field* levels of investigation. This chapter gives a brief review of these three methods of approach, because there has been a strong tendency for each individual worker, interested as he is in all aspects of population interactions, to confine himself to a single type of approach.

A Short Historical Survey: the Mathematical Approach

Historically, the mathematical approach seems to have preceded all others. Malthus[446] in his *Essay on Population* discussed one fundamental property of single species populations, namely their tendency to exponential increase. He inferred from this the need, in the case of man, for some artificial method of population control in order to avoid control by starvation. This idea inspired Darwin,[157] whose theory of "natural selection" due to selective survival of the fittest is still the main theoretical background idea of biology. Perhaps the driving force of his theory was the assumption of an almost unbelievable intensity of competition, as is shown by his reference[158] to "the infinitely various ways beings have to obtain food by struggling with other beings, to escape danger at various times of life, to have their eggs or seeds disseminated, etc., etc.," and again, animals "will be exposed to the mutual action of a different set of inhabitants, which I believe to be more important to the life of each being than mere climate." Still on the mathematical level we have the work of Verhulst[764, 765] who first applied the *logistic equation* to the growth of a single species population and then of Pearl[562, 563] who drew attention to Verhulst's work and, in the first example of the experimental approach, tested its applicability to experimental populations of *Drosophila*. In the field of *vertical* relationships Ross[620] worked out a theory of the interaction of parasite and host for malaria, mosquito and man.

The 1920s were a time of important innovation in the mathematical field, for it was in 1925 that Lotka's *Principles of Physical Biology*[415] and Volterra's analysis[768] appeared. Both these authors independently derived mathematical expressions governing the results of competition between populations and of the effect of interaction between predator and prey; both independently described the conditions under which, in simple systems, unstable conditions may arise and oscillations in number may start. There was still no practical investigation of these problems, although Volterra's thinking was started by fisheries statistics produced by D'Ancona. Lotka's book also contains the first attempt to apply the methods of human demographers to animals and advocates the use of the "intrinsic rate of natural increase" as a measure of the growth rate of populations. Meanwhile, Thompson[713, 714, 715] had developed independently the theory of parasite-host relationships, especially in connexion with the practical application of biological control. Two important theoretical works appeared in the early 1930s: first that of Nicholson[488] who extended Howard and Fiske's[327] idea of "facultative agencies" which he called "control factors" and introduced many other important ideas which are considered below. Nicholson's control factors were in turn renamed "density-dependent" factors and applied to biological control problems by H. S. Smith (1935).[664] Shortly after Nicholson's paper, Gause's (1934) *Struggle for Existence*[243] appeared containing a theoretical analysis based mainly on Volterra and followed by one of the first detailed attempts to carry out laboratory experiments and to test the applicability to ecological situations of the theories of the mathematicians. Nicholson was concerned both with *vertical* and *horizontal* relationships.

The Experimental Approach

Gause's work, important in itself, seems to have inspired others to attempt laboratory work of this type. A whole series of competition and predator-prey experiments[48, 49, 50, 54, 96, 135–9, 243, 324] was carried out mainly using grain pest insects. Single species population experiments on blowflies by Nicholson[493, 494, 495] should also be mentioned at this stage.

These important experiments introduced the quantitative study of competition and predator-prey relationships under controlled conditions and have shown in particular how very complicated such "simple" systems can become. A field of outstanding importance is that developed by Park[545–55] who, by numerous replicates of very long experiments, showed that in the two-species grain-beetle system, described by him, the outcome of competition is more accurately expressed as a statistical probability, it being uncertain whether the outcome of a particular situation will end in favour of one or the other species. He also showed how the presence or absence of a Protozoan parasite can reverse the outcome of competition and how fine, even in such a "simple" experiment, is the balance deciding the fate of competition.

A brief paper of Gause's[245] involving the maintenance, for a very short period, of an experiment in which eight species achieved an equilibrium, shows that work on these lines is practicable, but it was not analysed very fully. A more complete analysis of these data is given by Leslie.[403]

Field-population Studies

Meanwhile, studies had been begun on animal populations in the field. It had long been known[197] that some animals, particularly small herbivorous mammals and birds living in sub-arctic and temperate regions, undergo violent fluctuations in numbers, and Elton[199] suggested that there might be some link between these and the oscillations described by the mathematicians and demonstrated experimentally by Gause.[243] A long programme of work started by Elton in the 1930s investigated the mechanism of such fluctuations; this topic has already been discussed in Chapter 10.

A more direct offspring of Nicholson's approach to these matters is shown by Varley's[748] study of natural populations on the Knapweed Gallfly, in which the causes of mortality were analysed and it was stated that the factor controlling the size of the population—a hymenopterous parasite—was not that which caused the heaviest mortality. This work was believed to confirm Nicholson's ideas about the importance of density-dependent factors in biological control and it has since been supplemented by work on the analysis of mortality factors (see p. 258).

Field ecologists and particularly ornithologists have contributed much circumstantial evidence to two theories in this particular field; first, the question of the role of density-dependent factors in determining the size of populations, and second, "Gause's theorem" that two animals with closely related habits cannot exist together in the same ecological "niche."

A number of field studies are reviewed in Chapter 16 and it is demonstrated there that the ideas derived from theory and experiment are not without application to the admittedly more complicated situations in the field.

Contributory evidence about the interactions of species in the community has come from work on "biological control" of pest species, both plant and animal. As in much applied work there has been some tendency to restrict the theoretical basis to few principles and not much that is qualitatively new has come from this. However, a much clearer idea of the magnitude of the biological forces which are at work has been gained from these experiments which are often on a vast scale. The subject of biological control is considered in more detail in Chapter 18.

The chapters which follow cover the detection and delimitation of communities (Chapter 13), the horizontal (Chapter 14) and the vertical (Chapter 15) relations between species populations from both the numerical and the energetic points of view and finally a synthesis of community properties (Chapter 17). Before proceeding, however, it is necessary to consider how the term community has been used in the past and how it can most profitably be defined and used in the present context.

It is a debatable point whether it is preferable to attempt to define concepts such as that of the community rigidly or to use them loosely, fully recognizing that one is doing so, until more has been learned about their structure, properties and limits. Some of the attempts which have been made to define communities will be reviewed, the ideas which they have in common and by which they differ will be discussed and then we shall return to the desirability of attempting further definitions.

It is not unusual in science for everyday words to be given one or more special meanings by theorists, as a result of which the generality of followers of the science concerned, and often the layman too, are faced with a dilemma. If one uses the everyday word one risks being misinterpreted as a devotee of the new theoretical ideas, while if one invents a new word to replace the old one, one is labelled a pedant for making unnecessary additions to the vocabulary.

Seven Typical Definitions of the Community

The word "community" has more than once been given special technical meanings in the history of ecology and it is mainly for this reason that it is shunned by many today. A recent reviewer,[134] for instance, was echoing a widespread view when he wrote: "Perhaps the reviewer is not alone in asking his students to look at least twice at any statement in which the word 'community' occurs. Its meaning is limitless, for it ranges from a piece of shorthand denoting an assemblage of organisms to something endowed with the attributes of organization which, in the absence of factual support, rivals the daydreams of the alchemists." In the English language the word has at least four ecological meanings of which the following, including related foreign language definitions, are some—

1. Akin to Cragg's first suggestion above is the agreed definition of the Third Botanical Congress at Brussels that ecological communities are "ecological units of every degree." Coupled with this definition was one of an association as "a community of definite taxonomic composition presenting a uniform physiognomy and growing in uniform habitat conditions."

2. Conspicuous for its denial of some of the views implied in the definitions of others is Clark's[112] definition of associations as "due to mere coincidence of range . . . and not to any community structure."

3. Möbius[463] invented the term "biocönose," which he defined as "a community whose total of species is mutually linked and selected under the influence of the average external conditions of life." In this he implied interrelations between the members of a biocönose which result in their occurring together and which bring about groupings not solely due to chance overlap of ranges.

Palmgren[543] reviews definitions by many, especially Scandinavian and German, authors. Among these two main trends may be discerned, typified by the authors in the next two sections—

4. Resvoy[600] states: "A biocönose represents a population system that occurs under given ecological conditions and maintains in itself a dynamic balance." This is expanded further by, Friederichs,[236] who claims that "the capacity for self-regulation is, therefore, included in the definition. This is in fact unnecessary in that this property is found in all biological entities, from the single cell to the whole world, and is not peculiar to living communities . . . the result of the self-regulation in the biocönose is the biocoenotic balance; this is never attained, but it results in a harmony, a relative order, which maintains the unity of the biocönose in given localities and its cause is that definite efficiency of all natural phenomena, without which the unity of the cosmos would be unthinkable." It is discussions of this sort which are largely responsible for the violent reactions of some ecologists when the word community is mentioned. However, the main theme of these definitions is evidently the concept of the ecological or biocoenotic balance.

5. On the other hand we have those definitions which stress the uniformity, in composition or in space, of the community. Thus, Wangerin,[781] a follower of Braun-Blanquet, states "an association is considered to be those separate and relatively stable local elements which agree in their essential sociological characteristics, especially in their floristic composition, their aspect and their ecological characteristics as determined by the local conditions." Hesse[318] states that "the biocönose is the grouping together of the living beings which dwell in a uniform part of the habitat and, in the selection and requirements of the species, correspond with the average prevailing conditions."

6. Emerson[210] wrote that "the same factors which bring about the integration of the organismic units within the species can also be

shown to be active in the ecological community . . . the ecological community has an ontogeny (succession) and a phylogeny."

7. Allee et al.[7] define a community as "a natural assemblage of organisms which, together with its habitat, has reached a survival level such that it is relatively independent of adjacent assemblages of equal rank; to this extent, given radiant energy, it is self-sustaining."

Differences between Plant and Animal Ecologists

Many other definitions of communities have been given. Some authors have stressed the differences between plant and animal communities, as for instance Braun-Blanquet,[66] who points out that "communal relationships between plants are fundamentally different from the relationships among animals. . . . The principles of usefulness, of division of labour, of conscious support . . . do not exist in the plant world. The struggle for existence here rules undisturbed . . . herein lies the deep and fundamental difference between the vital relations of plant and those of animal communities." Others[700] have stressed the reverse aspect of the picture and the extent to which plant and animal communities are similar and indeed are part of a single "biotic" community. However, the above quotations will provide sufficient basis for a short discussion of what is common to these definitions and what are the main differences of opinion among ecologists on the subject.

Botanists tend to use the term community in the non-committal way of the Brussels congress and to attribute ideas such as these to "associations," while to many animal ecologists "community" is the more special term. It will be understood that in this discussion the concept of the community as something more than a mere chance assemblage of species is at the focus of interest and for convenience the term "community" will be used in this sense. Thus, the controversy between Cain[89, 90] and Emerson,[210] although ostensibly about "associations," is strictly relevant to the present problem.

Main Conceptions Involved

It will be seen that there are three main ideas and two lesser variants involved in definitions of communities: first, the mere presence together of a range of animals which, in the view of many, is the only well-established and indubitable property. Secondly, the recognition or the claim, depending on one's view, that collections of virtually the same groups of species recur both geographically and in time, and thus that there are many examples of a given "community type" which can be recognized and distinguished from other "community types"; this is based on the idea of constancy of composition. Third, the idea that communities have a tendency to dynamic stability as a result of which a "normal" or "usual" composition is recognizable and that this composition tends to be restored when it has been upset by natural or artificial interference. Fourth, the idea, originating presumably from Whitehead's philosophy,[803] that the community exhibits characteristics which could not be predicted from the properties of its constituent organisms and that one is therefore justified in regarding the community as embodying a different and higher level of organization. Fifth, the community is claimed to be a superorganism and analogies with plant and animal bodies are stressed (the fourth idea carried a step farther).

Coincidence of Range and Constancy of Composition

The difficulty of recognizing the boundaries of communities seems chiefly to have been experienced by marine biologists concerned with the bottom fauna or "benthos." They have often experienced large areas of sea-bottom supporting faunas which show only gradual and indistinct changes. It seems quite possible that the sea-bottom does, in fact, support very few communities and it has even been argued that an area lacking any primary photosynthetic source of food cannot be regarded as a biotic community but should be considered part of a wider community which includes the plankton. Some authors have denied altogether the applicability of the community concept to the benthos (and hence extended their argument to the entire globe). On the other hand, Caspers,[94] for instance, after comparing the virtues and failings of many definitions, concludes that by considering the biotic community together with its environment as a single entity, and by using indicator species and *Leitformen* (characteristic animal life-forms) it is possible to distinguish closely related associations and to maintain the existence of communities in the benthos. This concept of *Leitformen* will be mentioned in Chapter 13.

Dynamic Stability

The main difference of opinion centres around whether the self-restoring tendency and the existence of a higher level of organization exist and are demonstrable or not, and the intermediate shades of meaning will not be considered further. It is therefore necessary to consider the validity of these ideas and the desirability of restricting the terms to one particular special meaning.

The nature of the dynamic balance[488] achieved by populations in the field will be discussed later (Chapter 16). While no one would contend that animal populations in nature are constant in size, it is generally agreed that the same species are usually found in the same habitats at the same seasons for many years in succession, and that they occur in numbers which are of the same order of magnitude. It is shown that this fact can only be attributed to the operation of density-dependent factors which will tend to depress the numbers of swollen populations more than those of diminished populations.

It must be conceded, since we have no surveys of complete associations of plants and animals over long periods, that dogmatism about the characteristics of such associations is unjustifiable. Nevertheless, the Darwinian method of argument from much circumstantial evidence has had a fruitful history in biology and is justifiable where there is no alternative. Those who would deprive the scientist of theories until he has accumulated an indigestible mass of facts misunderstand the methods of science and ignore the value of the working hypothesis in providing a theme and a means of organizing the facts.

The mere fact that competition within one "trophic level" for the same resources and that the intensity of predation and parasitism between trophic levels both tend to act in a density-dependent manner will ensure that a group of organisms living together and ecologically interrelated will have many tendencies towards self restoration. The self-restoring tendencies can, of course, be so adjusted that violent oscillations in numbers occur owing to the relations between the sensitivity of reactions and the delays in their initiation. This (see Chapter 15) was predicted from a consideration of very simple mathematical models by Lotka and Volterra, was demonstrated in simple experimental models by Gause and is well known in the field from regions of the world where ecological situations involve few species, as in the arctic and in artificially simplified areas under human cultivation. That such things do happen in nature is indisputable evidence that biotic relationships between populations do act in no uncertain manner and that Clark's generalization is unacceptable. Presumably the fact that such violent oscillations are uncommon in parts of the world and in natural communities where more species exist together is due to the far greater number of alternative restoring biotic relationships which are called into play when a population is displaced from its normal level; each species has more potential predator species and competitors available to suppress any rapid increase in numbers, while the predators and competitors in turn have more alternative sources of food to which they can switch their attention without a temporary shortage reacting immediately on their numbers; these factors result in the damping down of incipient oscillation. The prevalent tendency for man to grow large areas of a single crop is, of course, a reversion to the greatly simplified conditions in which violent oscillations are more likely to occur.

We can, therefore, argue from our knowledge of the interrelations between the component organisms of a community that they are likely to lead to a dynamically stable system and from our observation of the continuity and reproducibility of the community that such systems do exist. To this extent one is justified in postulating the existence of something more than is implied by the "association" of the Brussels definition, at least until more direct evidence from prolonged observation of natural systems is available.

That plant associations are self-regulating systems is widely conceded, although a number of qualifications are usual: first, all but "climax" associations are generally recognized to be but steps in a process of evolution from simple to more complex assemblages of species. It is one of the outstanding features of this process, however, that the periods of relative stability are much more distinct than those of change and continue far longer. The fact that stages in the succession are recognizable implies the existence at each stage of conservative forces which tend to delay the onset of change until the evolutionary forces are overwhelming. Similar situations are familiar both in space and time in the evolution of species and in that of human institutions and civilizations, and seem to be an outstanding characteristic of organic processes.

Secondly, it is recognized that many apparently stable associations in fact show cyclical changes of a few years' duration. Such have been described[787] from the vegetation of breckland, blanket bog, and many other communities. The patches of one species increase in vigour and size and then decay, often from the centre, are invaded by one or more series of sub-dominant forms, and finally are re-established.

The process may be related either to the depletion of minerals or the operation of physical factors, such as wind action. The net effect is that, although the proportion of the different plants in the area as a whole may remain constant, the pattern of species in any one area is constantly changing and the "balance" is thus an average effect of short-term cyclical changes. The extent to which this sort of thing occurs in animal populations has not been much studied. Naturally, in most animals, which are far more mobile than plants, the scale would be very different and Elton's conception of "interspersion"[203] is more appropriate. In the case of microscopic soil animals, however, there is evidence of very rapid fluctuations in numbers of Protozoa and Bacteria.[146, 702] The small soil insects may also be related to the cyclical vegetational changes occurring in arctic soils due to solifluction,[436] but this is a problem not yet adequately investigated.

Thirdly, it is evident that the dominant component species of an association may gradually change over a wide geographical area as one species is replaced in its niche by another, while the essential structure of the community remains. The existence of this feature has been made the basis of Cain's[90] rejection of the plant-community hypothesis. However, as Braun-Blanquet[66] stated in his analysis of plant sociology, geographical replacement of one dominant by another does not imply a change of community. The structure of the community is the object of study and not the detail of its component parts just as a church is a church whether made of brick or of stone.

This is not the place to argue the case for and against the concept of plant communities.[89, 90, 210, 355, 700, 701, 739]   At least part of the confusion among botanists is due to their concentration on the formal study of plant associations and the neglect of the essential structure of the biotic community as a whole involving animals and other heterotrophic organisms. It is shown in Chapter 13 that the results of "biocoenological" studies provide evidence for the unity and overlap of animal and plant communities and to this extent provide an argument for the objective reality of both.

Organismic Unity

One property which we considered would support the existence of the community in nature was organismic unity. The ancient argument between the "vitalists" and the "mechanists" no longer occupies biologists' attention today largely because it has been shown,[824] by the application of the "organismic" concept due in the first place to Whitehead,[803] that it was largely based on the misuse of words. It will probably be conceded by followers of this line of thought that an association of organisms such as we have been discussing shows properties of a higher level of organization than those possessed by the individual animal. The most important of these properties is, of course, the tendency to self regulation both at the level of the single species population and that of the association of species. If one were to use the properties of the single species population as a guide, one would naturally expect a collection of species to expand indefinitely, and there is nothing about their individual properties which would enable one to predict the outcome of their doing so in a limited universe. The self-limiting, self-regulating properties of such a collection of species when they happen to constitute a biotic community must therefore be properties of the community itself and characteristic of that level of organization. Any characteristic patterns of change found in such a collection, whether evolutionary or cyclical, are quite unpredictable on the basis of the characteristics of the individual species alone. In this sense, therefore, the existence of biotic communities as entities with a new level of organization is indisputable.

When Emerson[210] and others refer to the community as a super-organism, is anything more implied? A great deal has been written which would suggest that there is, but the arguments, however, are largely based on analogy, and although statements such as those made by Emerson and Friederichs are obviously not amenable to demonstration, it is doubtful whether their authors intend them to be taken literally. It is also doubtful whether the use of such loose terminology helps the advance of an already difficult subject and it is certain that it discredits it in the eyes of more literally-minded biologists.

Conclusions

We have seen that views on the meaning and validity of the biotic community cover a wide range and that there seems to be little *theoretical* reason for attaching the word community to any particular one of them. The *practical* function of a scientific term is to represent unambiguously an agreed set of properties, but in the present case agreement on properties is not to be expected because the properties to be anticipated depend on the ecologist's views on the ultimate aims of his science. Should the term, therefore, be among those which are, by agreement, used in many different senses? Disagreement in this case is seen to represent something more fundamental than a question of word use, because different groups of people are using the same word to indicate what they think ecology ought to concern itself with and how it ought to be studied.

The invention of new jargon being particularly abhorrent to the present author, it is not intended to propose here a set of words to represent the ideas of what a community should be from seven different points of view; it shall suffice to indicate the sense in which it has been used in the present book. It has been a main theme that when the life of the earth is studied, not from the point of view of the individual organism, or its component parts, but from that of taxonomically-discrete populations, we are able to discover generalizations about such populations and their interactions with one another which are peculiar to population systems and are not to be predicted from the behaviour of the individual. Some of these properties are reviewed at the end of Chapter 16. The word community is applied here to such a relatively isolated and discrete population system. Because we have experience of the functional and demographic ties between populations and of the operation of density-dependent processes we recognize that such systems show the properties of constancy of species composition, dynamic stability and organismic unity. Because we recognize such a system to be an organization in its own right we see no particular reason, pending its further justification, why it should conform to analogies derived from other levels of organization, such as are implied in the "super-organism" concept.

In other words, the term community is a shibboleth and a label for a working hypothesis. It is used to denote an important part of their field of study by those who anticipate that the study of population systems will be a productive approach to ecology. Because each community has its peculiar features and because we have not yet collected enough information about any one community to analyse it fully, we cannot make very specific generalizations about the pro-perties of all communities. Nevertheless, from the success of the working hypothesis and the clues so far discovered, we have a clear conception of what to expect and this includes the properties of species constancy, dynamic stability and organismic unity. At the same time the word community is also used, without prejudice, in the sense of an assemblage of species populations which can be segregated by means of the methods of ecological survey discussed in the following chapter. This use of one term should really be separated from the other by calling it a biocoenosis, but in fact there is seldom any doubt as to which sense is intended, because the two fields are seldom studied by the same people. It remains to future ecologists to demonstrate whether these two conceptions of the community are in fact identical.

Note

The translations included in this chapter have been checked by Dr. A. K. Thorlby to whom I am most grateful. The original German versions are appended—

Resvoy[600]: "Eine Biocönose stellt ein sich in einem beweglichen Gleichgewichtszustand erhaltendes Bevölkerungssytem dar, das sich bei gegebenen ökologischen Verhältnissen einstellt."

Friederichs[236]: "Die Fähigkeit der Selbstregulierung ist also in der Definition aufgenommen worden. Dies ist zwar insofern unnötig, als diese Eigenschaft jeder biologischen Einheit zukommt, vom Einzeller bis zum Erdball, und nicht etwa der Lebensgemeinschaft eigentümlich ist. . . . Das Ziel der Selbstregulierung in der Biocönose ist das biocönotische Gleichgewicht; sie erreicht aber niemals dieses, sondern ihr Resultat ist die Harmonie, eine relative Ordnung, welche die Einheit der Biocönose bei Bestand hält, und ihre 'Ursache' ist jene begrenzte Zweckmässigkeit aller Naturerscheinungen, ohne welche die Einheit des Kosmos nicht denkbar wäre."

Wangerin[781]: "Als Assoziation werden diejenigen in sich abgeschlossenen und relativ stabilen Lokalbestände zusammengefasst, welche in den wesentlichen soziologischen Merkmalen, insbesondere in ihrer floristischen Zusammensetzung, in ihrer Physiognomie und in ihrem durch die Standortsverhältnisse bedingten ökologischen Charakter übereinstimmen."

Hesse[318]: "Die Biocönose ist die Vergesellschaftung von Lebewesen, die einen einheitlichen Abschnitt des Lebensraums bewohnt und in der Auswahl und Zahl der Arten den durchschnittlichen äusseren Lebensverhältnissen entspricht."

Chapter 13

"BIOCOENOLOGY": THE DETECTION AND DELIMITATION OF COMMUNITIES FROM DISTRIBUTION DATA

In later chapters we shall attempt an analysis of communities in terms of their feeding relationships and the impact of populations on one another by competition, predation and similar activities. This approach is an ambitious one and has yet to achieve a synthesis for any living community. An alternative approach which, in the hands of plant ecologists has achieved a high level of generalization is the analysis of species distribution in order to describe the spatial pattern in each species and to detect regularities and coincidences between the patterns of different species. On the whole functional relationships are ignored by this approach, although some recent work which relates it to other ecological fields will be mentioned. It might also appear that a static approach by way of distribution patterns is of limited usefulness in animal ecology except in the case of sedentary forms; to some extent this is true but successful studies of numerous small species by sampling methods and even of large mobile forms such as birds demonstrate that the methods are not so limited as might appear at first sight.

Classification of work in this field is difficult because individual workers have often shown an interest in many aspects. However a primary division into, firstly, studies aimed at describing the relationships of organisms *within* a community and secondly, relations *between* communities appears to be logical and to separate two main fields of work. Of the *intra*-community studies we can recognize on the one hand those concerned with the primary relationships between pairs of species such as their affinity and tendency to have correlated or complementary distributions. On the other hand there are investigations of the relation of a species to the whole community, i.e. its status as measured by various numerical indices from simple abundance per unit area to more difficult concepts such as fidelity.

Among the *inter*-community relationships ecologists have been concerned firstly with attempting to detect discontinuities in distribution which might be interpreted as boundaries of communities; this is an important field on which much activity is being concentrated at the present time. Secondly, having established limits to such "communities," whose relationship with the "communities" discussed in the last chapter remains to be demonstrated; it is natural to attempt to classify them in a hierarchical structure and to create systems which indicate their affinities in terms of species content, successional status and so on. In this section, we shall also consider attempts to relate this more statistical approach based on distribution to the more biological approach usual in other fields of ecology.

Some Definitions

These terms are widely employed in plant ecology and will be used here in the following senses. *Abundance* is simply the number of individual organisms of the species in question per unit area. Difficulties in assessing this are sometimes encountered when species reproduce vegetatively. *Dominance* is the proportional abundance expressed as a percentage of the number of individuals of the species in question when compared with the total of all species. Obviously dominance has a biological meaning only when applied to plants of much the same size, but "areal" dominance is sometimes used, in which case the ratios of ground area covered by the species are measured instead of numbers of individuals. *Frequency:* if a large number of samples are taken within a chosen area some species will appear in most of the samples, others in but a few of them. This will depend not only on the abundance, but also on the regularity of distribution. Frequency is thus an index of the proportion of samples in which the plant in question appears; its numerical value in any particular instance will depend on the relative sizes of the sample and the plant. It is easier to estimate than abundance, because the numbers present in each sample are not counted, and has sometimes been used as a substitute for abundance, which is obviously an unwise procedure. When organisms are of similar size and, if sample size is carefully chosen, some idea of patchiness of distribution can be given. *Constancy:* by some Scandinavian authors this term is used to mean the same as frequency. In reality it should be used when comparing the occurrence of a species in samples taken from different associations of plants over a wide area, and not from the same association. *Fidelity:* this is a mainly subjective measurement of the extent to which a plant is restricted to one association. It allows for the extent to which the species is absent from different associations as well as the extent to which it is regularly present within the chosen association.

INTRA-COMMUNITY RELATIONSHIPS

Measurements of Affinity and Related Concepts

Two distinct approaches to the measurement of the distributional relationships between species have recently converged. Both are based on the measurement of the extent to which species overlap in a set of samples or quadrats. The older method[374, 599] was to prepare a set of species lists for each sample and to work out an index of the affinity (i.e. frequency of common occurrences) of each species with respect to every other species. Those species showing closest affinities were grouped together by means of a *trellis diagram* in a manner closely similar to that used for determining affinities between samples discussed on page 194. This technique is not now widely used in its original form.

Secondly a number of authors have proposed indices of association between species based on a 2×2 contingency table in which the number of samples containing both species together is compared with the number in which one species is present alone. In earlier treatments samples containing neither species were ignored but later formulae (e.g. by Cole[122]) allowed for this category as well. Cole's method which was applied first to parasites and their hosts is based on a comparison of the measured degree of common occurrence with that to be expected on the assumption that both species are distributed independently and at random. This method is not generally applicable for the present purpose because it is influenced by whether the two species occur in a high or a low proportion of the samples tested, or in other words whether the sample size is large or small compared with the density of the populations.[217, 472] Alternative indices have been prepared by Fager[217] and by Morisita.[472] In Fager's index the probabilities of the occurrence of the two species are related, not to the total number of *samples* taken but to the total number of *occurrences* of both species. Independence of sample size is demonstrated and a table of significance (over a rather limited range) is provided so that from a knowledge of the numbers present of both species and their joint occurrence, the minimum number of the latter for significant association can be seen at a glance. Morisita's presentation makes fewer concessions to the non-mathematical biologist and does not claim an index which is entirely independent of sample size but has two indices of "interspecific overlapping" and "interspecific correlation" appear to be more easily extended to complex problems involving a number of species.

Properties of Species Distribution within the Community

The properties which follow, while often important in themselves, will be found to have an additional significance as the parameters often used in inter-community analysis which is discussed in the next section. Much of the plant ecological work with quadrats aimed to measure the "status" of particular species in the community has been concerned with measurements of abundance (in terms of numbers or area covered) and frequency. The latter, as already explained is dependent on quadrat size, absolute abundance and regularity of distribution but is often much easier to measure than abundance. Obviously for studies of, for example, productivity and population dynamics frequency is no substitute for abundance but it is questionable whether, in biocoenology, the ecologist when offered the choice of a few samples accurately counted or many samples checked for presence or absence, should not use the latter more often. Davis[164] for instance found a close logarithmic relation between log abundance and frequency in sets of 36 samples and concluded that either could be used equally effectively in an analysis of the relations between soil fauna and a series of plots. Again Fager has advocated the use of ranked data (simply scoring the different species first, second, third and so on in order of abundance) followed by rank correlation-analysis methods due to Kendall[359] in place of total counts. Indeed it seems likely that much of the time which ecologists spend counting, especially when this is performed on material obtained by inefficient sampling methods and derived from heterogeneous populations, would be better spent thinking about how to improve the efficiency of their work.

A property of species within communities which has proved particularly elusive is that of *fidelity*. Originally put forward in purely qualitative terms by Braun-Blanquet,[66] whose definitions fail to account for species which are widely common but absent from one or two samples, it has been the subject of an index invented by Goodall.[275] This resembles Cole's index of affinity between species with figures of *samples* containing common species replacing figures of cohabiting *species*. Goodall also introduced the use of discriminant functions, (see below) in this context. Although not specifically claimed as such Fager's[217] method of analysis of recurrent groups discussed below also seems to provide a quantitative measurement of fidelity.

A further property which determines the distribution of species within and between communities is that of ecological tolerance range. There are many species which are widespread in a range of communities and others confined within a limited niche in a single community type. In order to measure this Agrell[2] introduced the idea of calculating a coefficient of variation (ratio of standard deviation to mean density) of numbers of individuals over a range of habitats and comparing the coefficients over a range of species. This coefficient can only have a comparative significance unless based on an extremely wide range of samples.

A type of study which goes some way to bridge the gap between distribution statistics and biological factors is the use of various kinds of statistical analysis to relate distribution of organisms to that of environmental factors. The traditional approach is through multiple regression and analysis of variance and covariance; techniques which were more particularly evolved for use in agricultural experiments in which varying combinations of physical factors are held at known levels and the resulting changes in response by organisms correlated with the different factors. The more advanced techniques in this field permit the segregation of effects due to interaction of different factors and a good sample of their application to a semi-field experiment is provided by Satchell's[628] demonstration of the dominating importance of pH in the species distribution of earthworms despite the fact that calcium carbonate and other factors were also correlated. This work was followed up by experiments which confirmed the hitherto unsuspected importance of pH in earthworm physiology.

On the other hand the appearance of precision and generality given by such studies should be accepted cautiously. Glasgow[265] for instance used correlation analysis of this kind to determine the factors responsible for the depth distribution of *Onychiurus armatus* near Rothamsted. Dhillon and Gibson,[174] however, were lead to quite opposite conclusions using the same technique in a different place. In view of the labour attached to such analyses it is important to realize that conclusions reached may be very limited in their application.

An approach perhaps better adapted to the less well controlled conditions in the field is that of multivariate analysis.[55, 277, 360, 593, 595]

Multivariate analysis provides a means of expressing, in terms of vector quantities (having both magnitude and direction), which, of all possible combinations of factors are most closely associated with the variations in the quantities observed. Unfortunately the mathematical techniques have not been fully developed yet for the use of ecologists.

INTER-COMMUNITY RELATIONSHIPS: THE DELIMITATION OF COMMUNITIES

The detection of the boundaries of consistent groupings of species necessarily involves large-scale sampling, usually with quadrats in the case of plants and cores or similar units in the case of animals in solid or liquid media. These are then analysed for consistencies and discontinuities of fauna or flora. The direct approach is to look for changes in presence or absence of species. This may be qualified by giving weight according to abundance, dominance, frequency or fidelity. More sophisticated approaches make use of various mathematically determined distributions derived from field observations or models, intended to describe the expected relationships between species and numbers of individuals as the range of sampling is extended. "New" methods are reported in this field of biology at an astonishing rate and in order to judge the efficiency of some of them it is advisable first to relate the problem to our experience of field conditions.

Intuitive Perception of Plant Associations

When a botanist goes into the field it is generally possible for him to recognize with confidence characteristic associations of plants which recur over wide areas of country and about the limits of which most botanists will agree. Thus, an oak-sycamore wood, a chalk-down grassland or a salt-marsh flora contain groups of species which can be easily recognized and recur in many parts of the British Isles. Individual examples differ much less from one another than from examples of other vegetation types. Admittedly there is dispute among botanists as to how these facts should be interpreted, a matter which has already been discussed in Chapter 12, but a statement such as the above is common ground to all schools and in this chapter the word "association" carries no further implication. The following quotations from Lousley[418] are typical—

"If I appear to have given undue prominence to rarities it is because they so often provide the most suitable examples of plant geography and illustrate differences between habitats better than subtle variations in the proportions and behaviour of the common species." (p. 16.)

"The trained field botanist can tell at a glance in most cases when he passes from other soils to limestone; often he knows within a yard or two where the change takes place, but his deductions are based on the association of different species of plants which he sees, rather than on the presence or absence of individual species. Attempts to use these as indicators are usually successful only in the case of the rarer flowers whose requirements are more exacting. Efforts to show that widespread plants grow only in calcareous soils generally fail as wide experience reveals numerous exceptions." (p. 15.)

"The majority of flowers which are *constant* in chalk grassland are not *confined* or nearly confined to this community. Those which are, tend to be local, and each locality has its own selection." (p. 42.)

Examples of the value of animals as community indicators include Strenzke's[694] use of Mites to typify soil types, Reynoldson's[603-4] a relation of Tricladida to lake types and Macan's[423-4] and Armitage's[24] studies on the littoral fauna with the same object. Davis has demonstrated by an independent technique that soil Arthropods can be a more sensitive indicator of soil conditions than plants.[164]

Other Methods of Delimiting Associations

The problem is, therefore, to distinguish and delimit plant associations from each other despite the fact that the rare species are too rare to be used for delimitation and the commoner ones too catholic in their distribution to be used for making clear distinctions.

This problem was first tackled by Braun-Blanquet[66] and his school of plant ecologists at Geneva who elaborated the nomenclature of abundance, dominance, frequency and fidelity now generally accepted. Their methods are qualitative and descriptive in nature and somewhat limited by the intractability of the concept of fidelity, which was held to be an important criterion for discrimination. Their work has been appraised by Poore[583-5] who, after demonstrating the subjective nature of some of their methods has adapted them for use in discriminating plant communities in Britain, and by Dahl[151] who has extended them for use in montane vegetation in Norway.

Gisin[257-62] has used somewhat similar methods based on the concept of the "vicariant" or "differential" species, in the case of soil animals. These are chosen subjectively to have a rather narrow tolerance range but to be fairly constant over a wide range of samples. They are used to "label" associations in a way which obviously leaves much to the skill of the naturalist, but is less laborious than more meticulous methods. This approach has been criticized on the grounds of subjectivity[1, 3, 4] and that the rules cannot be applied consistently.[217]

A variety of methods have been used in practice to sort out extensive collections on the basis of those species which are most vicariant,[257, 436] frequent,[694] or most abundant;[386] it is sometimes doubtful whether these reveal more than could have been detected by the practised naturalist and there is a real need for the application of more objective methods. It should be remembered however that "objectivity" in this context is rather a relative term for not only should there be no bias in the taking of the samples, but also in the choice of the exact sampling points and further, since few collecting and extracting methods are equally efficient for all species these too can easily introduce bias into the results.

Methods Based on the Trellis Diagram

The Uppsala school in Sweden are responsible for two important contributions to plant sociology: first, Raunkiaer's conception of plant "life forms" or characteristic structural features shared by widely different plants and recurring in a range of associations, and second, the use of statistical methods to attempt an "objective" division of the flora of an area into associations on the basis of the floristic[387, 682] or faunistic[2, 3, 374, 375, 399] similarity of groups of samples taken within the area. A commonly-used device is the "trellis diagram," a coincidence table which is familiar in the form of fare tables in buses or summaries of the results of athletic contests. For instance, it may be desired to make use of a number of lists of species present in samples covering a considerable area in order to see whether the samples fall into groups with a similar flora. An index of relationship or correlation is worked out for every possible combination of two samples. The methods for calculating such indices vary and are the subject of rival claims; they may be based simply on presence and absence, or they may take into account the dominance or abundance or frequency of the species in the samples. The indices are arranged in the squares of the trellis diagram (as shown in Fig. 21), the linear order of the samples being the same in the rows and the columns. This linear order is then shuffled round by trial and error so as to bring the highest numbers

Species	Sample Locality												
	B1	B2	B3	B4	B5	B7	B8	B9	B10	B11	B12	B13	Q7
Hypogastrura succinea.			1·2					6·5					0·9
Xenylla humicola .	45·1	70·8	33·6	77·9	45·0	71·7	64·6	69·6	61·8			97·4	63·9
Onychiurus groenlandicus . .						5·1	5·9		1·6				
Onychiurus macfadyeni	18·3	5·8	1·2	1·7					4·8	13·2			0·5
Onychiurus debilis .								8·7		20·6	57·7		
Onychiurus arcticus .										1·7			
Tullbergia krausbaueri	30·1	2·7	11·6	1·7	5·0				14·3				
Tullbergia arctica		1·8	3·1	5·1	30·0				1·6				
Folsomia sexoculata			22·4			15·4	11·8	6·5	15·9	61·2	42·3	2·6	
Folsomia bisetosa		18·1	36·5	10·2	5·0					3·3			34·7
Folsomia sensibilis						2·6	5·9	4·3					
Isotoma notabilis	4·3			1·7									
Isotoma viridis .	1·1	0·4	0·4	1·7	15·0	2·6	11·8	2·2					
Smithurinus concolor .	1·1					2·6		2·2					

(a)

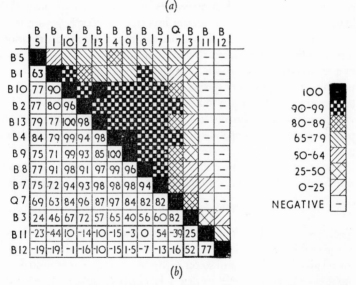

(b)

FIG. 21. EXAMPLE OF THE USE OF A TRELLIS DIAGRAM IN COMMUNITY
ANALYSIS

The data (from Macfadyen, 1954) are given in (a), which shows the dominance
(percentage abundance) of fourteen species of Collembola in thirteen sample
localities. These figures are used to compute a correlation coefficient "c"
according to the formula $c = \dfrac{\Sigma ab}{\sqrt{\Sigma a^2 \cdot \Sigma b^2}}$ where a and b are the deviations
from the average value.

The linear order of the sample localities is then rearranged in a figure such as
(b) (the trellis diagram) in such a way that the maximum number of higher
values of "c" come to lie nearest the central diagonal. The process is facilitated
by the use of shading as in the top right-hand half of (b). From the results shown
it would be concluded that the sample localities come from two separate
associations of Collembola.

nearest to the centre diagonal and the low numbers farther from it. A moment's thought will show that this results in samples with high affinity, as measured by the index, coming together. The arrangement is thus opposite to the bus-fare table where the nearest fare stages have the lowest prices. When rearrangement has been carried as far as possible it is usually found that some of the samples fall into distinct groups. It is then claimed that the constituents of such groups of samples are members of the same community and are biologically distinct from those in other groups.

A different method of analysis which could be applied to abundance or other figures but has so far been restricted to presence or absence data is that of Williams and Lambert.[812, 813] This aims at providing a hierarchical subdivision of species lists from a very large number of quadrats by determining those species groups whose distribution is least significantly associated. This is done in the first instance by means of a trellis diagram approach, followed by tests of affinity between all possible combinations of species. With the help of a computer a very large number of samples taken from a complete "chess-board" of vegetation was analysed and significant differences in vegetation pattern—later and independently correlated with unsuspected environmental factors—were detected.

The precise *index of association* used in analyses by trellis diagram and similar method, can be based on presence or absence as in Sørensen's[682]

Quotient of Similarity which is simply $\dfrac{2j}{a+b}$ where $j =$ number of species present in both samples, a and $b =$ number of species restricted to each of the samples separately. More complicated quotients account for relative abundance and so on or are based on different models. For instance Mountford's[475] index I is given by $e^{aI} + e^{bI} = e^{(a+b-j)I}$ assuming a logarithmic relationship between numbers of species and individuals as in Williams' logarithmic series (see Chapter 8). This should render the index independent of sample size. Kontkannen[375, 376] believes the Sørensen index to be at least as good as Kulczynski's,[387]

which is $\dfrac{1}{2}\left(\dfrac{1}{a} + \dfrac{1}{b}\right)$ while Davis[164] found some slight advantage, which was doubtfully commensurate with the great labour of calculation, in using Mountford's index. This index was used by Satchell for a range of small Arthropod woodland samples and discriminated between those from acid and from alkaline soils.

Methods Based on Mathematical Models

A second approach to the delimitation of communities is based on mathematical models of the distribution of species as the number of samples or the area sampled increases.

Earlier work was based on the idea of "minimal area." If a series of quadrats of increasing size is taken and the area included is plotted on a graph against the number of species found, the resulting curve tends to fall off as the area included is increased, until that size of sample has been taken which includes virtually all the members of the community. The area at which this occurs is the "minimal area." In the case of a mixed assemblage of species covering more than one association, or where factors, such as interference by man, have resulted in a transient phase in the vegetation succession, no clear limit can be detected and the number of species continues to increase as the area of the samples is enlarged. A related method of demonstrating a similar phenomenon is due to Chouard,[107] who plotted as ordinate the number of quadrats of a fixed size containing x species and as abscissa the number of species x contained in a quadrat. He found that there is, in the case of a well-defined association, a single peak to such curves, i.e. that there is a tendency for quadrats taken at random to contain a certain number of species which is characteristic for the community. When a group of species not part of an association are treated in the same way there is no clear peak.

Alternatively, the logarithm of the area of a series of quadrats of increasing size can be plotted against the mean number of species per quadrat so that the points tend to fall on an S-shaped curve. Archebald[23] attaches special significance to the area corresponding to the point of inflexion of the S-shaped curve and to the mean number of species per unit of area and claims that these can be used to characterize different types of community.

These and other similar methods have been justifiably criticized by Goodall[274] in a useful review article. His conclusions, which are perhaps slightly less favourable than those of most ecologists, are antagonistic to the use of such methods especially where it is difficult to find an ecological interpretation of the figures obtained.

Margalef[449] used an index of diversity—

$$d = \frac{S - 1}{\log_e N} \qquad \begin{array}{l} \text{where } S = \text{number of species} \\ N = \text{number of individuals} \end{array}$$

and applied it to marine phytoplankton data. He detected changes in the index when the samples taken were extended to waters of different origin and justified the use of this index (which is not independent of sample size) by comparison with an artificial population of letters taken from a manuscript. This point has been criticized by Hairston.[297]

A useful test of several different indices was made, Looman et al.,[414] on data from prairie vegetation. They decided that the usefulness of Williams's index of diversity[808]* was limited to detecting the existence of heterogeneity, that Kendall's rank correlation method[217] is cumbersome but has the great advantage of permitting the estimation of errors, whilst Sørensen's K is easy to calculate but gives no estimate of error.[682] They, therefore, used Sørensen's index on all their data and Kendall's on a limited set of samples in order to determine, for that particular set of samples, the order of variation in Sørensen's index which could be regarded as significant.

More recent models have come closer to reality and three, at least, attempt to use parameters which can be given biological meaning.

Kershaw's[363, 364, 365] method is to carry out a spatial analysis of the variance of counts of plants with increasing sample size and to plot mean square variation against area covered. Discontinuity is revealed by a step in the curve. This method has the advantage that it can also be used to measure association between two species because when association is negative the pattern size of "lumped" data will be increased, while no change in pattern size accompanied by increase in variance indicates a positive association. This technique makes use of information on abundance and on inherent size of natural pattern, both of which are neglected in earlier methods. Odum et al.[533] suggest a model based on the concept of a hierarchical organization of "niches" on the analogy with a human society in which only a medium-sized town can provide jobs for people such as lawyers and a city for university professors. On this sort of basis one would expect a plot of log individuals (as abscissa) against increment in cumulative species (as ordinate) to be a straight line. Thus $S = k \log N$. If samples extend into new communities upward "kinks" in the curve are to be expected whilst a levelling off in the curve would indicate an "immature" community too "young" for the "professional classes" to have moved in yet.

MacArthur[427] tested three models of which the most successful was

---

* In a population which conforms to the logarithmic series, the number of species obtained by doubling the sampling area should be constant.

based on the assumption that the total number of individuals effectively "fill" the environment without overlap of their niches. The environment is represented by a stick broken at random into a number of segments whose number is equal to the number of species and whose length is proportional to the abundance of all individuals. The expected length of the rth shortest interval is given by—

$$\frac{N}{S} \sum_{i=1}^{r} \frac{1}{(S - i + 1)}$$

when S = number of species
N = number of individuals
i = interval between successively ranked species and the rarest
r = rank in rareness

When plotted with abundance of each species (as ordinate) against rank in rareness on a log scale (as abscissa) this distribution gives a convex curve.

MacArthur found that while some bird populations fitted this curve well, others showed a preponderance of very common and very rare species which could be accounted for on the basis that two or more communities were included in one set of samples. This interpretation has been challenged by Hairston[297] who also found rare species too rare and abundant species too abundant in the case of soil samples. Hairston makes the interesting point that the patchiness of his species populations is not independent of abundance. The more abundant species tend to be more randomly distributed partly because, in the regions where they are successful they can occupy a whole area while the rare species are restricted to small enclaves in a mainly hostile region. Thus MacArthur's assumptions of random distribution of all species demand an extra hypothesis while Hairston's model would account for the departure of field data from MacArthur's curve. Hairston's conclusions receive support from a similar analysis of snake populations by Turner[738a] who tried the effect of grouping populations from the same and from different habitats on their fit to McArthur's curves.

CLASSIFICATION AND RELATED TOPICS

The classification of communities detected by methods such as those we have outlined and their arrangement in hierarchical systems is subject to all the problems inherent in morphological classifications in addition to those which stem from the greater difficulties in defining the characters by which particular "species" are to be recognized. Much of the work of the Montpellier school of plant sociologists is concerned with these problems but animal ecology, apart from the Clements and Shelford school has, perhaps fortunately, neglected this field. Generalizations about succession of communities are sometimes more fruitful but on the whole these are best based on functional studies and will be considered in Chapter 16.

Life Forms in Animal Ecology

On the continent of Europe, and especially in Germany, the more empirical approach is usually combined either with results of Gisin's differential species method, or else with the conclusions of the morphological-ecological studies of exponents of *Lebensformtypen*.[385, 598, 728] According to this doctrine, which has some affinities with Raunkiaer's "plant life forms," there are characteristic morphological features which are particularly adapted to certain environments and which tend to be analogously developed in a wide range of animals of systematically very different origins. For instance, the peculiar fauna inhabiting the deep layers of the sand by the sea shore (Psammon)[598] includes many very elongated animals whose size varies over only a limited range. This may be related to a need to move through the interstices between the sand. A special vocabulary of technical terms is used to describe the inhabitants of different habitats and, where the fauna is consistently of one life form type, this is considered to justify the recognition of a distinct community. In some parts of Europe "ecology" is almost synonymous with work of this sort.

A Method Based on Structural Habitat Classification

Another approach to the detection and delimitation of communities is that of Elton and Miller.[207] They frankly face the problem that animal communities are extremely complex, that the species composition of a given locality may change rapidly in time and be discontinuous in space and that one dominant species may replace another according to the effect of the impact of physical factors and of other species. They recognize that the accumulation of information from which community structure can be determined is the work of many generations of men. They propose, therefore, to accumulate over a period of many years information obtained from a limited area, the information being derived from observations by naturalists of "ecological events" involving two or more species, from more detailed studies of life histories and general ecology by specialists and also from relevant information from books. All this information is classified and analysed under species, and also according to a system of habitat structure which aims to be very clear-cut, easy to understand and to apply in practice. By the use of suitable punch-card and filing systems and backed by museum collections information is obtained on both the ecology of individual species and also the composition of the fauna of characteristic elements of the habitats; for example, the herb layer under oak-sycamore wood or water-filled tree hollows are such habitat elements. Such a system has the advantages of permitting the use of the voluminous information obtained by naturalists, and the sifting of the accidental from the ecologically significant events over a long period of time, and no theories about the nature or structure of communities are assumed. It will provide material for the testing of such theories and the determination of the limits of communities and the ecological relationships between species.

Such methods are obviously only possible to an institution whose continuity in time is reasonably assured, but they do permit the use of information obtained by amateurs who tend today to find it more and more difficult to co-operate with scientists as their interests tend to become more specialized. Another important function of such an institution is that the ecological information obtained by workers in one field is available to those in another; if the notes and collections of the coleopterist are used in this way the student of, say, aphids, need not learn all about the taxonomy and feeding habits of beetles before he can begin to understand an important cause of mortality. A student of any particular group can rapidly, by means of collections, survey the biotic environment of any one habitat element and assess its significance for his own group. This system has recently been adopted and extended by the Nature Conservancy in Britain.

Inhabitants of "micro-habitats" such as water-filled tree-holes,[423a] acorns[822] or the flower heads of flowering plants[720] often contain highly characteristic groups of species including several trophic levels and it is a matter of dispute whether these should be regarded as "communities." This partly depends, of course, on which of the many possible definitions is adopted and when the word is used in its most general sense there can be no objection. Alternatively the hierarchical nomenclature of the Clements and Shelford school can supply terms such as sere and microsere to those who prefer them.

Conclusion

Clearly the terms "community" and "association" are used in biocoenology in a number of different senses and there is no logical reason why any of these should have any particular affinities with any definitions of a community given in the previous chapter other than the "weakest" of them agreed by the Third Botanical Congress. Methods of this kind cannot be expected to throw light on the more biological features discussed in that chapter and a discussion of the relationships between the "biocoenological" and other concepts of the community will therefore be deferred until these features have been discussed in the next three chapters.

Chapter 14

COMPETITIVE RELATIONSHIPS BETWEEN POPULATIONS IN THE SAME TROPHIC LEVEL

THIS and the following chapters are concerned with inter-specific relationships, that is to say with the biological properties of interacting populations. These properties have been studied in the past through simplified theoretical models, through laboratory experiments and through field observations on population interactions and their effects. More recently these approaches have been unified to some extent by attempts to base more realistic mathematical models on observation of nature rather than on more or less plausible assumptions.

It is convenient, if not strictly logical, to divide this vast field of work into (a) relationships between animals which potentially share common resources at one trophic level. These we shall call *competitive* or *horizontal* relationships. On the other hand (b) we shall consider relationships involving feeding, predation and parasitism which we shall term *vertical*. It can be justifiably argued that the effects of parasites on their hosts for instance are similar to those of "competitors," in that they are competing for the same food supply. However the nature of the population reactions in two cases is usually different because the growth of the parasite population tends to lag behind that of the host. Both horizontal and vertical relationships can be studied at the theoretical, laboratory and field levels, but since the latter usually reveal situations of great complexity containing both intra-specific as well as inter-specific relationships it is more practicable to deal with field examples separately.

Therefore these three chapters are arranged as follows: in this chapter and the next we cover horizontal and vertical relationships respectively. In Chapter 16 the population dynamics of populations in the field are considered especially with regard to problems of population control. Finally in Chapter 17 we consider the integrated effect of these properties on natural communities.

Competition means here inferred *or* proven interaction between species which share a common population-limiting environmental resource such as food or shelter. It is not extended, as Nicholson extended it, to cover parasitism and predation, despite the fact that the bodies of prey are, in a sense, a common resource for the two component populations of such a system. Elton and Miller[207] have distinguished from the general term competition those cases where "it is known that one species affects the population of another by . . . reducing the reproductive efficiency or increasing the mortality of its competitors." This more limited use is termed by them "interference." They justify the introduction of this term because "competition" has already acquired many shades of meaning for geneticists and others concerned with evolution and the isolation of species and because many examples of implied competition "just suggest that allied species tend to evolve into different ecological niches, which is another way of stating that the facts exist and that one believes in natural selection." Harper[302a] seems to use these two terms in opposite senses.

(a) THEORETICAL STUDIES. Volterra[768–70] considered the case of two species competing for a common food resource and showed that if ε_1 and ε_2 are the coefficients of increase of the two species with unlimited food ($N_t = N_0 e^{\varepsilon t}$) and if h_1, h_2 are the constants of food consumption and if γ_1, γ_2 are the constants of susceptibility to food shortage and N_1, N_2 the numbers of the two competing species, then—

$$\left.\begin{aligned} dN_1/dt &= \varepsilon_1 N_1 \\ dN_2/dt &= \varepsilon_2 N_2 \end{aligned}\right\}$$

The total removal of food by both species is then $h_1 N_1 + h_2 N_2$, and this removal reduces ε_1 and ε_2 to a new lower level such that ε_1 and ε_2 change respectively to—

$$\left.\begin{aligned} \varepsilon_1 &- \gamma_1(h_1 N_1 + h_2 N_2) \\ \varepsilon_2 &- \gamma_2(h_1 N_1 + h_2 N_2) \end{aligned}\right\}$$

Therefore

$$\left\{\begin{aligned} dN_1/dt &= N_1[\varepsilon_1 - \gamma_1(h_1 N_1 + h_2 N_2)] \\ dN_2/dt &= N_2[\varepsilon_2 - \gamma_2(h_1 N_1 + h_2 N_2)] \end{aligned}\right.$$

Then if $\varepsilon_1/\gamma_1 > \varepsilon_2/\gamma_2$, the second species population approaches zero, the first approaches $\varepsilon_1/\gamma_1 h_1$, i.e. the species which shows the greater susceptibility to food shortage will be eliminated in competition with that which shows the lesser susceptibility.

Volterra then traced the possible fates of the two species under different combinations of initial conditions and vital parameters, the consequences of competition between more than two species, of combinations of competition with predation and of the effects of adding new species to associations already in a steady state.

Gause[243, 244] produced similar competition equations in the form—

$$dN_1/dt = N_1 b_1 \frac{(K_1 - N_1 - \alpha N_2)}{K_1}$$

$$dN_2/dt = N_2 b_2 \frac{(K_2 - N_2 - \beta N_1)}{K_2}$$

where α and β are the coefficients of competition and are proportional to the population-depressing effect of the one species on the other.

Gause recognized three cases—

(i) When $\alpha > K_1/K_2$ and $\beta > K_2/K_1$.

The population-depressing effect of each species is greater on the other species than on its own population. In this case only one species will survive, depending on the initial populations.

(ii) When $\alpha > K_1/K_2$ and $\beta < K_2/K_1$ or when $\alpha < K_1/K_2$ and $\beta > K_2/K_1$.

Competition results in the elimination of that species which is most harmed by the other; the case considered by Volterra above.

(iii) When $\alpha < K_1/K_2$ and $\beta < K_2/K_1$.

Both species survive in equilibrium indefinitely. This situation arises when both species have a niche in which they are more favoured than the other species. This condition was realized by Gause in experimental conditions when two species of *Paramecium* (*P. caudatum* and *P. aurelia*) were able to live together in culture (see next section).

(b) GAUSE'S THEOREM. Although Gause himself does not appear to have enunciated any "law" or "theorem" to summarize these results, "Gause's theorem" is the term very widely used to signify the theme which was, perhaps, first enunciated by Darwin[157, 307]—

"As the species of the same genus usually have, though by no means invariably, much similarity in habits and constitution and always in structure, the struggle will generally be more severe between them, if they come into competition with each other, than between the species of distinct genera."

A similar idea, without reference to taxonomic affinity, is contained in Nicholson's second corollary (Section 1 (a)). To most ecologists the attribute of taxonomic affinity is not a *sine qua non* of "Gause's theorem," but only a corollary of it, and to this extent Hartley[307] would appear to be wrong in equating Darwin's and Gause's statements. The theorem is usually rather loosely stated in some such form as "two species with the same ecology cannot co-exist." A recent comparison and a criticism of different formulations[255] does not include Hutchinson's and Deevey's[339] version that "two species with the same niche requirements cannot form steady-state populations in the same region."

Quite obviously the theorem as usually stated is not intended to be a rigid law, and its main implication that competition is more severe between animals whose ecological requirements are most similar can very easily become a circular argument. It could be made "watertight" if three principles were followed: first, any formulation must be adequately supported by definitions of words such as "niche," "the same," "co-existence," etc. Secondly, it is patently obvious that taxonomically-related species often do occur in close physical proximity. It is therefore desirable to separate from the theorem itself, which is concerned with ecological affinity, the further corollary that ecological affinity implies taxonomic affinity, for this may not always be the case. For the same reason, and because spatial proximity may be no real index of ecological overlap, this part of the theorem needs much more careful consideration, if only because Gause's formulae apply only to species in competition under conditions where the total population is limited. Both Nicholson and later Crombie[138] emphasized the latter point, that the theoretical results of competition will only ensue if a density-dependent, population-limiting factor is actually shared by the two species. Crombie emphasized the importance of Gause's third case when two species each have their own part of the environment in which each can increase more successfully than its competitor. He concluded that the elimination of one species by the other will not follow when both populations are held at a low level by some alternative mortality factor so that competition too is at a low level.

Hutchinson[336] also pointed out that continual fluctuations in environmental factors might effect the coefficients of competition in such a way as continually to reverse the theoretical outcome and, thus, the establishment of one species at the expense of the other would be prevented. He believed that such a situation may arise with the succession of phytoplankton algae in lakes. It is also widely believed that the marked climatic changes which occur in temperate latitudes through the seasons may operate in a similar manner and allow the continuance of species in seasonal succession which might otherwise compete more severely if weather conditions remained constant.

Although a satisfactory formulation of "Gause's hypothesis" presents difficulties and does not seem to have been achieved, there can be little doubt that the fundamental idea behind it has been useful as a stimulus to research and especially to field observation. For instance, valuable contributions to the natural history of titmice and of coarse fish by Hartley[306, 307] would appear to have been stimulated and oriented by this theme and, especially among ornithologists, "Gause's hypothesis" has been most useful in providing a unifying principle, a feature all too rare in ecology.

The Lotka–Volterra–Gause theory of inter-specific competition has been attacked[17] on the grounds that it contains a fundamental logical contradiction. The objection seems to be based on the definition of K, the saturation density, as defined by the "logistic equation"—

$$N_t = N_0 e^{r \frac{K-N}{K}} \quad \text{or} \quad \frac{dN}{dt} = rN \frac{K-N}{K}$$

In the logistic equation, which applies, of course, to a single species population, this saturation density is not exceeded by N, the number of animals present at any one time. On the other hand, K, as used in Gause's equations, is exceeded by the number of individuals in one population plus the equivalent number of units of the competing population. This, claim Andrewartha and Birch, is inconsistent because it implies that the maximum density can be exceeded by two species but not by one species alone. The inconsistency is due to the critics who compare the two sets of equations and not to the separate originators of the two sets. There is nothing magical about the saturation value, K, which is simply the upper asymptote of the logistic curve to which the single species population trends. It is well known, both in theory and from experimental results such as those of Gause[243] and of Park[550] that, owing to statistical variations this "upper asymptote" is, in fact, frequently exceeded both in single species populations and in experiments involving more than one species. Arbitrarily to give different definitions of K in the two cases obviously results in an inconsistency, and is not a valid method of argument. A more mathematical refutation of Andrewartha's and Birch's argument has also been published. [570]

The theoretical implications of statistical study of dispersal rates of populations [649] do not yet seem to have been applied to competition problems. Skellam demonstrates that competitors with different dispersal rates may continue to coexist if that with a faster dispersal rate has a lower reproductive rate. This indicates the need for a further modification of simple models, a need which has been met to some extent by Williamson's [814] theory of competition, which incorporates stochastic influences. It is evident, however, that many of the predictions of simple theory are borne out by experimental studies and that there is room for more theoretical work which will help to bridge the gap from the very oversimplified models which have been used so far.

(c) EXPERIMENTAL RESULTS. Gause himself was the author of many experiments on competition and he succeeded in demonstrating a number of the theoretical predictions in experiments on microorganisms. The Yeasts *Saccharomyces cerevisiae* and *S. kephir* were grown together with a limited daily ration of sugar, *Paramecium aurelia* and *P. caudatum* and *Glaucoma scintillans* among Protozoa were used as competitors. One of the most interesting cases was that of the two *Paramecium* species competing for the same yeast food; *P. aurelia* can survive at a greater depth in the culture tubes employed because it can tolerate higher concentrations of waste metabolites. *P. caudatum* has a superior competitive ability in less-crowded conditions and thus survives better near the surface of the tubes. This demonstration that even a small glass tube can encompass two "niches" is particularly significant in relation to Hairston's [295] analysis of five species of *Paramecium* in a 40-ft stretch of river.

A very extensive series of experiments was performed by Park [545-9] using cultures of *Tribolium confusum*, the flour beetle, to which was later added *T. castaneum* for experiments on competition (Plate III). The outstanding feature of Park's later experiments is that these were continued for very long periods (four years) and were replicated many times. In this way Park was able to demonstrate three important principles—

I. Even apparently simple competition situations can, in reality, be complicated. In earlier work, for instance, the presence of a Sporozoan parasite, *Adelina*, was neglected and under these conditions the outcome of experiments in which small quantities of flour were started with both species of *Tribolium* in equal quantities was always that *T. confusum* replaced *T. castaneum*. However, when a technique of rearing the beetle free of *Adelina* infection was developed it was found that the situation was completely reversed. This was apparently due to *T. castaneum* being much more susceptible to the parasite, as was shown also by single species experiments in which its total population size was much less in the presence of *Adelina*, while that of *T. confusum* was reduced to a smaller extent.

The complexity is further shown by the persistence, even in single species populations, but more so in the competition cultures, of fluctuations in total numbers and of the numbers in the different life stages—egg, larva, pupa and adult. These fluctuations, which persist through the longest cultures of 70 generations and more, have not so far been analysed; they presumably involve such density-dependent factors as cannibalism and interference with breeding, feeding and copulation of each species as well as intra-specific factors. The implication of the complexity of the *Tribolium* experiments for the interpretation of field results is, of course, that it would be naïve to expect to be able to demonstrate the operation of the simple mathematical situations by simple inspection except in the most exceptional circumstances. An impression of the manifold possibilities from the point of view of invertebrate herbivores, in the case of soil,[97] for instance, can be gained from a review of the enormous number of fungi which occur there.

2. Park's repetition of his experiments many times, over long periods, enabled him to demonstrate that the outcome of a particular competition situation, beginning with certain definite proportions of the two species in a fixed amount of flour medium, is not rigidly fixed, but, like any other population system is subject to statistical probability. He was forced to express his results in the form that a given outcome has a given probability of occurring. Again the implication for field-data interpretation is obvious and important.

3. The great length of Park's experiments in relation to a life-cycle enabled him to show that the outcome of competition is frequently not decided for many generations; this again affects the probability of a given outcome occurring and might well permit, under more "natural" conditions, the survival together of two species although theoretically one of them was doomed to be eliminated by the other.

Park's later work[54, 550–55] has been mainly concerned with the analysis of the mechanism of population dynamics in the cultures, and in the relations between the outcome of single species population experiments and those in which the same species are in competition. Thus, the equilibrium population level for two species of *Tribolium* living separately was determined in six different combinations of temperature and humidity. The two species were then cultured together in the same sets of environmental conditions, but in competition. Under these circumstances, Park found that in some cases the species which alone maintained the higher density in a particular environment was also the "winner" in competition, while in other cases the reverse was the case. Experiments on the effects of a wide range of initial ratios of the two species, but under equally favourable conditions for both, gave the surprising result that, in 92 out of 97 cases *T. castaneum* "defeated" *T. confusum*, which event was heralded by the disappearance of all females in the latter species. Many further questions are posed by these experiments which serve to illustrate the great complexity of superficially simple systems.

Among many experiments which have been done with grain-insect populations, those of Crombie[135–9] covered a considerable range of competition phenomena. Crombie worked with the beetles *Oryzaephilus surinamensis* and *Rhizopertha dominica* as well as *Tribolium confusum* and with the moth *Sitotroga cerealella*. *O. surinamensis* can normally survive in the presence of the other species owing to its rather different ecology. In a *Rhizopertha dominica–S. cerealella* system the only part of the life cycle at which competition appears to operate is in the larval stages, when space for development is short. Lack of food or oxygen or "conditioning" of the medium by excreta did not act as density-dependent factors of any importance.

One of the most interesting of Crombie's results[138] was obtained from a *T. confusum–O. surinamensis* system. In single species populations of both these beetles (according to Crombie, but see Chapter 10) the rate of increase of the population is determined by the balance between oviposition rate, and rate of cannibalistic eating of the eggs and pupae by the active larval and adult stages. This, in a dense population, accounts for over 99 per cent of the mortality and also determines the maximum population density reached. In wheat both species live together but in flour *T. confusum* survives on account of its more voracious cannibalism. When, however, glass tubes of a suitable bore are mixed with the flour, *O. surinamensis* is able to survive in addition to *T. confusum* because the larvae are able to find refuge in the tubes. Crombie claimed that this small change in the medium is, in fact, not only able to provide "niches" for two species instead of one, but that *Rhizopertha dominica* can also survive there as well.

Crombie's work, which suffers in most cases from being based on experiments with very few replicates, preceded Park's later long-term experiments and was of much shorter duration; it is possible that he might have had fewer examples of "Gause's third case" to report had his experiments lasted longer.

Crombie[138] fitted his experimental results to Lotka's and Volterra's equations and calculated the constants involved. He stated that the basic assumptions of these equations, namely (*a*) that the potential rate of increase remains statistically constant and (*b*) that factors inhibiting increase are linearly related to density are, in fact, justified in his experiments. He was careful to stress, however, that this is frequently not the case and that one should not accept these assumptions without first testing them in any given case. In addition to his experimental work, Crombie also contributed a useful survey of competition experiments up to that date.[139]

In experiments on intra- and inter-specific population systems of water fleas, *Simocephalus vetulus* and *Daphnia pulicaria*, Frank[231] was unable to determine the population-limiting factors operating in single species populations, but the outcome of mixed cultures was always the same, namely that *S. vetulus* was always eliminated and *D. pulicaria* survived. One of the most interesting aspects of Frank's work was his analysis of the effects of density on birth rate and death rate, the changes in which accounted, at least in part, for the outcome of competition. Another contributory factor, which reveals a new extension of the Gause's theorem principle, is the greater inhibitory effect of high densities of *D. pulicaria* on its own populations than on those of *S. vetulus*; on the other hand, *S. vetulus* populations are almost equally harmful to populations of both species. Frank, once again, was able to detect some differentiation of even the small culture bottles into two "niches," *S. vetulus* tending to concentrate at the sides and bottom of the bottle and *D. pulicaria* more in the centre. These habits correspond with their distribution in their natural habitats.

Although a great deal of work has been done on the above level of description, the subject has hardly begun to develop methods of causal analysis. Park's attempts to relate fecundity and mortality factors to success in competition which have already been mentioned, and Birch's[48, 50] demonstration that r was, in some cases at least, related to success in competition are important pioneer developments.

In the present state of ecological science it would be premature to draw any but very tentative conclusions from the results of experimental studies on population systems. The application of demographic analysis and of a more detailed treatment of such systems has only recently begun, and it is almost certain that great advances will be made in this field in the near future. The theoretical work of Lotka, Volterra and others has undoubtedly been an important stimulus to research, even when the basic assumptions have been too simple and arbitrary, but the need is now appearing for further methods of analysis and there is no doubt that valuable work could be done by mathematicians.

Metabolic Aspects of Competition

It will be argued in Chapter 15 that a consideration of the relative metabolic activities of competing populations is a useful and valid way of assessing their relative importance. The very approximate analysis of grassland communities clearly indicates the value of this approach to field problems, but this aspect of competition appears to be completely unexplored in the experimental field. It might be suggested that the great complexity of the approach just discussed, using data from population dynamics and demography, would be further complicated if combined with studies of metabolic activity. That the reverse may be true is indicated by the success of Frank's[233] and of Slobodkin's work discussed in Chapter 10, from which rather simple generalizations emerged in the case of single species populations.

Again, in so far as metabolic rate is likely to be a major factor in a high intrinsic rate of increase, the rather simple relation between this and success in competition which was discovered by Birch[48–50] poses questions which are an obvious challenge to the experimenter. The complete *analysis* of such experiments may demand the compilation of "metabolic life tables," but the existence of useful generalizations at the inter-population level could be revealed by quite simple experiments.

Chapter 15

FOOD-CHAIN RELATIONSHIPS BETWEEN POPULATIONS

THIS chapter is concerned with "vertical" or feeding relationships between populations. These are considered under three headings, the numerical population aspects, the general metabolic aspects of food chains and the special metabolic characteristics of the principal trophic levels. *Field evidence* on effects of predators on their prey and parasites on their hosts is mainly discussed in Chapter 16, but some important *ideas* derived from field and experimental studies are discussed here on page 220.

Theoretical Studies

Ross's work[620] was directed to an analysis of the practical problems associated with malaria control. He derived equations describing the progress of a malaria epidemic in a situation where mosquitoes and man were present, and was able to predict that the very practical question of whether or not malaria would persist in an area is mainly determined by the ratio of mosquitoes to men: below a certain level of infestation (about 40 mosquitoes per man in the circumstances considered) the disease will die out. This prediction was in opposition to those who regarded malaria control by the elimination of mosquitoes as impracticable and it gave a great impetus to campaigns to reduce the infestation of mosquitoes.

Thompson[713–15] treated the interaction of insect parasites with their hosts in a more general way with special reference to biological-control methods. He was able to demonstrate that the slow establishment of an intentionally introduced parasite does not mean that biological control will fail since the spread of the parasite may increase rapidly in time; also the effects of different reproductive rate of the two species and of variations in egg-laying behaviour of the parasite. His earlier work was restricted in its usefulness because the calculations were based on generation frequency and not on an absolute time scale, making it more difficult to treat cases when host and parasite generations are not of the same length.

In contrast, Lotka,[415] in a more general treatment, employed an absolute time scale. He made assumptions such as that one host killed is equivalent to one parasite born and derived the equations—

$$dN_1/dt = r_1N_1 - kN_1N_2$$
$$dN_2/dt = kN_1N_2 - d_2N_2$$

Where—

N_1 = number of host population
N_2 = number of parasite population
d_2 = death rate per head of parasites
r_1 = birth rate minus death rate from causes other than parasitism per head of hosts

Thus,

$K_1N_1N_2$ = rate of consumption of hosts by parasites
$K_2N_1N_2$ = number of hosts available
d_2N_2 = death rate of parasite population

Lotka then derived a graph representing the course of a parasitic invasion based on various simplifying assumptions (see Fig. 22 (a)). This was followed by a more complete treatment giving rise to the graph of Fig. 22 (b).

In graphs of this sort, which are used also by Gause [243, 244] and others to express relationships between two species, the ordinate and abscissa represent the numbers of the two species and the points are plotted as in a correlation or regression curve. Time is not represented along the axes but could be indicated by measuring the angle of a line drawn at right angles to the tangent of the curve through the "singular point" in the centre. Alternatively, the same data can be plotted with time as the abscissa and the numbers of *both* species as ordinates. This is done in Fig. 22 (c) for the same data as Fig. 22 (b), and it will be seen that the result is a distorted "sine curve" for each species, the numbers of the predator lagging behind those of the prey; this presentation is rather more familiar to and more easily understood by some biologists.

From the first, simplified, treatment it will be seen that interaction of the two species results in oscillations of constant amplitude; the time taken for the system to "go round" one of the circles is determined by the host reproductive rate and parasite death rate as $2\pi/\sqrt{r_1d_2}$. The different circles, representing different amplitudes of oscillation, result from the use of different values of an integration constant M^1 which depends on the relationship between the rates of increase of the two species. It seems most improbable, on common-sense grounds, that a system of two species would, in fact, continue to oscillate with a constant amplitude. The more general treatment in Fig. 22 shows

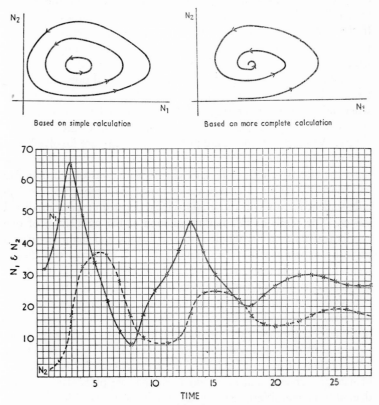

Based on simple calculation   Based on more complete calculation

FIG. 22. INTERACTION OF TWO ANIMAL POPULATIONS THROUGH PARASITISM

(After Lotka, 1925)

(*a: top left*) Based on Simple Calculation.
(*b: top right*) Based on More Complete Calculation.
(*c: bottom*) Plot on a Time Basis of *top right*.

what probably happens in nature; namely that, while the period of oscillation remains constant, the ratio of reproductive rates does not, and thus the amplitude of oscillation tends to change progressively so that the system either "unwinds," the oscillations becoming greater and greater until one species reaches zero and the system collapses or, alternatively, the oscillations tend to die down and the system comes to rest at the singular point in the centre. In the first case, the collapse of the system, if the host is the species to die out the parasite (in the limited universe which is postulated) will rapidly follow suit. If the parasite is the first to reach zero, the host population will presumably increase until controlled at a new level by a new density-dependent factor such as parasitism or food shortage.

The implications of these results for experimental populations will be considered below, but it is worth pointing out at this stage that when using them to interpret experiments it is best to regard the curves of the above figures as curves joining points of greatest probability. When reasonably large population systems are involved they may represent quite accurately what happens, but with small populations the effects of chance factors, chance variations of reproductive and mortality rates and chance variations of the intensity of density-independent factors will cause appreciable departures from predicted values. The result of this is that, as soon as the population of one species reaches zero the whole system collapses, and the poor success of many experimental systems intended to demonstrate this theory seems to be attributable, in fact, to the small populations involved and the greater liability of the systems to become extinct as a result.

Lotka's treatment only slightly antedated the independent work of Volterra,[768] a mathematician who became interested in the results of fisheries statistics in the Adriatic which were obtained by his compatriot D'Ancona, following the First World War. Volterra defined a "coefficient of increase" which is the same as Lotka's "intrinsic rate of natural increase" and he worked out the case of predation rather than that of parasitism, treating the results of competition between two species in more detail than Lotka did. (These have already been treated in Chapter 14.)

For a predator-prey system Volterra derived three "laws"[769]—

1. The law of the *periodic cycle*. Prediction that oscillations will occur, depending only on the coefficients of increase of predator and prey and on the initial relative numbers.

2. The law of *conservation of averages*. The mean numbers within each species remain constant, whatever the initial conditions, provided the intrinsic rates of increase and the efficiency of predation are constant.

3. The law of *disturbance of averages*. If two species are uniformly destroyed (e.g. by human fisheries operations) in proportion to their numbers, the mean numbers of prey increase and of predators decrease.

Further generalizations applicable to small fluctuations only are—

1. The period, T, of the cycle is not affected by the initial numbers nor by the efficiency of predation.

2. The period T is proportional to the mean number of times by which the prey population alone would double itself and the predator population halve itself. $T = 9 \cdot 06 \sqrt{t_1 t_2}$.

3. Uniform destruction of predators accelerates (and of prey retards) the rate of fluctuation. If destroyed uniformly the ratio of amplitude of prey to predator numbers increases.

The close similarity of many of these results to Lotka's is at once evident. There is, of course, no fundamental difference between the predator-prey and the parasite-host situation, except that the order of magnitude of the constants involved is very different because one predator in its lifetime usually consumes a large number of prey, whereas a single parasite is usually but one of many individuals to draw its nourishment from a single host. Some hymenopterous parasites of insects, in particular, which have but a single host for each parasite individual are to this extent intermediate between parasite and predator. One result of the different proportions between host and predator or parasite is that the predator is potentially a more useful biological-control organism since, other things being equal, it should become established faster. However, in practice the more specialized feeding habits of parasites and their greater reproductive rates usually outweigh this advantage.

Nicholson [488] developed a different line of approach to the problem of predation and parasitism when he put forward his theory of the "balance of nature" based especially on the concept of the "area of discovery." According to Nicholson the searching by a population for food, unless organized on a basis of co-operation by the whole population, will inevitably be random. (This premise is disputed by Thompson, who assumes systematic searching, and is evidently untrue in certain cases, as when an individual's searching activities reduce the probability of other members of the species searching the same ground. An extreme case of this occurs when a herbivore removes food which would otherwise be searched for and eaten by its fellows.)

Assuming random searching, which must occur very generally in nature, Nicholson illustrates the result on the consumption of prey by a "competition curve" of area against time which indicates the progressive difficulty of finding food as the population increases. This, as will be seen (Fig. 23), is an exponential curve in which the rate of increase is inversely proportional to the extent of departure from the upper asymptote, which represents 100 per cent searching success. It is rather unfortunate that Nicholson used the word "competition" to include parasitism. Williamson[814] has used it to cover predation as well; but most subsequent authors have followed the practice observed in this book of restricting the word to include species

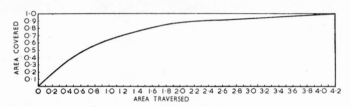

FIG. 23. THE "COMPETITION CURVE"
(From Nicholson, 1932)

exploiting the same food or shelter, etc., but excluding the interaction of predators and parasites.

Nicholson then correlated the "area of discovery," or area effectively traversed by the predator in its lifetime, with the power of increase of the species. (This "power of increase" is not r, the intrinsic rate of natural increase, but R, the number of times the population can multiply itself in a generation under the specific set of circumstances.) The power of increase and area of discovery were then related to the "steady state" at which the first is balanced by the mortality of the population.

On the basis of this equation Nicholson produced an elaborate series of conclusions about the interaction of parasite and host, some of which are the same as Volterra's, while others concern more specifically the "balance of nature."

Nicholson's first two conclusions, which link "competition" with the "balance of nature," foreshadow two ideas which have come to play a predominant role in theories about population. The conclusions are—

1. "Intra-specific competition automatically regulates the severity

of its action to the requirements of each population provided the inherent resistance of the environment is sufficiently low to permit the species to exist." This is fundamentally the concept of "density dependence" which was developed further by H. S. Smith[664] (see Chapter 10).

2. "For the steady state to exist each species must possess some advantages over all the other species with respect to some one, or group, of control factors to which it is subject." This is a direct corollary of the idea that two species with the same ecological requirements cannot exist together which was first stated by Darwin, but has frequently been attributed to Gause and has been a potent influence in certain fields of ecology. This has already been discussed, Chapter 14.

Nicholson criticized Lotka's treatment to some extent and developed it further in the predator-prey and parasite-host field, and came to a number of conclusions about the results of displacement from a "balanced" situation, and of introduction of further parasites or predators. He then considered the conditions for oscillation in a very simple host-parasite system and concluded that oscillations are likely to increase indefinitely but will, however, be reduced as more alternative hosts or parasites are introduced. Territorial behaviour and catholic feeding behaviour on the part of predator or parasite are recognized as further damping factors.

Nicholson considered that physical factors such as climate are non-density-dependent and contrasted their operation to that of density-dependent biotic factors, although these terms were not used. Certain, rather trivial, criticism of Nicholson's work is based on the fact that it has since been shown that climatic factors are not always density-independent and nor are biotic factors always density-dependent, in their action in any given instance.

The most serious defect of the earlier equations of predator-prey and parasite-host interaction is that they all make one or more of the following assumptions, namely, that changes in the population size of the one will be instantaneously reflected in a response by the other, that the appetite of the predator is infinite, that searching by the predator is truly random and that reproductive rate of the predator is proportional to the whole prey population size. These assumptions have been criticized by a number of authors some of whom have suggested improvements, for example Beverton and Holt, [46] Thompson, [716] Chitty[101] and Wangersky et al.[782] The latter for instance explore the possibility of introducing time lags in the interaction of the prey and conclude that it is only possible to predict the outcome of particular instances with the aid of a computer. A more radical revision of the whole matter is due to Watt[790] who constructed a model on the basis of practical experience and tried it out by substituting data from a wide variety of field populations. His basic equation is—

$$N_A = PK\left(1 - e^{-AN_0P^{1-b}}\right) \text{ where}$$

N_A = number of prey attacked
N_0 = initial number of prey liable to attack
P = number of predators searching
A = coefficient of attack, the instantaneous rate N_A/P
K = maximum number of attacks that can be made per P during the period that N_0 are vulnerable.

Means of obtaining these measurements are discussed.

The inherent feedback in the system which may or may not lead to stability is demonstrated and it is shown how different biological properties of predators will increase their effectiveness at different densities.

A closer approach to natural conditions is also apparent in the attempts to develop methods of estimating mortality in populations which are changing rapidly due to continual or intermittent recruitment of new individuals[606] and where the incidence of attack is not independent of age.[804]

Newer Theoretical Ideas Derived from Laboratory and Field Experiments

More complex examples of predation phenomena in the field are discussed in the next chapter, but the recent tendency to base theoretical models on field experience and to carry out field experiments on specific aspects of population dynamics makes it more convenient to consider here a few examples more directly relevant to theoretical problems, especially as they throw light on the validity of assumptions made in earlier models. Varley and Edwards[757] tested the assumptions of Nicholson's approach in the case of experiments on the housefly and its Chalcid parasite *Mormoniella* by De Bach and Smith[168] and found (in contrast to the latter's conclusion that Nicholson's theory was well fitted by the data) that in fact, the "area of discovery" falls to low values when the host population is high and the number of hosts attacked then becomes independent of host density.

Varley and Gradwell[758] made use of an idea due to Haldane to analyse the successive effects of mortality in the field. Haldane expressed the differences between the logarithms of the population numbers before and after each of a series of mortality factors had operated as k_1, k_2, k_3 . . . Then the total mortality over a period K is equal to $k_1 + k_2 + k_3$ . . . Applying this to field populations of the Winter Moth it was shown that k_1 (= winter disappearance in the soil) over a number of years is largely related to K and accounts for most mortality. The mortality due to pupal predators, although less than that due to winter disappearance, operates in a density-dependent manner, being higher when the over-wintering population was larger.

Rather different approaches to the analysis of mortality are those of Watt,[792] who was able to incorporate simultaneously-acting factors in a single model by measuring their effects independently, and Lloyd[412] who related various aspects of breeding success over a series of years to ranked estimates of a number of mortality factors. Thus we have three quite distinct techniques suitable for the analysis of mortality factors acting in succession through one season, all together and to different extents in different seasons, respectively.

Another study derived from Varley's work is that of Dixon[177, 178] on the searching behaviour of the Coccinellid bettle *Adalia decempunctata* and the reactions of the aphids on which it feeds. Contrary to earlier suppositions aphids have a variety of very effective defence mechanisms and, unless the beetle is at least as large as the aphid, are not usually eaten. Once a young *Adalia* has received its first meal however its chances of survival are greatly increased. The behaviour of *Adalia* is such that simple suppositions about the relations between random searching, rate of supply of aphids and rate of increase of predators are invalid. The aphids occur in clusters and adult *Adalia* search for these and lay their eggs there, thus effectively increasing the area of discovery of their young.

An example of predation which varies in intensity with the age of the prey is provided by Connell's[126] study of predation by *Thais lapillus* on *Balanus balanoides*. The predator (more widely known to ecologists as *Nucella* or *Purpura*, according to their generation) requires more time to remove the barnacles than to eat them and so, by concentrating on the larger barnacles, increases both its own production and that of the barnacles (which are largely limited by competition for living space). One result of this age-dependent mortality is that earlier estimates of growth rate were seriously at fault.

This very rapacious predator is responsible for a very high proportion of barnacle mortality in summertime and is also very destructive to *Mytilus*.[369] These authors refer to an old record reporting that population *cycles* can result from *Thais-Mytilus* interaction but are unable to throw light on the question.

Experimental Studies

Gause[243-5] was the earliest worker to do extensive experiments on predator-prey systems with the intention of testing whether Lotka's and Volterra's predictions can be applied to laboratory populations. He was particularly interested in the maintenance of oscillatory systems, and these he was able to achieve on a number of occasions. In none of the experiments quoted in his book[243] was this possible without arranging for small daily additions at a regular rate of one or other of the species. This was regarded as immigration by Gause. It is generally agreed that the numbers of animals present were too small to avoid accidental extinction of one or other species, as discussed above (see p. 216).

However, in the experiments[244] on *Paramecium bursaria* feeding on *Saccharomyces pombe* and *P. aurelia* on *S. exiguus*, several complete cycles of oscillation were maintained before extinction occurred. On the basis of the figures he obtained, Gause calculated the values of the parameters in Volterra's equations—

$$dN_1/dt = b_1N_1 - k_1N_1N_2$$
$$dN_2/dt = k_2N_1N_2 - d_2N_2$$

In the first case the birth rate, b_1 of *Saccharomyces pombe* was artificially maintained by doubling the numbers of unconsumed yeast cells daily, while in the second the numbers of *Paramecium aurelia* were reduced to 0·45 of their level at the end of each day, thus achieving an artificial mortality d_2 of 0·45. To this extent even these experiments were not free from objection, but presumably they show that, had animals with these particular vital characteristics been available, oscillations would have occurred.

As far as is known to the author, no laboratory predator-prey populations have been maintained in oscillation for long periods without manipulation of some sort and it is evident that such "simple" systems are not easy to achieve. A usual fate of such systems is shown by the experiments[243] with *Didinium* feeding on *Paramecium* in which the prey population was usually completely destroyed and the predator then starved. When, however, "cover" in the form of sand grains was provided, a few prey individuals usually survived even the most intense predation and the predator then starved—to be followed by a new outburst of the numbers of the prey.

Certainly in nature small amounts of migration between relatively isolated populations are frequently found and under these circumstances, at least, the perpetuation of erratic oscillations could be predicted. However the role of emigration and immigration in modifying the effects of inter-species interactions has been studied very little experimentally.

An interesting experiment on two mite species on strawberry plants is reported by Huffaker et al.[330] and summarized by Andrewartha and Birch.[17] The predator is *Typhlodromus cucumeris* and the prey, which is an economic pest is *Stenotarsonemus pallidus*. Experimental plants kept free of the predator by means of chemicals bore heavy infestations of the pest while those in which the predator was allowed to flourish remained very lightly attacked. These results were repeated under field conditions and in no cases did either predator or prey disappear (except because of the insecticide). This is thought to have been due to the availability of refuges for the prey which prevented complete extermination. Further experiments[329] with different but related mites and a "universe" of oranges were designed to investigate the effect on the outcome of an experiment of this kind of rates of dispersal and of refuges. Huffaker was able by using many oranges and with the aid of petroleum jelly barriers to maintain the predator-prey system in operation for six months (or about twelve prey generations).

An example of a more complex situation is provided by the report of Flanders et al.[223] of an experiment in which the moth *Ephestia* and its parasite *Idechthis* were cultured together. The parasite normally kept the number of its prey down to a low level but when a mite predator *Melichares* which fed on the eggs of *Ephestia* was introduced, the number of the host rose. This can be interpreted theoretically as an example of Volterra's law of the disturbance of averages or of Nicholson's compensatory reactions.

METABOLIC ASPECTS OF THE "VERTICAL" (FEEDING)
RELATIONSHIPS BETWEEN POPULATIONS

In Chapter 6 the theory and methods for studying metabolism were briefly reviewed and in Chapter 11 the metabolic characteristics of whole populations were considered. In both cases, the relation between animals and their food organisms was necessarily mentioned. In this chapter the effects of feeding relationships on the structure of whole communities are the centre of interest. At a descriptive level this involves a consideration of the food chain and related ideas; it is then demonstrated that these can be made quantitative by tracing the flow of energy through the ecological links in the chain.

The first attempts to describe the functional relationships between populations were based on the food chain. This idea goes back to the French "Physiologists" of the last century, and, according to Brewer[71] to Semper in America. But it was neglected until Elton[199] extended its use. He pointed out that the number of links of successive predators and parasites is quite small, not usually more than three, giving a total of about five stages when the plant and herbivore links are included. He also drew attention to the great disparity between the numbers of species in the successive stages or steps of the food chain. This he expressed by saying that in a single community there is a "pyramid of numbers," whose basal layer is the abundant mass of plants, while the herbivores and successive carnivores constitute successive layers of rapidly decreasing size until there are quite small numbers of the larger predators. This conception has come to be called the "Eltonian Pyramid" by American workers in particular. The construction of food chains or "food webs" is an essential preliminary to an understanding of the biological structure of a community. The expression "food web" is American in origin as is "trophic level," meaning a "horizontal" stage in the pyramid of numbers, consisting of organisms consuming the same kind of food; both have been generally adopted in this country. The concept of the "pyramid of numbers" has sometimes been misunderstood in America, where papers have been published describing pyramids whose successive steps represent simply different species or size groups arranged in order of abundance. This seems a rather elaborate way of comparing the abundance of different species and has nothing to do with the original "Eltonian" conception whose essence was a *functional* analysis of the community. In work of this sort the food habits of the animals are frequently not studied at all, which must make things much easier for the experimenter, but correspondingly less informative for the reader.

Examples of valuable ecological work based on the food chain and the food web are many and references to them will be found in the standard textbooks. Three recent examples will be mentioned here, however, because the authors have been able to combine studies of

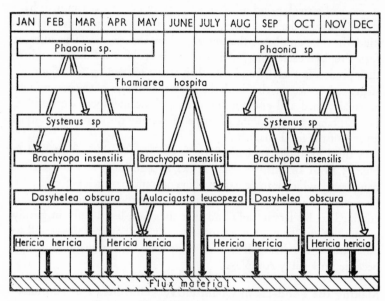

FIG. 24. FOOD CHAIN IN A BROWN FLUX
(From Robinson, 1953)

feeding habits with observations on the effect of time on the changes in the structure of the food chain. Thus, Glynne-Williams and Hobart[267] worked on the crevice fauna of rocky seashores. They found that there are two complete faunas, both involving scavenging organisms, herbivores and predators, and both showing zonation in two respects, namely a vertical zonation determined by the time of submergence by the sea and a horizontal one depending on the distance from the mouth of the crevice. These two faunas, the "terrestrial" one with Collembola as the main detritus feeders and mites and fly larvae as predators, and the "marine" one with Polychaet worms as the main predators, replace one another when the presence of water or air permits the activities of the swimming and walking animals in turn. In addition there are a number of links between the two sets of animals; the Collembola, for instance, include forms which feed on dead Mollusca.

Robinson's[615] work on the animals of a brown flux on elm trees introduces a community dominated by a very different time scale. In place of a twelve-and-a-half-hour cycle of change, the animals have their "exits and their entrances," as the melancholy Jaques noted of mankind, the time unit being the annual cycle of the seasons. The different forms replace each other, taking up their ecological functions where their predecessor left off and with their active and resting and migratory stages so interwoven that both the interrelationships of the community are maintained and also the life cycles of the members are fulfilled. Fig. 24, taken from Robinson's paper, illustrates the changing seasonal aspects of the food chain.

A third example, typical of recent German work, is illustrated in Fig. 25 from Brauns.[67] This shows in a striking way the sort of complexity which is to be expected in communities such as forest soils. However, it should be noticed that this particular "food web" is confined to fly larvae only and that these are listed only in family groups. If any attempt were made to cover all animal phyla and to differentiate the many hundreds of species such a diagram would become impossibly complex.

Making the Food-chain Quantitative: Numbers and Biomass

The food chain is not, as it stands, a device for measuring the magnitudes of the effects of the feeding of species on each other or in competition with each other. In practice, however, the more we learn about an assemblage of animals the more numerous do the biological ties prove to be and the more complicated does the food chain become. There is a great need, therefore, for a means of distinguishing the important from the irrelevant "links" in the chain and for distinguishing those species whose absence would profoundly alter the whole structure from those whose importance is trivial. The necessity of being able to select the important species is most apparent in the complicated terrestrial communities such as those of grassland and woodland which often contain nearly a thousand species of animals.

Since the organisms exploiting a given food resource may range in size from bacteria to elephants, the census must be converted to estimates of total protoplasm or biomass. However there are two fundamental limitations to the use of biomass in food-chain studies. The first is that the measurements we want are not represented by the standing crop of the species at all. As stressed in Chapter 11 standing crop is, for many reasons, a very poor index of production because metabolism is not directly related to it. Secondly, while it is possible to measure the food-chain links in terms of the quantities of organic matter which pass along each in unit time, it is difficult in practice to label and recognize particular parcels of food. Phillipson's[571] ingenious technique of presenting different coloured foods to a predator is one possible approach. Another is used by Cushing[143] who worked with a rather simple food chain in the sea in which two types of Copepod fed on virtually a single species of Alga. Here measurements of algal division rates, Copepod grazing capacity and reproduction and mortality figures sufficed to calculate productivities and to show how the spring outburst of Algae, the nutrient cycle in the sea and the capacity of the Copepods to "overgraze" the Algae are related.

Another method which has been used in the plankton community is to follow the levels of particular chemical elements in the water.

However there is a fundamental difficulty which was originally realized by Thienemann,[708] in using chemical elements such as phosphorus or nitrogen in estimating production. If one considers the fate of a certain atom of the element taken up by a certain planktonic plant, say a diatom, it may be excreted into the surrounding water and taken up again by a second plant almost immediately; alternatively, it may be eaten with the plant by a water flea, there to remain for an indeterminable period, short or long, before excretion; or again, it may remain inside the diatom until the latter dies and sinks to the bottom of the water, there to remain perhaps until the annual "turnover" of the lake in autumn, or to become incorporated in the bottom mud in such a way that it is not made available to living organisms again until the lake dries up in thousands of years' time. These are but a few of the many possible fates of such an atom and, since the extent to which any given element may circulate in the community is both unpredictable and also irrelevant to the productivity of that community, it follows that the concentration of chemical substances cannot be used for estimating productivity of whole communities.

Furthermore, in most communities of any complexity, such as a lake, the generation times of the members of the different trophic levels are very different. Thus the liberation of substances at death occurs with different frequencies according to the species and it is not possible to sum the productivities of the different species when these have been estimated with biomass as a basis. Bacteria and Algae have several generations in a day, Nematoda and Parasitid mites live for a few weeks, while springtails have three or four generations a year and many larger organisms live for a year or more. Again, organisms such as fungi, which do not produce discrete individuals are difficult to treat quantitatively for obvious reasons.

The Advantages of Using Metabolic Activity in Studying Food-chain Relationships

There is, however, one measurable entity which does not recirculate in the community, which is independent of the biological idiosyncrasies of the organism and which appears to be a suitable basis for estimating productivity of whole communities and to permit comparisons within them; this is energy. Energy enters the community as a proportion of the radiations emanating from the sun and intercepted by the earth. Of that which penetrates the atmosphere and enters plants a high proportion, probably about seven-eighths, is liberated as heat even in the processes of photosynthesis. [224] However, the remaining one-eighth is transferred by the plant to organic substances of high energy content—carbohydrates, fats and proteins.

The plants themselves, in addition to their photosynthetic activity, are continually respiring, that is to say, are liberating energy, breaking down organic substances and reducing oxygen to carbon dioxide. In this way a proportion of their energy intake is dissipated. However, a larger proportion is made available to other organisms in the form of fresh green stuff which is grazed, of storage organs which are plundered or of decaying remains of plant matter which are decomposed. These sources of energy are the supply for the herbivores, predators and decomposing animals of all the remaining "trophic levels."

Similarly, the members of the successive trophic levels partly break down their ingested organic matter and liberate energy either in the direct production of heat or in the form of mechanical work used in locomotion and similar activities which ultimately produce heat in their turn. *But*, and this is the important point, the energy does not

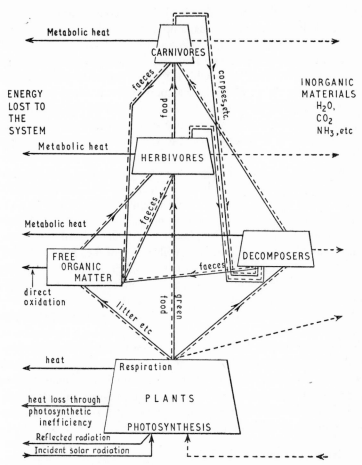

FIG. 26. MATTER AND ENERGY RELATIONS IN THE ECOSYSTEM

Paths of energy ———— high energy organic matter – – – – and inorganic matter – – – – – in a (greatly oversimplified) perfectly isolated ecosystem. Intake and output of energy to the left; of inorganic matter (plant nutrients) to the right. Note that photosynthetic energy input (gross primary production) equates with the total of all metabolic heat losses and is an index of total turnover.

recirculate in the community as chemical substances do. An individual stores part of its energy intake in its tissues and liberates part as heat or mechanical work. This happens throughout the food chain. It is thus possible to draw up a balance sheet for a community in which the debtor side is the sum total of all the "packets" of energy liberated by the individuals, plant and animal, in the community, while the credit side is almost entirely made up of the single vast contribution which the plants make by their photosynthetic activities Fig. 26.

The measure of the energy flow can be taken at all the different points in the community at which it passes from one population to another when the productivity of components is being compared; it can be taken at its entrance to the plants and the sum total of its exits from all the members when that of the whole community is to be measured. It is directly related to the common-sense idea of the "productivity" or "activity" of a community. An "active" community is one in which the plants are capturing a high proportion of the incident solar energy; a balance is achieved between the activity of the plants and the rate of supply of nutrient substances to these (through the liberation of mineral matter from the animals and decomposer organisms). The photosynthetic activity of the plants, which should equate with the energy liberation of the "heterotrophic" element, is thus a measure of the activity of the whole community, for, if the non-photosynthetic organisms were to disappear, the plant life would rapidly die out for lack of nutrients.

From the point of view of the constituent organisms in a community, the relative importance of different species can be compared more simply on the basis of their contribution to the energy flow of the community than in terms of biomass. The population which exploits the greatest quantity of stored energy is contributing most to the rapid liberation of nutrient substances. These will ultimately find their way back to the plants and thus contribute to raise the energy intake of the community as a whole.

Efficiency and the Food Chain

The concept of efficiency was first associated with the food chain by Lindemann[409] who used it to compare the production (i.e. the total calorific content of the food exploited by all members) of the successive trophic levels in a hypothetical food chain. Efficiency in his sense is therefore the ratio of food made available to a "higher" trophic level divided by that available to the level under consideration. This has been termed the *Food-chain efficiency* by Slobodkin[659] in contrast to the *ecological efficiency* (see Chapter 11) in which the denominator is the energy content of the food actually consumed by the lower level. Lindemann suggested that efficiency is greatest at the lower levels of the pyramid and least at the higher but most later authors doubt the validity of this generalization.

A great number of other energy ratios can of course be recognized and some of these have been tabulated by Pattern[558] who also introduces the concept of entropy in a stimulating paper. At the present stage of ecological theory and practice, however, there appears to be little to gain from the substitution of the concept of increase of entropy for that of reduction of energy as he has done.[659]

Some Examples of Quantitative Food-chain Studies

During the past few years a number of pioneer quantitative studies of food chains have been carried out in the United States: these have mainly derived from the precept and example of E.P. and H.T. Odum and have now been summarized, together with much valuable information on the energy dynamics of natural and man-dominated communities.[527] This work has provided us with practical figures of total production, trophic level production and efficiencies in the case of two freshwater communities,[706, 531] the *Spartina* marsh already mentioned[529] and an oceanic coral reef.[534] Since then H.T. Odum has published some figures for tropical rain forest[532] and Golley for a grassland community.[271] Some of these communities are reasonably self-contained and show normal types of numerical, biomass and energy pyramids, but others such as the spring investigated by Teal[706] are based on the import of practically all plant-produced energy in the form of dead leaves and show a very restricted photosynthetic layer and a great preponderance of decomposer organisms. The coral reef is interesting especially because the corals containing zoochlorellae combine in one individual two, or possibly three, trophic levels. The relative importance of the Algae from the production angle was not measured and has since been disputed[828] on the grounds that it is insignificant—although the Algae are important as a kind of excretory organ for the corals and to this extent contribute to increased turnover. The section to follow serves to illustrate the approximate outcome of a study of this kind when applied to one particular community—in this instance to grassland.

The Structure of the Grassland Ecosystem

No terrestrial ecosystem has yet been studied thoroughly enough to provide material for a complete synthesis. However, it is possible, by drawing data from a number of separate studies to compile a general energy flow picture for a permanent grass field grazed by cattle and to arrive at a number of, admittedly tentative, conclusions about its main features. In Fig. 27 (*a* and *b*) the standing crops of the main groups of organisms are represented by "boxes" whose area is proportional, on a logarithmic scale to their calorific content. These are joined by energy flow "channels" whose width is also proportional, on a logarithmic scale, to their mean annual energy flow in calories per unit time. Obviously since the time unit is arbitrarily chosen the size relationship between the boxes and the channels is also arbitrary and of no special significance. If we first compare the ratio of the boxes to the channels we see that there is a progressive increase in ratio of flow/standing crop, i.e. of rate of turnover of organic matter as one passes from grasses to man through the above-ground diagram. No such generalizations are possible for the subterranean diagram. That is to say a stock containing about 1,000 calories of plant, 200 calories of beef and 160 calories of man respires a calorie per day. The micro-organisms require 400 calories content to respire one calorie, the large soil invertebrates about 1,000 but the smaller ones about 200. This means once more that biomass (proportional to calorific content) is not a good indicator of activity. The main features to notice about the *widths of the flow channels* are that about one-sixth of the energy of photosynthesis is respired by the plants, about two-thirds goes in the form of dead plant matter to the decomposer organisms, mainly in the soil and less than one-quarter is consumed by all herbivores. Even of this proportion about half is returned to the soil as non-assimilated faeces. So in a field which the farmer believes himself to be fully using in this way less than one-half per cent of total biological production is harvested by man and about three-quarters goes to the soil. Obviously, the soil is in a privileged position. Of the energy flow entering the soil all is ultimately respired provided no appreciable accumulation as peat, etc., is taking place. About five-sixths of the respiration is microbial and one-twelfth (a very uncertain figure this) is by Protozoa and the remainder is shared between the larger fauna such as earthworms and Myriapods on the one hand and the "mesofauna" (mites and Collembola) on the other.

An attempt has been made in Table 11 to work out in more detail the abundance, biomass and metabolism of some commoner soil animals. It should be stressed that no figures have yet been obtained following

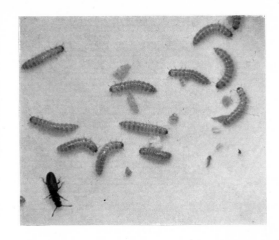

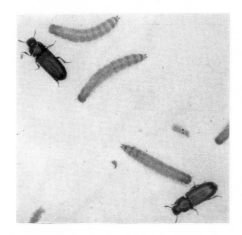

PLATE III
Grain-living Beetles widely used
in Ecological Experiments

(*Above*) *Oryzaephilus surinamensis*,
adult and larvae.
(*Centre right*) *Tribolium castaneum*,
adults and larvae.
(*Below*) *Tribolium confusum*,
adults and larvae.

PLATE IV

Grain-living Beetles widely used in Ecological Experiments

(*Above left*) *Rhizopertha dominica*, adults, larvae and pupae on wheat.
(*Above right*) *Calandra oryzae* on wheat.
(*Below*) *Calandra granarea* on wheat.

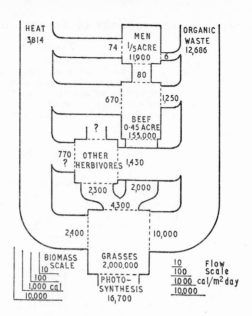

FIG. 27. (a) ENERGY FLOW THROUGH A MEADOW: ABOVE GROUND ORGANISMS

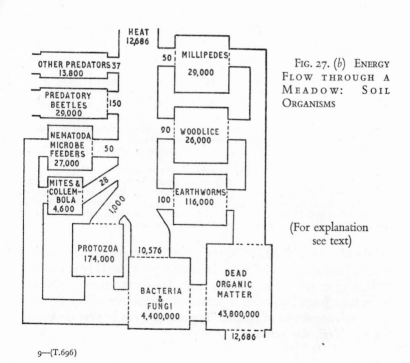

FIG. 27. (b) ENERGY FLOW THROUGH A MEADOW: SOIL ORGANISMS

(For explanation see text)

TABLE 11

Figures from a hypothetical grassland community showing order of magnitude of numbers, biomass and metabolism for the main invertebrate groups. Numbers and biomass are typical for areas in which the respective groups are abundant, i.e. most groups would be uncommon in some grasslands and none of them would be as common as this in one place together. Also the balance of groups would be quite different in, say, moorland or woodland. Figures in the same horizontal row do not necessarily correspond where independent estimates are available.

Group of organisms	Results of Metabolism Experiments				Approximate Estimates Grassland, per sq m		
	Weight of organism, mg	O$_2$ uptake Cu mm per hour per individual	Temperature °C	calories per day per g at 16°C†	Numbers	Mass g	Calories per year§
Bacteria*	10^{-9}	7×10^{-9}	20	575	10^{15}	1,000	—
Fungi*			20	161		400	—
Protozoa*	0·05	10^{-2}	22·5	14	5×10^8	38	113
Nematoda	0·001	$1·2 \times 10^{-3}$	16	144	10^7	12	355
Lumbricidae	5,000	300	16	7	10^3	120	180
Enchytracidae	0·14	0·117	16	100	10^5	12	160
Mollusca‡	1,500	1,000	28	29	50	10	62
Myriapoda	25	10	19	36	500	12·5	96
Isopoda	22·7	9	19	36	500	5	38
Opiliones	18	10·5	19	53	40	0·4	5
Acari—							
Parasitids	0·2	0·5	16	280	5×10^3	1·0	64
Oribatei	0·25	0·12	14	72	2×10^5	2·0	30
Araneae	10	3·0	19	27	600	6·0	34
Coleoptera	250	60	13	39	100	1·0	8
Diptera	610	105	13	29	200	1·0	6
Collembola	0·46	0·55	16	144	5×10^4	5·0	153

* Figures for micro-organisms are only available per g of soil; these have been multiplied by 10^4 to give an *extremely approximate* estimate on a square metre basis.

† Metabolism figures are corrected to 16°C by means of Krogh's graph.[60] Values are in small (g) calories.

‡ Molluscan figures based on snails, weight of soft parts only.

§ Daily metabolism figures for 16°C are multiplied by 212 to correct for annual temperature cycle in N. Europe; (based on Neilsen[509]). Values in large Calories. Owing to effects of microbial antagonism (see p. 270) rates for natural conditions are far lower than in the laboratory, but no valid estimates are possible. Note that the total from field experiments on undisturbed soil is around 5,000 Cal/year.

all the precepts advised in Chapter 6, that many groups show marked seasonal and spatial variations and that the figures should be regarded as indicating an order of magnitude at best. However, the comparisons of abundance (on a log scale), biomass and metabolism of Fig. 28 show that one's assessment of relative "importance" can be very dependent on which criterion one uses.

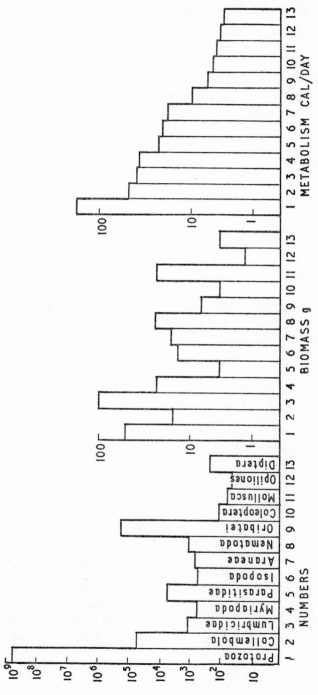

FIG. 28. COMPARISONS OF THE ABUNDANCE, BIOMASS AND METABOLISM OF SOIL ANIMALS

The figures are based on a purely hypothetical meadow population of invertebrates and are intended to show the change in relative importance of different groups according to whether numbers, biomass, or metabolism is used as a criterion of importance. For want of better information the metabolic rates given in Table II are used, although these are only indications of order of magnitude.

It may well be questioned, however, on the basis of the discussion on p. 270 whether even metabolic rate is to be regarded as a good criterion of "importance." If it is true that micro-organisms determine some 90 per cent of the soil metabolism in any case, is it not likely that some of those insignificant species which happen to spread fungus spores or destroy antibiotic substances in their digestive tracts may outweigh in importance others which are metabolically more active? This is a question which only further quantitative measurements can decide, but it is perhaps worth mentioning that other important functions of soil animals include mechanical mixing, drainage, aeration and crumb formation, all of which are performed most efficiently by earthworms and that when these animals are absent the entire structure of a soil is degraded—as has been shown by Raw[597a] in the case of an apple orchard sprayed with too much copper.

In general, then, there seems to be little doubt that in grassland and probably most terrestrial communities[33, 296, 297, 271] by far the greater part of net primary production is channelled not through the herbivores but through a decomposer food web, and also that the actions of the various soil organisms on the ecosystem as a whole are of greater significance than their "importance" in the sense of numbers, biomass or even metabolic rate.

SOME SPECIAL PROPERTIES OF SPECIFIC TROPHIC LEVELS

Plants and Photosynthesis

Green plants are almost entirely responsible for the primary production of the whole community and for this reason can be set apart from the animal and other consumer organisms. (Chemosynthesis by Bacteria is generally agreed to be a relatively unimportant phenomenon, in comparison.) Because the energy intake of plants in a closed system is equal to the integrated total of respiration throughout the community photosynthesis is the best and most practicable measure for determining the productivity of the whole community. The proportion of photosynthetically bound energy which is liberated again in the plants' own respiration seems to vary over a wide range amounting to well over half in the tropical rain forest studied by Odum et al.[532] and in tropical plankton communities according to Ryther.[622] In Golley's study of temperate grassland on the other hand it amounted to about one-sixth. Since the photosynthetic efficiency and total primary production are higher in the tropics this may have the effect of reducing the non-respired energy available to the rest of the food chain to a more even level.

The most direct method of determining primary productivity is to measure the difference between (a) oxygen production, carbon uptake or mineral uptake associated with *apparent* photosynthesis in sunlight and (b) the quantities of these elements exchanged in the reverse direction due to the simultaneous respiration of the plants, as measured in the dark. This is the basis of the dark and light bottle method for plankton and some gas train methods on land. A less direct method of determining gross productivity is the chlorophyll method in which the quantity of chlorophyll present is multiplied by an independently determined factor which related it to photosynthesis.

The *net* primary productivity, i.e. that remaining after plant respiration and animals and other heterotrophic organisms have taken their toll, can be measured by one of several *harvesting methods*. These are mainly applicable to seasonal plants. When feeding by other herbivores is reduced to a minimum in man-controlled systems such as vegetables and corn crops the human harvest may represent quite a high proportion of the difference between gross primary productivity and plant respiration, e.g. man may harvest up to two-thirds of the gross primary productivity in an alfalfa crop during the six-month growing season.

Primary Productivity Methods Based on Chemical Exchange

The classical method used to determine gross productivity of plankton is the light and dark bottle method already mentioned.[622] The rates of increase of oxygen in a clear bottle and of decrease in a dark bottle are added. They are determined by the Winkler oxygen-concentration method.[230]

Alternatively the rates of carbon dioxide absorption in light and production in dark can be determined, either chemically by titration or with a pH meter.[759, 760] The validity of results obtained in this way has been disputed on the grounds that the inner surface of the dark bottles are sites of increased bacterial respiration,[513] and that the lower turbulence inside the bottle reduces photosynthetic rates.[762] Both these effects would appear to indicate that published figures of productivity are too low. Early estimates in which nanoplankton were neglected are also far too low.[616, 617] Steemann–Nielsen[510, 511, 512, 513, 514] introduced an alternative method of measuring carbon uptake. He added solutions of sodium bicarbonate containing ^{14}C to the samples in bottles and after exposure to sunlight measured the quantity of radioactive carbon present in plants filtered and centrifuged from the water. Short exposures were used to reduce the passage of carbon to heterotrophic organisms. Neilsen's estimates were lower than those generally accepted. According to Ryther,[622] Nielsen was really measuring net and not gross productivity because photosynthesis and respiration are virtually contemporaneous and only storage in excess of immediate requirements is measured. The practical details and comparative advantages of these methods have been usefully reviewed by Goldman,[270] who demonstrates that measurement of primary productivity is not an easy matter. Rohde[616] has helped to explain discrepancies on the grounds of the rapid variation in productivity during the day.

Similar methods have been used for the measurement of gross primary productivity of terrestrial communities; carbon dioxide, absorbed in alkali from a stream of gas, is estimated by titration. A simple field technique for low herbage, and some results have been published by Wallis and Wilde,[778] and the use of transparent plastic bags in conjunction with a similar apparatus to determine production of tree leaves is mentioned by Odum et al.[532]

Alternative direct methods employ the measurement of mineral uptake, particularly phosphorus by chemical analysis. As already explained these are really methods of measuring *net* primary production and are only applicable in rather simple systems such as plankton communities during the period of seasonal increase.

THE USE OF CHLOROPHYLL AS AN INDEX OF PRIMARY PRODUCTIVITY. The quantity of chlorophyll present in a sample of water can be determined by a number of elegant physical and chemical methods and on the whole is surprisingly constant at particular latitudes.[508, 448] As a practical measure of productivity in the sea it has been criticized by Gillbricht[256] because up to five-sixths of the chlorophyll may in fact be in the faeces of Copepods and not living in algal cells. The quantity of chlorophyll on an area basis is much more difficult to determine for land communities but it appears to lie within a narrow range of values. Bray[69] surveyed a wide range of native and managed plant communities and obtained values between 0·3 and 3·0 g dry weight per sq m. The quantity of chlorophyll was higher in forest than in grassland, in lowland meadows than upland grassland and at the later stages of succession. Odum et al.[532] give figures around 3·0 g per sq m for tropical rain forest and Gessner,[253] 1·0 for grassland and 1·2 for forest. When suitably related to measurements of productivity chlorophyll appears to be a useful index of *potential* productivity, but, of course, actual short-term productivity is always subject to the influence of environmental conditions and particularly light and temperature.

Harvesting Methods of Productivity Measurement

As already explained harvesting methods measure net primary productivity and are best adapted to seasonal crops. Harvesting methods have been applied to timber production by Muller and Møller[476] by Ovington [540, 541] and by Pearsall.[542] These all involve fairly straightforward, if technically difficult, measurements of weight or volume of organic matter produced.

The Range of Primary Productivity Values Found in Practice

Total annual gross productivity values expressed in g carbon per sq m per year range from less than 45g for deserts to 450g for favourable agricultural areas and up to 2,250g in exceptionally fertile situations.[527] A very approximate calorific content (in gramme calories) can be obtained if these figures are multiplied by 10,000. Many figures have been published for *net* production of managed and natural communities[70, 357, 527] although it is not always clear whether roots are included with aerial parts of plants. When reduced to the above basis of g carbon per sq m per year (1 g carbon ≈ 2·5g organic matter) normal values for temperate conditions range from 150g to 370g[70] but tropical crops range up to about 2,500 for Cassava.[357] English coniferous and deciduous woodland each produce up to 540g and 270g,[540, 542] a reflection of the seasonal interruption of production in the latter. Golley[272] obtained grassland production figures of 580g gross and 490g net. The most recent estimates of world annual photosynthesis put the activities of marine plants at $2·5 \times 10^{10}$ tons and of land plants $1·7 \times 10^{10}$ tons of carbon equivalent to a total world turnover of some $0·63 \times 10^{24}$ g calories.[477]

The Food-chain Efficiency of Primary Production

Primary production efficiency is low when based on comparison of calorific content of plant products with the energy in solar radiation.

As already mentioned some 30 per cent of gross production is dissipated as plant respiration, but this is a small loss in comparison with the 50 per cent loss of radiation between arrival at the plant and absorption by chlorophyll and an efficiency of only about 10 per cent in the actual chemical changes in photosynthesis itself.[224] Estimates of overall efficiency from reception of solar energy over large areas of the earth's surface to production of organic matter usually vary from about 1 per cent to 5 per cent[357, 527]; Golley estimates 1·25 per cent for grassland and Ovington and Heitkamp[541] quote about 2·7 per cent for pine wood or 3·5 per cent when roots are included as a maximum for British woodland. Kalle[357] quotes 0·04 per cent for the North Sea where photosynthetic efficiency is reduced by turbidity of the water but assisted by mechanical mixing of nutrients and water with the Algae; however for the reason given below this should probably be nearer 0·14 per cent.

H. T. Odum[530] has pointed out that, since conditions for maximum photosynthesis are usually below the optimum and since production rate rather than efficiency is likely to be of importance to the survival of a community, selection of those systems with higher production but lower efficiency is likely to occur. This point is discussed below.

A variety of figures for incident solar radiation can be found in the literature referred to above, in papers by Fogg[224] and Strickland[696] and also in climatological and physical publications, for example that by Hilsum.[322] Ovington and Heitkamp[541] give a formula for calculating radiation at the earth's surface in terms of climatic factors. Typical figures of radiation available to plants are $2·5 \times 10^8$ calories per sq m per annum in Britain,[541] 47×10^8 in Michigan.[271] Kalle[357] gives $8·4 \times 10^8$ for the North Sea, but this is based on a midsummer value and is not corrected for seasonal changes in radiation.

The Herbivore Trophic Level

This is the secondary level which is most widely exploited by man and as a result has perhaps received an undue prominence. Of the net production of a typical meadow grazed to capacity by cows, for instance, less than one-third is consumed by herbivores,[439] and the general impression from unexploited terrestrial communities is that a much smaller proportion of plant energy goes to the herbivores.[33, 296] In the marine plankton community the herbivores appear to ingest a higher proportion of plant production but to assimilate less of it.[145]

The food-chain efficiency of domestic herbivores suitably managed can reach high levels as was shown in Chapter 6 but hunted prey are considerably less efficient. Productivity maxima for U.S. sports fisheries are about 5 g per sq m per annum compared with a primary production of about 300 g. It will be remembered (Chapter 11) that Allen[8] obtained a figure of about 17 per cent as the overall efficiency for trout of which never more than 10 per cent was harvested by man, the rest going to natural predators. In both this and Watt's[788] studies the high proportion of production which is lost as young fish to other predators points to the need to eliminate predators or to accept a smaller fish in the catch if productivity is to be increased.

The Carnivore Levels

These have been very little studied. Lindemann[409] was of the opinion that carnivores are less efficient than herbivores because they use more energy in searching out and catching their prey. Certainly among mammals the *basal* metabolism of carnivores appears to be no higher than that of herbivores[5 Table 150] in relation to size. This index might not be the ideal measurement if it were shown that carnivores are capable of periodically raised metabolic rates and herbivores not. Among terrestrial invertebrates there is some evidence of greater *total* metabolic activity among carnivores than herbivores (Chapter 11). At present Slobodkin's opinion that food-chain efficiencies vary little from one trophic level to another seems to be the safest generalization,[659] and values of the order of 10 per cent are to be expected.

Decomposer Levels

These have been much neglected in the past but in terrestrial systems, at least, probably process a higher proportion of plant production than do the herbivore and carnivore levels. As Hairston[297] has pointed out, wherever a community is relatively static the impression of abundant food available to herbivores is deceptive; ultimately all the food is consumed and much of this by the "reducer or decomposer" organisms. The same opinion has been expressed by other biologists also.[33, 252] Aquatic communities vary in this respect: most of the animals in Teal's[706] spring were decomposers and in Odum's[531] Silver Springs study most metabolism was through decomposers although their biomass was less than that of herbivores. In typical grassland communities both standing crop and production of decomposers appear to exceed that of herbivores as illustrated above.

It appears that terrestrial plants as a whole have evolved methods for keeping their energy stores away from herbivorous organisms during their lifetimes; many grasses are armed with silica spines and store their food reserves below ground in winter. Trees are only exploited by defoliating insects and some specialized browsing mammals. Thus Ovington and Heitkamp[541] point out that in managed forests the energy content of the litter is small compared with that of the timber. However, this is no index of the energy turnover in the litter and it is not, of course, any guide to the state of affairs in natural woodland where the whole of man's harvest is added to the intake of the decomposer organisms as each tree dies and releases its hoarded wealth of organic matter. The estimates of tree litter contributed to the soil vary considerably; Pearsall[564] quotes 1·5 to 1·6 kg per sq m per annum or about 6×10^6 calories for oak wood; Ovington and Heitkamp's figures for oak indicate about $1·5–2·5 \times 10^6$ as a standing crop (no annual figures are given but in such woods the annual fall disappears during the year).

Liberation of 5×10^6 calories per sq m per annum spread over the year represents the amount of heat required to boil about 150 cc of water per day—or enough to make a cup of tea.

Chapter 16

THE APPLICATION OF POPULATION DYNAMICS

In the last two chapters we have reviewed theories concerning, and experiments with, relatively simple population systems. In this chapter we turn to the study of populations in the field.

The Influence of Population Dynamics on the Study of Field Ecology

The theoretical and experimental work detailed in the last two chapters has had a very great influence on the interpretation of observations on natural populations in the field, especially in three important respects. First, the concept usually termed "Gause's theorem" has dominated a whole field of work, particularly connected with the extent to which closely-related species occur together and share common resources. On the whole this idea has generally been vindicated, at least as a pointer to rewarding fields of research.

Secondly, the distinction between density-dependent and density-independent mortality factors discussed at the end of Chapter 10 has greatly influenced the thoughts of those concerned with biological control and the regulation of numbers of animals.

Thirdly, observed oscillations of the numbers of natural populations have been a challenge to the ecologist and attracted much study and speculation. Early hopes that they would be easily explicable in terms of the equations of competition and predation, although often disappointed, have resulted in problems being tackled which would otherwise have appeared hopelessly complicated. From the few cases of clear-cut oscillations which have been analysed in very abundant species, such as the mammal species which show marked cycles, it is beginning to appear as if oscillations are often the result of intraspecific, rather than inter-specific factors; this may well be untrue of the less common species, however.

Therefore, despite the over-simplifications of the mathematical equations, despite the disappointments which have resulted from a too naïve extension of experimental results to field conditions and despite frequent mistakes, it cannot in general be disputed that the theories of population dynamics have stimulated much useful work in a field where guiding principles are sorely needed, have simplified the interpretation of natural phenomena and, for the first time, have introduced the use of measurement in a field where quantitative method was unknown thirty years ago. The extent to which this "leaven" of ideas has produced results in the fields of the interpretation of natural communities, and that of the control of populations of economic importance will be judged from the last two chapters of this book. In this chapter we shall consider the factors which limit the size of natural populations and the light thrown by population dynamics on an understanding of these.

Some Examples of Field-population Studies

In order to provide a basis for the discussion of population-limiting factors some of the few reliable studies of field populations from this point of view will be briefly described as examples. As far as possible the facts in each case will be separated from the authors' interpretations and it should then be possible to judge the kinds of influences at work in these cases, at least.

1. STORED-PRODUCTS INSECTS. Solomon[672] provides a useful analysis of population-controlling factors in insects which inhabit grain and other stored products. His article also includes many references to work in this field, arrives at some general principles and can be recommended as an introduction to population control in stored-products populations.

In this particular type of habitat a nearly unique feature is the "competitive" effect of metabolic heat which so raises the temperature of the habitat as to make it uninhabitable when the animals, in the case of Laemophloeus for instance, reach a density of 2·5 animals per gramme. At populations of 5·5 per gramme the temperature rises by 0·7°C per day and, owing to the poor heat-conducting properties of wheat, lethal temperatures are reached in bulk wheat in a few weeks. As a result the populations only reach a high density quite close to the surface of the wheat. Similarly,[819] when individuals of Rhizopertha were released under conditions in which the temperature, moisture and population density could be measured, it was found that this beetle at a depth of five feet in grain is reduced to a density of 0·3 individuals per gramme. The important point made by Solomon is that these densities are well below those at which other density-dependent mortality or fecundity-reducing factors would normally operate to control the population.

Although *Callosobruchus* fecundity is reduced at low densities due to the infrequency of meeting and of copulation between the sexes, this effect is *linearly* related to density and there appears to be no confirmation of experiments on *Tribolium* which indicate a more powerful population-depressing action by this factor.

Solomon provides some interesting estimates of the order of population density at which different factors start to have a significant effect on population increase rate and mortality rate. Arbitrary levels of increase in mortality rate or decrease in fecundity are taken and it is shown that, over a wide range of insects, a 20 per cent effect is produced at population densities of 0·25 to 32 insects per gramme. An 80 per cent effect (i.e. increase in mortality or decrease in fecundity) occurs at densities between three and several hundreds per gramme. More precise figures are available for particular species, but even orders of magnitude are useful where so little information is available.

2. BEETLES WHICH EAT ST. JOHN'S WORT. Clark's important study [110] of the ecology of two species of beetles which have been introduced to Australia to control St. John's wort raises a number of interesting issues, of which only two can be mentioned here. The beetles have not by themselves proved to be a very satisfactory means of controlling the weed (see Chapter 5), because they are very near the limits of their physical tolerance range. They suffer density-independent mortality from the effects of frost, high temperatures and soil desiccation, while idiosyncrasies of behaviour prevent them from entering woodland areas where these factors are less severe. The usual history of a local population of *Chrysomela gemellata* or *C. hyperici* is that the population gradually expands until it eats out the food supply of *Hypericum*. The population is then made far more vulnerable to the normally density-independent climatic factors owing to the absence of cover and the more severe microclimate which results. Also the beetles fly far less under Australian conditions than they do in California and thus find their food less easily. There are also more usual density-dependent predators and diseases. This combination of mortality factors results in the complete local elimination of the beetle population, usually through the action of climate or the defoliation of the St. John's wort. The St. John's wort then recovers and becomes a pest long before the beetles have reached a density at which they are able to

damage the wort. The violent oscillations in numbers of the beetle would appear to provide an example of oscillations resulting from interaction of a herbivore and its host plant.

3. THE TAWNY OWL AND ITS PREY. Southern[684] gives a preliminary account of the only field study so far published in which populations of both a predator and its prey have been measured. The species concerned are *Stryx aluco*, the tawny owl, *Apodemus sylvaticus*, the wood mouse, and *Clethrionomys glareolus*, the bank vole (Plates V, VI). The owl population was followed for twelve years in a 1,000-acre woodland estate and that of the rodents in an area of 250 acres in the midst of the same estate; nearly 20,000 rodents were handled and marked with metal leg rings during this time.

The owl has the convenient habit of swallowing its food whole and then rejecting the inedible parts of the food (fur, bones, etc.) in the form of pellets. These pellets were analysed for their content of food species and also passed under a magnet which removed the metal leg bands.

Owing to "trap addiction" (Chapter 8) which was discovered during the course of this work, the estimates of the rodent numbers are subject to revision, but Southern was able to obtain a preliminary estimate of their significance by ranking the years in order of availability of rodent food, the best year being scored 10 and the worst year 1. Fig. 29 shows how three important sources of owl mortality were related to the rodent scores; all three factors, number of pairs breeding, size of clutch and breeding success are correlated with rodent supply, the first two rather more closely than the last, as might be expected. Throughout the twelve-year period there was a consistent trend in the number of pairs present, namely an increase from 16 to 30 between 1947 and 1958. This trend, involving a halving of the mean territory size, may be due to changes of forestry practice in the wood or to the fact that the population was badly hit by the severe winter at the start of the study and probably consisted mainly of birds which were increasing in age (and hunting skill?) throughout the period of study.

During the first six-year period when there were, on average, less than 25 pairs present in the area breeding success was significantly greater than in the second six years when the average was above 25. This provides further evidence that juvenile mortality could be density-dependent. From the results in Fig. 29 it is clear that food supply has a density-dependent effect on the owl population despite the very

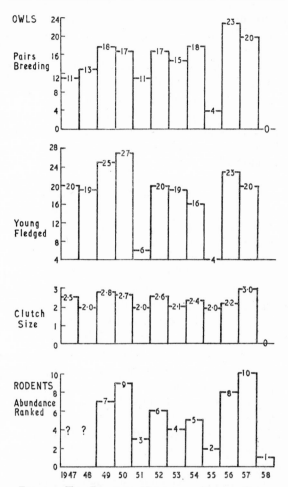

FIG. 29. THE BREEDING HISTORY OF TAWNY OWLS
(After Southern)
Figures from Witham Woods, Berks., 1947–58.
(For further explanation see text.)

powerful "damping" influence of territorial behaviour which, Southern showed, results in a very high mortality of surplus young adults each year.

The prey populations fluctuated rather violently.[683] From a preliminary examination of the ratios of the two prey species in the pellets it is clear that in 1949, which was a peak year for both species of rodent, the owl fed mainly on *Apodemus*; this was followed by a marked decline in numbers. In 1950 there was a peak for the *Clethrionomys* population and the owl turned its attention to this food. Simultaneously the vole population fell to a low level and did not recover for at least a year. In 1951 there were very few of either prey species and the owl breeding season was a failure, only about 25 per cent of the normal number of young being raised. The owl population was low and the rodent numbers recovered during 1951 and 1952.

It is natural to wonder what part the owl had in the reduction of the prey numbers; here we must await further analysis of the data. The general impression given from most small mammal studies is that predation is not of primary importance in the generation of cycles, as shown in Chapter 10; however, the behaviour of the predator in changing its attack from one rodent to the other until the "crash" phase is virtually complete, may well serve to accentuate the violence of the cycle and possibly to change its phase.

4. PREDATION BY SPARROW-HAWKS. Tinbergen[725] made an extensive study of the effects, on the populations of four species of passerine birds, of predation by the sparrow-hawk. Since the sparrow-hawk population in Holland is partly migratory it was not possible for him to obtain full data on the predator as Southern has done, but the effect on the prey species is estimated with some accuracy, although it is difficult from Tinbergen's data to be certain that the predator actually controls the prey species because mortality and density are not related throughout the year. The magnitude of the errors was estimated at all stages. The house sparrow suffers most from the attentions of the sparrow-hawk, which accounts for over half its mortality. In the chiff-chaff and the great tit this is rather less than half, while in the coal tit the effect of predation on the population is almost negligible. The importance of factors in the birds' behaviour, such as the use of cover and conspicuousness, is demonstrated for these four species and also other birds. The population-limiting factors of the coal tit were not finally decided but Tinbergen believed that parasitism may play a role in controlling this very rapid-breeding species.

Evidence is provided to show that, in 1942, when goshawks were short of their normal food and turned their attention to sparrow-hawks as prey, the resulting reduction in the population of the latter was reflected in an increase in that of the passerines. Tinbergen is insistent

Plate V

(*Above*) *Microtus agrestis* (short-tailed field vole).
(*Photo* H. N. Southern)

(*Below*) *Apodemus sylvaticus* (wood mouse).
(*Photo* H. N. Southern)

(T.696)

248

PLATE VI

(*Above*) House Mouse Feeding at a Pile of Bait.
(*Photo* H. N. Southern)

(*Below*) *Clethryonomys glareolus* (bank vole).
(*Photo* H. N. Southern)

that any natural community must suffer many such unpredictable changes as this, which may have a wide influence on the population under study. He therefore deprecates the uncritical application of such theories as Nicholson's to field populations and points to the many population-limiting mechanisms, including territorial behaviour, which are found in birds and which reduce or prevent oscillations in numbers when these might be predicted from theory.

5. CONTROL OF THE KNAPWEED GALLFLY. Varley[748] carried out an intensive study of the factors which control the population density of the knapweed gallfly (*Urophora jaceana*), whose larvae are responsible for galls in the flower heads of the knapweed (*Centaurea nemoralis*), as shown in Fig. 30. A census of 92 square-metre plots for two years was made and from this the population density of the flies was determined and a kind of balance sheet of mortality was drawn up showing the proportion of flies killed by the various mortality factors at each stage in the life history. A very large proportion of the mortality (some 96 per cent of the larvae in the 1935–6 generation) was due to factors which were probably not density-dependent—the eating of larvae in the knapweed heads by caterpillars and by mice and losses due to flooding of the area. However, since the fecundity was found to be between 50 and 70 eggs per female, it would only be necessary for a few insects to suffer a density-dependent mortality for control to be achieved. The only effective density-dependent factor was considered to be parasitism by a Chalcid *Eurytoma curta*.

Varley made use of Nicholson's[502] "area of discovery" concept and estimated this parameter at 0·25 sq m. From this he estimated that the parasites could keep the gallfly down to a level of 0·68 per sq m (see Chapter 12). This level was lower than that actually found for the gallfly. When, however, allowance was made for the reduction in the efficiency of the parasite by factors which operate on both host and on parasite because they kill the parasitized gallflies, the figures were found to fit very satisfactorily. (This is Volterra's "Law of the disturbance of averages," Chapter 15.)

As Varley himself states, the exactness of his figures should not be misinterpreted, for, in a fluctuating environment subject to many external influences, the results predicted by simple theory cannot be expected to be very precise and the precision in fact obtained may have been partly due to good fortune. However, this is most important as a pioneer study in which an attempt is made to measure the

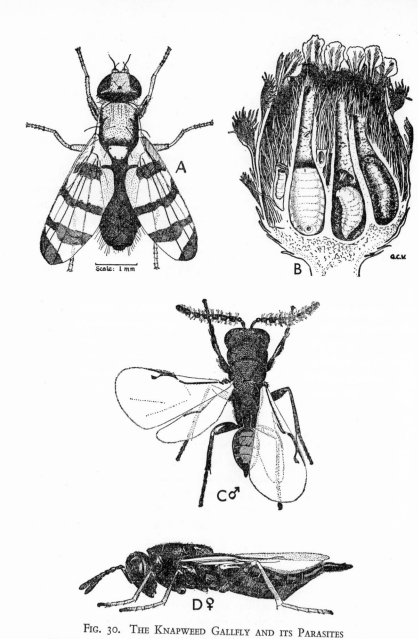

FIG. 30. THE KNAPWEED GALLFLY AND ITS PARASITES

(A) *Urophora jaceana* male; (B) Gall with larva of *U. jaceana* (*left*), puparium (*right*) and larva of *Torymus* (*centre*); (C) *Eurytoma curta* Walk; (D) *Habrocytus trypetae* Thoms.

magnitude of ecological forces of this type and it is most encouraging. It is also important because it indicated that a population can well be controlled by a factor which is only responsible for a small proportion of the mortality, provided that the factor in question operates in a density-dependent manner. Further, the reduction in efficiency of the parasite by the later-acting indiscriminate mortality factor shows how, by simply killing animals of an undesirable species without regard to its ecology, one may well increase and not reduce the size of the population, an argument, it will be remembered, put forward by Nicholson (see Chapter 10). Thus, the eating of knapweed heads containing gallflies by mice which killed 64 per cent of the available larvae tended to increase the gallfly population and not to reduce it.

6. CONTROL OF GERMAN FOREST PESTS. A great deal of work has been done on the Continent on forest insect pests and the fluctuation in their numbers.[638, 639, 750, 773] The enormous changes exhibited by four species in German spruce forests can be gauged from the fact that logarithmic graph paper covering five orders of magnitude (from 1 individual per 1,000 sq m to 10 per sq m) is still not able to show all the annual numbers in the case of one of the species. Apart from the original author's useful critique of theories about population fluctuations, which are considered below, Varley's review is valuable for the demonstration that the fluctuations of the different pest species are not significantly correlated and that these four species which at first sight frequently defy "Gause's hypothesis" do in fact have very different life histories, the onset of the different life stages being "staggered" over a period of four months or more. Varley also shows that the periods of high numbers are usually those during which parasitism is at a very high level, highly-specific parasites being involved. This is important because Nicholson[488] concluded from his theoretical study that increasing oscillations will result when a host is controlled by a single parasite. Schwerdtfeger's data do not permit a critical appraisal of the causes of mortality, but there seems little doubt that this situation, in which crops of a single forest tree carry a greatly simplified fauna, is especially likely to favour violent fluctuations in this way; this topic is discussed by Varley.[749]

7. BIOLOGICAL CONTROL OF A COCO-NUT MINING BEETLE. An example reported by Taylor[705] which indicates the unexpected repercussions which may follow an apparently irrelevant change in an ecological community and which illustrates the kind of factor which

can decide whether a population is to remain at an economically unimportant level or to achieve serious outbreaks is that of the control of the leaf mining beetle of coco-nut palms in the Fiji islands. This is but one of many examples of the successful applications of biological control methods in these islands.

The beetle, *Promecotheca reichei* (Fig. 31), is indigenous to Fiji, and so are a number of hymenopterous parasites, including *Oligosita utilis* and *Elasmus hispidarium*. Until 1920, *Promecotheca* was never important enough as an economic pest to cause alarm because small local outbreaks were promptly suppressed by the parasite species. Under these circumstances, the generations of *Promecotheca* overlap one another at the same time, which results in the parasites, which have rather short life histories, being always able to find hosts. However, in 1921 a very widespread predatory mite, *Pediculoides ventricosus*, was first reported in the islands; it had probably arrived some years previously but remained unnoticed. Soon after this, in the late 1920s, local but very severe attacks, resulting in complete defoliation of the palms, were made by *Promecotheca*, especially on the small islands of the Lau group.

The characteristic history of these attacks was found to be that *Promecotheca* was attacked by the mite *Pediculoides*, which thus appears at first sight to be beneficial to man. However, the mite was an extremely successful predator during the dry season but suffered heavy mortality by the flooding of the galleries in the wet season. Thus, having reduced the *Promecotheca* population to an extremely low level, the mite itself suffered a severe "crash," often, apparently, being completely eliminated. During the long period of virtual absence of *Promecotheca* the natural parasites died out through lack of hosts.

Under these circumstances the stage was now all set for a completely unhindered revival of the *Promecotheca* populations. A few individuals which survived as resting stages or were transported between the many small islands of the group by human agency, started to increase and, in the absence of parasites or predators, caused great economic damage.

The story of the successful control of this situation can be only briefly mentioned. Evidently, if the indigenous parasites had had longer resting stages, resulting in a more prolonged life history, it would have been possible for them to remain on a given island until the *Promecotheca* populations returned or built up again and thus to

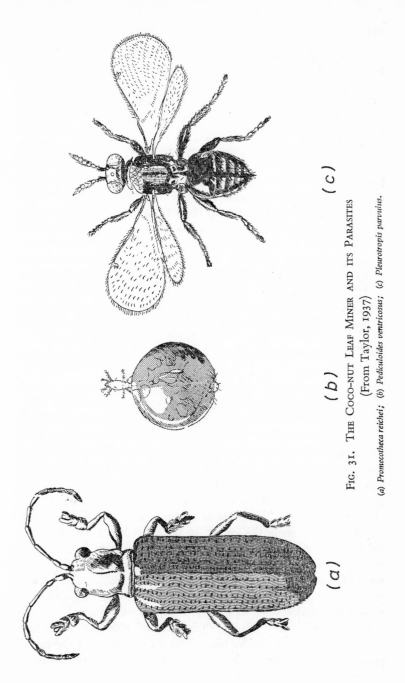

Fig. 31. The Coco-nut Leaf Miner and its Parasites
(From Taylor, 1937)

(a) *Promecotheca reichei*; (b) *Pediculoides ventricosus*; (c) *Pleurotropis parvulus*.

overtake the pest species. An insect which would be a specific parasite for *Promecotheca* and would fit this specification was sought and eventually found in Java in the form of another Hymenopteron, *Pleurotropis parvulus*, and, when introduced, this species was successful in preventing the fluctuations and restoring *Promecotheca* to a very low level of no economic importance.

The history of this encounter provides many lessons in ecology, not least of which are the unexpected repercussions which may follow from an accidental introduction and one way in which population control mechanisms may work and may break down.

8. CYCLES IN CANADIAN FUR-BEARING MAMMALS. In a useful review of population cycles in Canadian fur-bearing mammals, Butler[84]

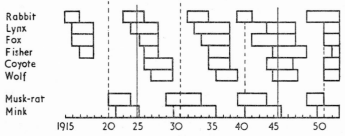

FIG. 32. THE RELATIONSHIP BETWEEN "GOOD" YEARS IN VARIOUS SPECIES OF CANADIAN MAMMALS

(From Butler, 1953)

relates the occurrences of population peaks in eight species during thirty-seven years (Fig. 32). The most outstanding point made by this comparison is that the snowshoe rabbit's rather regular peaks are always followed by those of the predatory mammals and that in all cases but one the "good" years for lynx, arctic fox, fisher, coyote and wolf begin about the middle of the snowshoe rabbit peak and continue some years longer. In the one case there is a delay of one year after the end of the snowshoe rabbit peak. There is a strong tendency for the predators to succeed the rabbits in the order given above. The muskrat and the mink cycles are independent of those just considered but are closely related to each other.

It has been shown[98, 200, 208, 209] that the peak years in different parts of Canada do not coincide, but follow a sequence with the central provinces leading, followed by the western and then usually the eastern provinces. Butler puts forward a theory to account for this involving the increased efficiency of reproduction at higher densities and the emigration of animals from regions of higher density. The evidence for the first factor is not very strong, but he is certainly justified in criticizing those who would base conclusions on the study of single small areas. One point which certainly seems to follow from the existence of this progressive delay in the population cycles and from the extreme regularity of the cycles (see Elton[200] for earlier data on these and other species) is that single climatic or other external factors are ruled out as direct causes of these cycles.

9. THE GREAT TIT IN HOLLAND. An excellent example of the operation of an internal population-limiting mechanism is provided by Kluijver's[370] study of the great tit. This was based on a population which roosted in winter almost entirely in artificial nest boxes and could therefore be counted quite easily. Kluijver found very distinct annual and local variations in the production of nestlings, due to changes in fecundity and in clutch size. Thus, figures from 3·9 to 14·1 young per brood were obtained and were correlated with population density, both fecundity and clutch size being lower in denser populations. Kluijver believes that disturbances due to fighting are responsible for the reduced fecundity. The strong tendency for higher breeding populations to be followed by lower ones and vice versa is attributed to the combined effects of the reduced tendency to emigrate and the higher reproductive rate in the lower population. Thus, annual fluctuations occur which are sometimes synchronous and sometimes not in different parts of the country. Kluijver invokes a theory similar to that of Chitty (see Chapter 10) to account for the synchronizing effect of major climatic disturbances.

10. SEWAGE-BED FLIES. A number of enlightening studies have been made of sewage beds and their fauna from an ecological standpoint.[311, 312, 601] Of these, Hawkes'[311] study of factors controlling population size in the fly *Anisopus fenestralis* is particularly relevant to the question of competition in natural populations. The populations of fly larvae, pupae and eggs were determined by sieving samples of the sewage bed material; it was found that they were of the order of 150 larvae and 100 pupae in a 27 sq in. sample, 6 in. deep. The actual numbers showed great seasonal fluctuations due to the successive generations of the flies. The magnitude of the peaks was determined by the amount of food available and intense intra-specific competition

occurred at the higher population levels. This resulted in a steady reduction of the fauna as the season advanced and the available food was reduced. At higher temperatures the frequency of generations and, therefore, of peaks was increased owing to accelerated development. It was shown that when the sewage beds were treated with insecticide the seasonal fall in the population did not occur because the food supply remained unconsumed and it was necessary to continue the application of insecticide at high rates to prevent the flies becoming a nuisance. At the same time, the efficiency of the filters was impaired owing to the accumulation of organic matter. There was evidence of inter-specific competition also and other grazing organisms, which are more susceptible than the fly to injury by chemicals in the sewage effluent due to industrial processes, were sometimes responsible for depletion of the food supply. On the basis of this study, which could provide a fascinating source of information on the population dynamics of the species concerned if studied from this point of view, Hawkes made practical recommendations for eliminating the fly nuisance without heavy expenditure on insecticides and without impairing the efficiency of the sewage beds.

11. INTER-SPECIFIC COMPETITION AMONG WOOD ANTS. One of the very few studies of inter-specific competition in the field is that of Brian[72] on a natural ant population. This work, which the author regards as a preliminary survey, combines observations of the normal distribution, population size and habits of the ants with an experimental study designed to change relevant environmental influences and observe their effects on the balance of competition. It provides a useful indication of the kinds of factors which determine the occurrence of competition in four species of ants, namely *Formica fusca*, *Myrmica scabrinodis*, *M. rubra* and *Leptothorax acervorum*. Only a few aspects of this work can be mentioned here. The experimental alteration of the habitat, by laying slates on the ground and in other ways, resulted in the replacement of one species by another by direct aggression or by infiltration during temporary absence. The main factors involved in this process are a clearly-defined "replacement order" due to superior fighting powers, differences in climatic tolerance and differences in building abilities which permitted the *Myrmica* species to improve otherwise poor sites. *Formica* can always compete successfully against the other species in acquiring the best sites, but is unable to occupy the poorer sites owing to inferior building ability. *Leptothorax*

is also a poor architect and is vanquished in battle by *Formica* but it has the unique ability to burrow into harder wood, where, being rather small, it constructs systems of galleries in which it is safe from its larger competitors. The *Myrmica* species both build mounds and can thus occupy damper and colder sites than *Formica*, but of these two *M. rubra* is inferior to *M. scabrinodis* in direct competition but extends into moister places.

This work clearly demonstrates how it is possible for four species to live in the same locality, their populations interspersed and their food the same and it is unique in combining a description of the *results* of competition with an analysis of the actual *processes* of competition at work. It has recently been supplemented by an analytical field study on two species of *Lasius*.[582a]

12. ROSE THRIPS IN SOUTH AUSTRALIA. A study by Davidson and Andrewartha[159, 160] of populations of rose thrips in a garden in Adelaide is of special interest because it appears at first sight to contradict Howard and Fiske's and Nicholson's and Smith's conception of the importance of density-dependent factors in population control and has sometimes been quoted in that context.

The thrips populations, which were collected from roses throughout six years, were at a low level of the order of tens per rose for the greater part of the year, but suddenly increased dramatically to numbers approaching a thousand per rose in early December. The peak period altogether spanned hardly two months. The rise in numbers was fitted by the authors to a logistic curve and the peak densities in the different years were mathematically correlated with weather factors in the previous autumn and spring. The duration of the peaks was shown to be determined by the time of onset of the dry weather which resulted in a sudden fall to low population levels once more.

During the dry period the impoverished thrips population was restricted to very few localities of less severe climate, one of these being the garden in which the samples were taken.

Davidson and Andrewartha were concerned to point out that Nicholson's theories did not apply to the thrips populations, for here was a population whose size is manifestly determined by climate which according to Nicholson, is a density-independent factor and therefore cannot control population size.

These arguments have since been challenged by a number of authors[501, 663, 678]. It is hardly surprising that the release of severe climatic restraints should be followed by the multiplication of the thrips and their extension into a much wider environment, nor that the size and duration of the subsequent population "peaks" should be related to weather conditions; the real question at issue is the nature of the factors which determine the year-to-year abundance of the population, especially in the unfavourable season. As has been repeatedly demonstrated, the control factors are not necessarily those which kill most animals; in the case of the knapweed gallfly and Varley's later experiments[748, 758] density-dependent factors whose incidence varied with population size normally killed only a small proportion of animals. By re-analysing Davidson and Andrewartha's data Smith[663] has demonstrated that factors of this nature were, in fact, present throughout the unfavourable season of the year because mortality at that time was inversely correlated with population size whereas there was no significant correlation between population growth and weather. It follows that these data far from supporting the authors' thesis, in fact provide evidence which contradicts it.

The Importance of Five Theoretical Questions in Field Ecology

The above accounts of work on the factors determining population size in nature provide a background for a consideration of the relevance of the principles derived from theory and experiment to conditions in the field. It is important to realize, however, that these accounts are greatly abbreviated and that very few ecological studies have yet been made on these lines; it is, therefore, most probable that tentative conclusions reached here will be modified in the near future and it is certainly essential that any serious student of ecology should read the original work and form his own conclusions in this vitally important field of study. In order to simplify our discussion it will be planned on the basis of the answers to the following set of questions—

1. What is the relative importance of density-dependent and density-independent factors?
2. Are competitive (and co-operative) relationships significant and what form do they take?
3. Are predator-prey relationships significant?
4. Are parasite-host relationships significant?
5. Are inter-specific or intra-specific factors the more important?

The following paragraphs are designed to answer these questions with regard, first to control of population size and then to causes of fluctuations in each case.

1. THE RELATIVE IMPORTANCE OF DENSITY-DEPENDENT AND DENSITY-INDEPENDENT FACTORS. The thesis has already been argued (Chapter 10) that theoretically only density-dependent factors can "control" a population in the sense of maintaining it at a level where it continues to exist but does not attain an undesirably high economic density. This argument was first widely applied to the practical field of biological control by Smith,[664] and he and his colleagues[665,666] have since provided many examples in the field of "biological control" to vindicate his arguments. By means of exclusion sleeves black-scale insects on citrus trees were protected from the attacks of the artificially-introduced *Metaphycus helvolus* and protected branches compared with unprotected. Thus the mortality due to *Metaphycus*, which is both a parasite and a predator and came originally from Japan, was shown to be decisive.

A great many examples of this sort, some of which are discussed in Chapter 18, are available from the literature of biological control and a useful comparison of different views on the subject from the practical point of view is given by Solomon.[670]

Alternative views are given, for example, by Bodenheimer,[58] Clark[112] and Andrewartha and Birch.[16] All the examples described in this chapter give evidence of the efficacy of density-dependent factors and almost all provide numerical information on the magnitude of the effects concerned. A feature, which may at first sight appear rather surprising, is that a density-dependent factor which causes but a small proportion of the total population mortality can be effective in control, while a density-independent factor, causing a much larger proportion of mortality, is ineffective. This is probable, for instance, in the case of the knapweed gallfly described by Varley.

The relevant feature here, of course, is that the excess reproductive capacity is automatically compensated by the density-dependent factor because its intensity of operation is adjusted to the host population size; thus, if the density-independent factors fell short of balancing the population increase by only a few per cent there would be no check on the gallfly. For instance, the numbers of animals in successive generations derived from 100 parents in which a 10 per cent increase is not compensated would, at the end of successive generations, become—

Generation	0	1	2	3	4	5	. . .	10	20	30	40. . . .
No. of Individuals	100	110	121	133	146	161	. . .	259	1,746	4,529	10,165. . . .

This, of course, is simply the exponential series once more (see Appendix to Chapter 9). Davidson and Andrewartha's work, which at first sight appeared to indicate control by a density-independent factor, is irrelevant for the reasons given. Serious analysis of mortality (e.g. Varley and Gradwell,[758] Southern,[684] Hughes[332]) usually reveals the presence of factors operating in opposition to density; the negative contention that density-dependent factors don't exist because not sought is unsatisfactory. Analysis of mortality is difficult in erratic populations (cf. Ricker's work discussed on p. 141) and theoretical interpretation seems to correlate closely with the kind of population from which one is (perhaps subconsciously) generalizing.[678]

The evidence that fluctuations in numbers are often caused by density-independent factors is, of course, overwhelming, but in this context it is useful to recall the distinction (Chapter 10) between "fluctuations"—regular *or* irregular variations—"oscillations"—showing self-restoring characteristics—and "cycles"—field phenomena thought, but not proved, to be oscillatory. That cycles can be the result of climatic effects of equal regularity has often been argued, but it is a theory whose vogue is steadily decreasing as more and more phenomena get out of step with the climatic changes with which they are supposed to be correlated. The theory that sunspot cycles acted in this way, at one time applied to many groups, has now been shown to be inadequate.[200, 466]

2. THE SIGNIFICANCE OF INTER-SPECIES COMPETITION AND CO-OPERATION. Of the examples given above, those of Brian's ant study and Clark's St. John's wort beetle investigations are the most relevant here. It is evident that inter-species competition can be a limiting factor in determining population size and that local elimination of species can occur as a result of such competition. Many other studies, including those discussed in Chapters 2 and 5, provide strong circumstantial evidence of the importance of competition in modifying the habits of birds and other animals because, as was shown in these discussions, the ecological niches of species are modified according to the presence or absence of closely-related competitors. Presumably such modifications occurred through the effect of competition on natural selection. However, the question of how exactly species in the field influence each other in competition remains one of the most obscure and little-studied in population dynamics and it is perhaps fair to say that some of the attention lavished on laboratory experiments might

be more profitably employed on field experiments. There is a tendency for the animal ecologist to think only of competition acting through a rise in mortality or a fall in birth rate. In plants, as Harper[302, 302a] has stressed, growth and reproductive rate are more flexible and some animals, particularly ant colonies must resemble plants in this respect.

It will be remembered that we showed (Chapter 14) that competition is the one type of population interaction which does not, according to theory, result in oscillations in the simple models used. Either one species eliminates the other or else, when the overlap in their ecological niches is insufficiently great for this to happen, both continue to survive indefinitely. This is conveniently summarized in "Gause's theorem." Elton's attempt to test the validity of this by a comparison of fauna lists from single communities with those from wider areas has been widely discussed.[201, 808a] The observation work of Hartley and a field study of thrips by Broadhead[75] provide much circumstantial evidence, however, which illuminates the situation after competition has occurred, rather than the process itself.

Although Allee's book[6] contains a number of examples of co-operation, as of passerine bird flocks hunting together, and though there are many examples of species co-operating on an individual basis in the form of commensalism and symbiosis, it does not seem that inter-species co-operation at the population level is sufficiently frequent to warrant further discussion.[339]

3. THE SIGNIFICANCE OF PREDATOR-PREY RELATIONSHIPS.   The relevant examples here are the studies by Southern on the tawny owl-rodent system in woodland, by Tinbergen on the sparrow-hawk-passerine population relationships and the work on Canadian mammal populations. An interesting study[266] of the efficiency of human control measures, as an example of predation, against the tsetse fly should be mentioned also, in which it is shown that numbers caught decrease as the prey population is rarefied in accordance with simple mathematical assumptions.

These examples show clearly that the size of predator and prey populations can be closely linked in the field and Southern's results show that the predator may have a reverse effect on the prey. The shortage of examples is probably no reflection on the rarity of this phenomenon, but rather on the great labour involved in collecting the relevant data for two or more species. Even in Southern's account, in which the owls' population size is partly limited by territorial behaviour there is probably a tendency for the production of oscillations due to over-eating of the food supply, although this is partly offset by the way in which the owl turned its attention from one rodent species to the other with changing abundance. In the case of the Canadian mammals it can hardly be disputed that the fluctuations of the numbers of the predators depend on those of their prey. However, in this case, there seems to be no evidence of a reciprocal effect as the oscillations in the snowshoe rabbit populations are apparently internally generated (see below), and to this extent the example does not resemble Gause's experiments.

An important point made by Varley[751] is that the direct effect of predators (or parasites) on the prey (or host) population is not strictly comparable with the reciprocal effect of the prey on the predator through reduction of its population and reduction of the predator's food supply. One difference is that this effect is felt only after a considerable delay, with the result that the ratios between the two populations cannot be the same when the predator population is increasing as when it is falling; that is, in the type of curve first introduced by Lotka (see Chapter 13, Fig. 22), in which numbers of predator are plotted against numbers of prey, the ratio of the two populations follows a closed loop, indicating a hysteresis effect. This kind of effect is absent, however, in the case of Protozoa which reproduce mainly by fission, and as pointed out by Nicholson (see Chapter 16, reference[497], oscillations about a balance level do not occur under such conditions. Varley points out that, so far, in field studies of insect populations the effects of prey on predator have not been measured, nor have the time delays involved. Only by measuring these quantities will it be possible to analyse the oscillations which owe their origin to this cause. Again, the transfer function method (Chapter 10) would appear to be appropriate to such an analysis. Varley also lists the criteria which must be fulfilled by a parasite if it is to control its host—

(i) it must reproduce faster at high host densities than at low, i.e. its reproduction rate must be related to host density.

(ii) it must find enough food under all conditions for the adult to mature its ovaries;

(iii) it must find many hosts at a sub-economic density;

(iv) it must search for hosts both *when* and *where* they are available;

(v) it must have a low mortality rate under the conditions in question.

In general, then, the control of population size by interaction between predator and prey undoubtedly occurs in the field; there is some very slender evidence for reciprocal interaction between predator and prey which, as in the simple laboratory experiments, could produce a tendency to oscillation. The many additional factors involved in any natural system should not, however, be forgotten.

4. THE SIGNIFICANCE OF PARASITE-HOST RELATIONSHIPS. Here the relevant examples are the study of the knapweed gallfly by Varley, Schwerdtfeger's and Voûte's work on forest insect pests, Clarke's on the St. John's wort beetles, and Taylor's on the coco-nut palm leaf miner. These and many examples of biological control of pest insects[503] leave no doubt that parasites can control animals in both the ecological sense of being the density-dependent factor which determines the long-term level of the population and also in the economic sense of preventing significant damage to crops. The fact that all these examples are derived from the class of insects is presumably due to the greater economic importance of this vast group and because widespread, lethal and intricately-adapted examples of parasitism abound among insects, while in the vertebrates at least parasites appear to have been more successfully resisted.

The case of *Promecotheca reichei* throws much light on the production of fluctuations in numbers and Varley's views on the greater tendency to fluctuations in systems involving control by highly specific parasites will be remembered. There can certainly be no doubt that when few species are involved and the system most closely resembles an experimental one, the results are also closest to those predicted by theory and imitated in experiments. The additional complications caused by greater numbers or more catholic habits of parasites tend to reduce the likelihood of violent oscillations; a conclusion which appears to have been so far appreciated by practical men that there is today a distinct tendency to avoid the culture of vast areas of single species of plants and to re-create habitats more akin to those of the undisturbed vegetation of the earth.

5. THE RELATIVE SIGNIFICANCE OF INTER- AND INTRA-SPECIFIC FACTORS. Hitherto, in this chapter, all the examples have been based on systems in which population limitation has been attributed to the operation of inter-specific factors. It will be remembered, however, that in Chapter 12 the existence of powerful intra-specific limiting factors was revealed, not only in experiments such as those involving

Tribolium and the blowflies of Nicholson's work, but also in field populations of small mammals where, as in the case of Chitty's study, the species' own physiological processes appear to determine the limits of population size. In the experimental examples too, other factors than shortage of food appear to be responsible. In the voles and also probably in the snowshoe rabbits of Canada these intra-specific factors synchronize with the cycles which are such a conspicuous feature of the biology of these animals.

In many birds and also in mammalian predators behavioural limitations to population size are common, usually in the form of territorial behaviour. It is usually considered by ornithologists[390a] but disputed by mammalogists, and has been demonstrated in some cases, that the population density which results is the maximum which the food resources of the habitat can support in normal years at some critical stage in the life history; either the breeding season or an unfavourable winter period.[393] In this sense, the territorial behaviour is only a behavioural adaptation ensuring that a, presumably less fit, proportion of the population dies rather than that food shortage has a more widespread effect on the whole population. Whether these speculations are true or not, it would appear that territorial behaviour is only a mediator, as it were, and not the controlling factor, of the density-dependent food shortage.

If intra-specific factors are sometimes prominent in determining the control of common and important species such as these small mammals and possibly certain insect pests, it is nevertheless true, as has been shown above, that the interaction of predators and parasites with their prey and hosts respectively can also both bring about oscillations and determine population levels. The one type of inter-specific interaction which does not appear to be important in bringing about oscillations is competition, although it is obvious that it is often extremely important in controlling population size.

It cannot be too strongly emphasized that the conclusions reached in this chapter are based on extremely few studies, that the accounts given are very much abbreviated and simplified. It follows not only that the reader should refer to the original sources and draw his own conclusions from them, but also that this branch of population dynamics, even more than others, is especially likely to change as more studies are made and more information obtained.

Furthermore, the situations which exist in nature are almost always extremely complex, and it is quite probable, therefore, that in many of the examples given different results might be obtained in different areas or on different occasions owing to the chance effect of unpredictable factors. The *Promecotheca* story and that of the effect of goshawks in reducing the predation pressure of sparrow-hawks on house sparrows should not be forgotten. Nor should the effects of introducing myxomatosis into the rabbit population of Britain,[18, 219] the repercussions of which are still becoming manifest in changes in the vegetation,[594, 711] in the diet of predators[406] and in the sizes of populations of potential competitors such as the hare and the rat.[621]

Conclusions: The Control of Population Size in Nature

The very meaning of the word control is far from agreed among ecologists (see Solomon[670]) but we shall assume it to mean the maintenance of a population level which does not differ from a long-term average by more than one or two orders of magnitude. This chapter should have illustrated clearly that the mechanisms of population control vary enormously with different species and under different circumstances. Ultimately, in reasonably stable and widespread species there can be little doubt that density-dependent checks operate quite regularly, even if only perhaps during a short season of the year as in Hartley's titmice (Chapter 14). There still remains the possibility that in unstable situations in which dispersal and rapid rate of increase are all important, refuges are few and whole populations frequently succumb to catastrophe, such checks will not operate at least for long periods, especially when the populations in question are constantly recruited from others in more stable circumstances. Of the density-dependent factors thought to control more stable populations some may be inter-specific and take the form of parasitism and predation. Among birds Lack's[390a] thesis seems to apply generally: that all aspects of reproduction including territorial behaviour and clutch size are so governed as to leave a maximum number of progeny under average prevailing conditions and that they can be modified by variations in these conditions. Under these circumstances most density-dependent factors operate by changing the death rate. On the other hand there is abundant evidence that this is not an invariable rule applying to all groups of animals. As Southern[684] has argued, it is sometimes rather an academic point whether the death of an egg in the female is to be counted as an increase in mortality or a reduction in fertility and perhaps the general term "repression" should be used when we are uncertain of the mechanism involved.

The generation of oscillations can undoubtedly arise through interaction between species as predicted by simple theory, but occasions when this happens seem to be confined to rather simple situations involving few species and there is no doubt that cycles can also be associated with intra-specific population-control mechanisms, even though the cycle may "spread" as it were from the prey to its predators. In fact the potentialities of biological rates of increase, as Hutchinson has stressed, would lead us to expect far more violent population explosions than actually occur and the remarkable stability of most natural communities provides the clearest evidence for the strength of these bonds between populations which are the framework of the community, and which human interference can so easily rupture with such devasting consequences.

We have now completed a review of the subject of population dynamics. It has been demonstrated that the size of populations is determined by a set of factors which can, despite our lack of experience in this field, be analysed and measured. It can hardly be disputed that, for an understanding of the success and local abundance of animals in nature, the methods which have been described constitute a tool which is superior to anything hitherto devised. The kind of work which we have discussed in the last chapter reveals clearly the powerful forces which are at work when a community of populations are brought into spatial and temporal contact with one another.

Chapter 17

THE ECOSYSTEM

In a most informative review Balogh[32] states that the concept of the ecosystem originated when Thienemann[707] and Friederichs[236] appreciated that the relationships between the *biozönose* of Möbius[463] and the biotope of Dahl[152] are reciprocal. In other words, not only is a characteristic community of organisms associated with and dependent on a characteristic habitat, but also the habitat is modified and to a greater or lesser extent created by the activities of the organisms. The two components evolve together in such a way as to develop into a single system. To this system Tansley gave the name *ecosystem*.[700a]

Succession and the Relationships between Communities

The subject of successional change in communities has been much studied especially by the Clements and Shelford school in the United States. This work was concerned at a descriptive level with the extent to which faunistic changes could be related to plant succession, and tended to produce somewhat nebulous results. The topic has been mentioned at a descriptive level in Chapter 4 and it seems clear that a greater insight into the structure of communities will be necessary before the mechanisms of successional change will be understood more profoundly. Lindeman[409] made the interesting suggestion that the climax community will prove to be that which exhibts the most rapid energy turnover, with the implication that where there are many different highly specialized forms at all trophic levels, productivity is increased because each species in competition with others becomes a specialist at rapidly exploiting a narrow range of resources. A similar point has been made by Hairston[296] who suggests that the local climax in any particular area is likely to be the most productive community available.

This raises the difficult question as to whether communities as such can be regarded as in competition with one another and subject to any kind of selection process. Odum[530] for instance, in discussing the efficiency and productivity of communities, appears to take it for granted that they can. He refers to the idea that "primary production of communities is important for their competitive survival" as Lotka's principle. He goes on to enunciate the point that productivity and not efficiency is the condition of success. Presumably this is because high productivity is associated with a rapid turnover of plant nutrients whereas low productivity implies that these will be locked up in inactive organisms which are then open to exploitation by the members of rival and infiltrating communities. These are attractive ideas but we certainly require more information before we can judge their applicability; in particular we require examples of the replacement of unproductive by more productive communities, but all our experience of human influence is derived from changes in the reverse direction.

It certainly seems to be justifiable to make some generalizations about complexity and stability of communities. Both in the natural series from highly complex tropical forest to simple tundra, and, in the man-made series, from the natural climax to the artificial monoculture of crops we see a rapid fall in the number of species, in the variety of niches available and an increase of the frequency and scale of instability in population size. These phenomena must surely be related to the damping effects of a variety of mortality factors, on the one hand, and, on the other, to an approximation to the conditions of the classical population experiments.

Free Organic Matter

The ecosystem at first appears a somewhat nebulous entity without much relevance to practical ecology. However evidence has steadily accumulated in recent years which not only vindicates the theoretical use of the concept but leads one to the conclusion that its application to the study of natural systems is a practical necessity. In the following paragraphs a number of examples are quoted which illustrate this point.

The activities of living organisms result in the liberation of very large quantities of organic matter into their surrounding environment. Fogg[226] for instance states that in aquatic environments from 6 to 4,000 times as much carbon is present in dissolved organic matter as in particulate matter and more than 100 times as much nitrogen is contained in this matter as occurs in an inorganic form. Radio carbon experiments show that up to 10 per cent of photosynthesized carbon is liberated by Algae and it seems probable that soluble compounds liberated by them are an important source of free organic matter. The rates of turnover of some compounds appear to be very slow but of others quite fast.

The biological significance of dissolved organic matter in water is a matter of controversy and its role in soil has hardly been investigated at all. It appears that at least some micro-organisms can obtain energy from this source but it should be recognized also that a certain amount of direct chemical oxidation has also been demonstrated[81] although admittedly under the rather peculiar circumstances of a very hot Australian desert. Furthermore in the conditions of tropical seas free organic matter is likely to be directly oxidized and to that extent the role of some decomposer organisms will be usurped by a non-biological process, without time lag. It seems certain, as Thienemann[710] pointed out, that nutrient levels tend to be higher in proportion to the standing crop of organisms in tropical lakes, although this is partly associated too with a much deeper photic zone so that the organisms are inevitably more deeply distributed in depth.

Over Feeding

It has now been demonstrated that many animals, in the presence of abundant food, ingest many times the quantity of food which they actually assimilate. This has been demonstrated for Copepods,[145] Cladocera[658] and Amphipods, and Isopods[241] in water, for *Orchestia gamarellus* in decaying wrack[28] and for many decomposer animals in soil such as Crustacea and Myriapods.[185, 252]

Their faeces often differ only slightly in chemical composition from the food they eat. It is of some interest, therefore, to find out what happens to all this organic matter. Presumably in water the soluble fraction is rapidly dissolved away and contributes to the dissolved organic matter; but there exists in the sea an enormous quantity of particulate organic matter and a vast fauna which depends on it. Fox,[229] for instance, points out that the mussels on three-quarters of an acre of rock shore filter about 22 million tons of water per annum from which they extract some 121 tons of material. The organic content of this material is uncertain but from feeding experiments the growth efficiency (including gametes) is about 15 per cent and the nutritive status must be high. The mussels at least are able to build up some 30 tons of protoplasm and so presumably assimilate about two tons of pure organic matter from a million tons of water. Fox estimates that the world's oceans contain about $1 \cdot 5 \times 10^{12}$ tons of organic detritus, with an annual turnover of about one-tenth of this value. Photosynthesis (see p. 239) produces about $2 \cdot 5 \times 10^{10}$ tons of organic matter per annum. Of course not all the organic matter mentioned above originates from animal bodies or faeces but most phytoplankton is either eaten or falls to the ocean bed and the proportion of shore plants is relatively quite small so that a considerable amount must in fact be of animal origin.

In the case of soil-decomposer organisms which produce large quantities of faeces in proportion to their assimilation rate it is clear that these faeces are of great biological significance. "Moder" soils are known which consist entirely of the faeces of Myriapods such as *Glomeris*[384] and even in temperate grasslands it has been estimated that *G. marginata* consumes as much decaying plant material as is produced annually by the plants[508] (much material must be consumed more than once). These faeces constitute a very rich medium for the growth of Bacteria and Fungi[745] and also for small Arthropods[779] apart from the external metabolite effect discussed below.

External Metabolites

In addition to the effects just mentioned which result from the liberation of food materials there is much evidence that both plants and animals have a more subtle effect on the community through chemical substances which either stimulate or suppress the activities of other species. An able review of the state of knowledge in this field at the time by Lucas[421] discusses many aspects of the problem and more evidence has been obtained since then. The presence of free vitamins which are required by many micro-organisms has been demonstrated in sea and lake waters although their importance is a matter of controversy. On the other hand there seems to be no doubt that microorganisms indulge in a kind of chemical warfare both in aquatic environments[226] and in the soil, where it is probably one of the main causes of "fungistasis" or the suppression of both growth and germination in normal soils of many perfectly viable moulds. The fact that antibiotic substances are not always demonstrable in soil is not considered very relevant here because, firstly they are very unstable and secondly, owing to the minute scale on which the soil is constructed and its extreme heterogeneity, effects may well operate in soil which cannot be demonstrated on a gross scale with homogenates.[83] The provision of a new surface such as a glass slide and other simple changes which involve no addition of nutrients are sufficient to cause an abundant germination of spores.[556] There is an annual cycle of inhibition usually building up to a peak in summer and apparently associated especially with the development of a slow-growing Basidiomycete flora. Ascomycetes, on the other hand, exploit a more ephemeral habitat which, in the absence of stasis, results from disturbance of the soil.[83] The importance of animals in such situations has only recently been appreciated. Van der Drift and Witkamp[745, 823] have shown in simple pot experiments that the introduction of larger soil invertebrates results in an enormous increase of spore formation by fungi, presumably due to the breakdown of stasis in the faeces or to the mechanical mixing of soil which is normally a very heterogeneous medium.[82] In the case of the terrestrial Trichopteran larva *Enoicyla pusilla* about 9 per cent of the leaf fall was consumed by this species which, by chewing, increased the surface area some fifteen times. The larva only assimilated about 7 per cent of the ingested food and extracted from the leaves about 50 per cent of the non-cellulose carbohydrate and very little other food. However, the faeces had fungal and bacterial counts respectively about 50 times and 10,000 times as high as in the food. The metabolic activity of the faeces resembled that of artificially ground up oak leaves and reached a value about 15 times as great as that of whole oak leaves. In the case of *Glomeris* reduction in cellulose content to two-thirds by the microflora was demonstrated in six weeks at 25°C. In addition Witkamp has demonstrated that single small Arthropods can very rapidly inseminate sterile soil with fungal spores either carried on the body or passed out unharmed in the faeces. It has been argued[439] that the magnitude of these "catalytic" effects on soil metabolism may greatly exceed that due to direct feeding by the animals, for not only is the microbial metabolism normally much greater than that of animals but also there is much indirect evidence of a reduction in total soil metabolism in the absence of such activities by the animals.

It seems clear, therefore, that it is not sufficient, when studying the action of organisms on the community as a whole, to consider each species population in isolation and then to add together their separate effects. Nor is it wise to neglect the effects of the organisms on their environment. For the incidental properties of by-products and metabolic wastes of one species may dominate the activities of many others and thereby control the flow of energy through alternative pathways in a manner which can only be compared to the action of chemical catalysts or mechanically operated valves. At first sight this may appear to invalidate the energy flow approach which has been so laboriously expounded above. It does indeed reduce the value of extrapolation from *simple* laboratory experiments to the field, but metabolic rate measurements remain the simplest and most powerful experimental tool we have and when suitably adapted in experiments designed to take account of the reciprocal interactions between species and the environment will surely enable us not only to detect but also to measure these powerful forces.

Chapter 18

CONCLUSIONS

In the preceding pages an attempt has been made to reveal the outlook with which the ecologist approaches the study of living systems. Even if this attempt has been successful in describing the outlook of only one ecologist—and it cannot of course be accurately representative of many—the reader should have been able to form his own conclusions about the claim made in the introductory chapter that ecology is developing a consistent system of ideas and principles which not only justify its recognition as a distinct science, but which are also heuristically successful in producing results. It would appear that the main features which mark off an ecological treatment of living phenomena are first, the recognition of the population as the centre of interest, second, the appreciation of the complex system of inter-relations between populations which makes the living community a population system worthy of special study and third, the realization that the ultimate aim of ecology is the understanding of the principles governing these relationships in nature even when, as so frequently happens, they must be studied in the laboratory with the help of simplified systems for the purpose of analysing communities and of providing analogies. To the author at least, the "watertight compartments" between sciences represent the boundaries not between fields of subject-matter, but between attitudes of mind, and the attitude of mind of the ecologist is at least as distinct as that of any other long-recognized biological discipline.

The Ecological Approach to the Control of Living Things

Because we are concerned with phenomena which can never be exactly repeated and with systems of relationships which never terminate abruptly, but "only fade away," we have learned by bitter experience that the snap decision, the sweeping generalization and the precise prediction are not characteristic of ecology. Hitherto, the main emphasis of applied ecology has been on biological control and, because the introduction of a new species into a country is obviously hazardous, the economic entomologist has been forced to take the ecology of the animals he deals with into consideration. However, in recent years the enormous growth in man's powers of changing his environment and of transporting materials and animals to new countries, combined with the inadequacy of empirical methods for dealing with the resultant situations, have created problems which can be solved only through an ecological approach.

An outstanding example of the application of ecological technique to a problem of this sort is provided by the reindeer–caribou–Eskimo system in Alaska. [155, 156, 400] In this case the impact of "civilization" on a native culture has had damaging effects not only on the Eskimoes, by introducing disease and destroying traditional social structure and hunting skills, but also on the caribou on which they traditionally fed and on the reindeer which were introduced as an additional food supply. The diversion of the Eskimoes from their previous occupations of hunting, and of herding the reindeer, resulted in the latter becoming extremely numerous, over-eating their food supply and staging a classical "crash" from over half a million to about 26,000 animals. Burning of the climax plant association of lichens in an effort to produce summer pasture for the reindeer accentuated this effect because it robbed both species of their winter pasture, while the caribou were drastically reduced in competition with reindeer and with moose, which are better adapted to feed on the woody plants which follow burning. Before this analysis of the situation, the only measures taken to deal with the situation were based on killing the wolves, whose predatory activities had been quite insufficient to depress the phenomenal upsurge which was followed by the inevitable "crash" as starvation and disease decimated the caribou herds.

An example [667] of the use of ecological methods which would have been incredible a few years ago is the deliberate maintenance of a low population of pests in order to retain a population of available predators. This case at least shows that biological control systems can be most reliable in their action.

There must be many more cases where urgent ecological problems are misunderstood and ecologically unsound action is taken. The current strife between the Chilean guano industry and Peruvian fisheries, both of which depend on the same fish, illustrates how human and political problems must complicate the situation, but the magnificent co-operation between Russia, Moslem, African and European countries which has been achieved by the Anti-locust Organization shows that the most unpromising political obstacles can be overcome where the need is great and the scientific advice firm.

Because they are a resource which is often shared among nations, fisheries have provided many instances of international co-operation on these lines, but here the ecological problems are more usually those concerned with the relationship between productivity and yield. This, as shown in Chapter 11, is a field in which much remains to be done from the theoretical point of view; some work has been done, however, on problems of overfishing and its prevention.[9]

Fields in which the Ecological Approach is Lacking

In two fields today, however, an ecological approach is only beginning to make headway in competition with other supposedly "scientific" practices. These are the practice of "monoculture," which has steadily grown up with the increased mechanization of crop production, and the uncritical spreading of lethal chemicals over the land. Some of the ecological results of the first practice in encouraging pest organisms are discussed in Chapter 16. The ecological basis for deprecating the uncritical use of poison chemicals is two-fold: first, they act in a density-independent manner and thus do nothing to control pest populations in the sense of causing greater mortality in denser populations; the result in practice is that the spray programme, once introduced, tends to become more and more elaborate and costly. The second reason is that they are usually not specific in their action and thus kill a great range of other animals in addition to the pest species against which their use was aimed. Thus predators and parasites of the pest are killed and any density-dependent action which they exerted is prevented. This makes the continuation of the spraying programme all the more necessary as a short-term measure, a result which benefits the pocket of the chemical manufacturer more than that of the farmer.

One result of the extensive use of chemical sprays which resembles the effects of monoculture, has been to simplify greatly the animal communities associated with crops.[450a] The number of insect pests associated with the apple in Britain has been reduced from over 100 to about five in the last half-century, but this benefits us little because these five are susceptible to only the most persistent applications of very potent chemicals and the economic cost of spray programmes is far higher. The red-spider-mite's assumption of the role of a major pest is entirely due to the successive elimination of its natural enemies first by tar oil and then by D.D.T. and B.H.C. sprays.

A further disadvantage of the use of chemical sprays as agents in pest control is the enormous selection pressure which is automatically set up in favour of individual animals which can withstand the poison. As is well known, resistant strains frequently arise and many cases of resistant insects are known already.[20, 35, 77] The situation deteriorates into a race between the chemist and the pest species, with the chemist always and inevitably in the second place.

The support of these assertions is hardly necessary here as the literature from many countries has been well reviewed.[667, 674] It is, however, worth quoting a sentence from Pickett[574] on the situation caused by the excessive use of D.D.T.—

"While it is true that we can now control almost any specific pest with which we have to deal, nevertheless the problem of controlling pests is more acute than ever and the expense of the control programme has increased many fold with the end not yet in sight."

One type of chemical spray holds out prospects of acting in a highly-specific manner against pests, namely the systemic insecticide which is taken by juice-sucking insects in the sap of the plant. Unfortunately, the most successful sprays of this type are the extremely lethal phosphorus group which have provided the most outstanding examples of another undesirable aspect of uncontrolled use of chemicals, namely the effect on the wild vertebrate fauna.

The Dissemination of Poisons

Many reports have appeared in recent years on the effects of these and other chemicals, and there is now no doubt that the death roll of vertebrates is very great indeed.[131, 249] This is hardly surprising in view of the fantastic toxicity of some of the substances used. D.D.T. kills fish in rivers and streams when adjacent land has been treated at $\frac{1}{4}$ lb per acre (1 lb per acre = 1·1 kg per ha) and birds when applied at 2 lb per acre. Substances such as Aldrin and Dieldrin kill birds when applied at rates down to 1 oz per acre and rodents at 1 lb per acre. The organo-phosphorus compounds are more than twice as poisonous again. The immediately toxic effects are not the only ones to be considered, for sub-lethal applications of D.D.T. applied over a period have been shown to be associated with a chronic fall in fecundity and of fledging weight in birds. The application rates just mentioned are of the same order as normal levels used in agricultural practice, but, usually, patchy application will result in local concentrations at far higher densities. The effects of these chemicals on native invertebrate fauna have hardly been studied; in 1955 Satchell[630] could report one case of harm caused by insecticides upsetting the balance of the soil fauna, but since then far more toxic chemicals have been introduced, despite our ignorance of the consequences of using them. Ripper[614] has ably reviewed the effects of these substances on the fauna of crops and shown that a more enlightened attitude to their dissemination over the countryside is beginning to appear.

The Positive Role of the Ecologist

In the face of demands for increased food production and the financial pressure of an industry whose annual turnover is approaching half a billion dollars in America alone, the ecologist's approach to the control of living resources cannot be a purely negative and defensive one. In a number of fields there are signs that the advantages of attempting to work with the biological forces of the community are being appreciated. A more sophisticated approach to pest control[690b, 777, 614, 807] involving a combination of biological and chemical methods, the adjustment of methods to the ecology of the animals and the use of mathematical models for predicting the outcome of different actions by the applied biologist[793] are examples. The ecological approach to maximizing production of species on which man preys (Chapter 10) is another: in the large areas over which we have as yet little control the population approach to fisheries management provides examples which could profitably be imitated in other fields of wildlife management. In the exploitation of agricultural crops a superficially straightforward, if unending struggle against rival predators and parasites obviously has much to learn from an ecological approach to pest control, soil conservation and, as shown in Chapter 15, the more efficient exploitation of natural resources. Finally, although the more unorthodox attempts to reduce the metabolic wastage associated with agricultural practice such as growing of Algae and Yeasts as foods appear at first sight to render an ecological approach superfluous, it should be remembered that the rationale of this approach can profitably be assessed from an ecological viewpoint, as has been most entertainingly done by Pirie.[577] Even a conclusion that a reduction in human natality would be a small price to pay for the loss of the pleasures of the table is mainly an ecological one.

Conservation

Perhaps the most important field in which applied ecology has made headway recently is that of conservation. Once again this is not to be regarded as a negative affair but as a positive, if rather long-term attempt, to set up ecological systems which are viable, stable and productive. This approach has been discussed as regards its general implications and as an insurance policy against ecological "explosions" by Elton,[204] it has also been applied to a particular instance, the management of a Scottish island by Pearsall.[565] Perhaps the most satisfactory feature of a positive approach to conservation is that one is working towards a state in which stability of numbers, productivity and the aesthetic satisfaction which comes from taxonomic variety are all combined; the very opposite in fact of monoculture with its monotony, tendency to catastrophic pest outbreaks and to loss of fertility. Of course we are not always able to identify our needs with the promotion of natural climax vegetation, but we certainly have much to learn from the conditions which prevail there and even in the case of food production under farming conditions it is clear that the further we depart from the integrated community the more likely we or our progeny are to suffer from our ignorance and carelessness.

It may be of interest to attempt a brief summary of the fields in which ecology appears most likely to contribute to human knowledge and to practical affairs. In the latter field it appears to provide an attitude and a set of principles for understanding and learning to control living systems which can already be used to guide us through the forest of unconnected facts which smother the student of living communities. This attitude involves an unpretentious effort to comprehend the effects of living populations on one another and is as incompatible with arrogance as it is dependent on faith in natural order. In view of its success so far and the failure of more superficial attempts to "control nature" we can hardly afford to neglect it.

As a contribution to human knowledge and understanding, ecology is in the fortunate position of being concerned with the most complicated systems of organization, apart from human societies, with which we have to deal. For this very reason it provides a constant challenge to the imagination as well as to experimental ingenuity. It is more difficult to analyse and to isolate the relevant factors in a living community than in some simpler system, but the gain in significant understanding of the material world and in comprehending the beauty of its organization is perhaps greater in proportion.

General Conclusions

The objects of this book were stated to be first to provide an introduction to the objectives of animal ecology and the way in which the ecologist attempts to gain information about the relations between animals and their environments, and secondly to provide a justification for regarding ecology as a subject in its own right, possessing distinctive methods, its own outlook and its peculiar subject-matter.

Ecology, as it has been described here, owes to natural history many important attitudes and principles, of which the ideas of the food chain, of competition and the living community are perhaps the most important. An attempt has been made to show that a quantitative science is being built upon these principles with the help of five powerful methods of measurement. These methods are—

First, the use of statistical methods in producing a population census of known accuracy and relating population density to the distribution of measurable environmental factors. In this way it has been possible to extend to the ecological field the principles of measurement and analysis, despite the fact that the factors concerned cannot be physically isolated—as is usual in the more venerable sciences.

Second, the quantitative study of the effect of the density of a population upon its own growth rate and that of other populations with which it comes into contact by competition or by sharing a food-chain link. The chapters on population dynamics have shown how, by a combination of the simple mathematical model, the analysis of laboratory experiments on populations and the measurement of such effects under field conditions, the factors determining the size of at least some field populations have been measured. Much still remains to be done to bridge the gap between theory and field and to apply, for instance, the quite specific measurements of competition, predation and parasitism proposed by the mathematical theorists.

Third, the use of demographic methods, developed for the study of the growth rate and population age structure of man, to animal populations. Because the potentialities for growth of different species can be compared with one another and more of the same species can be compared in different environmental situations, we now have a potential method of measuring the effects of one species on a most important population characteristic of another, and of expressing quantitatively the previously vague concepts of optimal conditions and of tolerance range.

Fourth, the use of quantitative methods for studying the food chain and the flow of energy and matter between populations in the same community. From the measurement and comparison of the activity of different member populations in a community, a hitherto descriptive device can be made quantitative, and at the same time greatly simplified; the importance of different links in the food chain can be compared and assessed on a common system of values. Also, different communities can be compared with one another and biological meaning can be given to indefinite conceptions such as rich *versus* poor localities, key species in the exploitation of a niche, and so forth.

Fifth, the combination of a practical and ecologically-valid method of habitat classification, with modern methods for the mechanical handling of large masses of information about the occurrence of ecological events, provides a basis for the survey, description and delimitation of communities and for overcoming the intractable difficulties of separating the accidental record from that which is ecologically valid.

These five tools, the statistically-valid census, the measurement of inter-population forces, the measurement of population growth rates, the measurement of energy flow in communities and the methods of ecological survey, have a number of factors in common. They all measure properties not of individual animals, but of populations, they provide the parameters of "synecology" as opposed to "autecology," and they are certainly not limited to the study of individuals.

Secondly, they are all quantitative methods of analysis and thus satisfy the requirement, which was indicated at the end of Chapter 5, for a means of refining and making more precise the methods of autecology. Thirdly, they are all potentially capable of greatly simplifying what at first sight appears to be an overwhelmingly complicated subject-matter.

While each of these methods by itself would appear to hold out great promise for the systematization of our knowledge of ecology and thus for predicting the outcome of new situations, it is clear that the studies which incorporate any one type of method have tended in the past to be relatively isolated. However, within the last few years a number of important studies have been completed which have helped to bridge the gaps between these fields. As examples it is only necessary to mention the work which unites the data of population dynamics and energetics by Slobodkin, Ricker, Watt and Frank for example, on demography, population dynamics and genetics by Park, Leslie, Chitty and Birch, on the extension of population dynamics into the previously isolated preserves of "biocenology" by Balogh, Hairston and Mac-Arthur and the wide scope of Margalef's introduction of information theory into many different branches of ecology. The traditional barriers are falling and the whole subject is coming to share a system of ideas which not only justifies the contention that ecology is a biological science in its own right, but provides the present-day biologist with an intellectual experience which can hardly have been enjoyed since the great days of genetics in the 1920s and, before that, Darwin's introduction of the theory of Natural Selection.

A SHORT LIST OF AVAILABLE TAXONOMIC WORKS FOR THE IDENTIFICATION OF THE BRITISH TERRESTRIAL FAUNA OTHER THAN BIRDS

General

SMART, J. and TAYLOR, G., *Bibliography of key works for the identification of British Fauna and Flora* (The Systematics Association, 1953).

Protozoa

SANDON, H., *The Composition and Distribution of the Protozoan Fauna of the Soil* (Oliver and Boyd, 1927).

Tardigrada

RAMAZZOTTI, G., I Tardigradi d'Italia, *Ist. Ital. Idrobiol.*, **2**, 29–166 (1945).

CUENOT, L., Tardigrades, *Faune Fr.*, **24**, 96 pp. (1937).

Nematoda

GOODEY, T., *Soil and Freshwater Nematodes* (London, 1951).

PENNAK, R. W., *Freshwater Invertebrates of the United States* (New York, 1953). Contains a useful key to Nematodes, many species being terrestrial.

Rotifera

DONNER, J., Rotatorien der Humusboden, *Osterr. Zool. Zeitschr.*, **2**, 117–51, 287–335, and *Zool. Jb. (Syst.)*, **79**, 614–38 (1949–51).

Annelida

ČERNOSVITOV, L. and EVANS, A. C., Lumbricidae No. 6 of *Synopses of the British Fauna* (Linnean Society, 1947).

OVERGAARD NIELSEN, C. and CHRISTENSEN, B., The Enchytraeidae, a critical revision and taxonomy of European species, *Nat. Jutland.*, **8, 10** (1959, 1961).

Mollusca

ELLIS, A. E., *British Snails* (Oxford, 1925).

QUICK, H. E., Testacellidae, Arionidae, Limacidae (Slugs), No. 8 of *Synopses of the British Fauna* (1949).

BARNES, H. E. and WEIL, J. W., Slugs in Gardens, *J. Anim. Ecol.*, **14**, 71–96 (1945).

QUICK, H. E., British Slugs, *Bull. Brit. Mus. (Nat. Hist.) Zoology*, **6** (5) (1960).

MACAN, T. T., *Fresh and Brackish-water Gastropods*, 2nd. edn. (Freshwater Biological Association, 1960).

MORTON, J. E. C. and MACHIN, J., A key to the land snails of the Flatford area, Suffolk, *Field Studies*, **1** (1), 57–71 (1959).

Arthropoda

Crustacea

WEBB, W. M. and SILLEM, C., *The British Woodlice* (Duckworth, 1906).

EDNEY, E. B., The Woodlice of Great Britain and Ireland, *Proc., Linn. Soc. Lond.*, Session **164**, pp. 49–98 (1953).

VANDEL, A., Isopodes Terrestres. Pt. 1. (Trichoniscidae and Ligiidae only), *Faune Fr.*, 64 (1960).

Opiliones

TODD, V., Key to the determination of the British Harvestmen, *Ent. Mon. Mag.*, **34**, 109–13 (1948).

SAVORY, T. H., No. 1 of the *Synopses of the British Fauna* (Linnean Society, 1946).

Spiders

LOCKET, G. H. and MILLIDGE, A. F., *British Spiders* (2 vols.) (Ray Society, London, 1951–3).

SAVORY, T. H., *Spiders and Allied Orders* (Warne, 1935).

Pseudoscorpions

KEW, H. W., A synopsis of the false scorpions of Britain and Ireland and supplement, *Proc. R. Irish Acad.*, Ser B., **29**, 38–64 and **33**, 71–85 (1911 and 1916).

EVANS, G. O. and BROWNING, E., Pseudoscorpiones, *Linn. Soc. Synopses of the British Fauna*, No. 10 (1954).

Mites

HUGHES, A. M., *The Mites of Stored Food* (H.M.S.O. for Ministry of Agriculture, Fisheries and Food, 287 pp. 1961).

HULL, J. E., Terrestrial Acari of the Tyne Province, *Trans. Nat. Hist. Soc., Northumberland, Durham and Newcastle-on-Tyne*, New Ser., **4**, 381–409, **5**, 13–82 (1909, 1913).

VITZTHUM, GRAF VON, *Die Tierwelt Mitteleuropas*, **3** (3) pt. 7, 112 pp. (1928). *Acarina in Das Tierreich*, **6** (4) pt. 5, 1,011 pp. (1942).

THOR, S., *Das Tierreich*, Nos. 56, 60, 70 (1931–41).

WILLMANN, C., *Die Tierwelt Deutschlands*, **22** (5), 200 pp. (1931).

MICHAEL, A. D., *British Oribatidae* (Ray Society, London, 1884, 1888).

SELLNICK, M., *Die Tierwelt Mitteleuropas*, **3,** (3), pt. 8 (1926).

TURK, F. A., A number of papers in *Ann. Mag. Nat. Hist.* since 1932. "A Synonymic Catalogue of British Acari," ibid., Ser 12, **I** (61), 1–26 and 81–99 (1953).

BAKER, E. W. and WHARTON, G. W., *An Introduction to Acarology* (New York, Macmillan, 1952).

EVANS, G. O., A series of papers is appearing, covering especially Parasitidae, in the Zoological journals and in official British Museum journals.

Myriapods

TURK, F. A., *Northwestern Naturalist*, **20,** 137–44 and **22,** 223–34 (1945).

BROLEMANN, H. W., Chilopodes and Diplopodes, Vols. **25** (405 pp.) and **29** (369 pp.) in *Faune Fr.* (Paris, 1930, 1935).

BLOWER, G., British millipedes with special reference to Yorkshire species, *The Naturalist, Lond.*, 145–57 (1952).

BLOWER, G., Yorkshire Centipedes, *Naturalist*, Oct/Dec (1955).

EDWARDS, C. A., Keys to the genera of the Symphyla, *J. Linn. Soc. Lond.*, Zool., **44** (296) April (1959).

EDWARDS, C. A., A revision of the British Symphyla, *Proc. Zool. Soc., Lond.* **132,** 403–439 (1959).

Insecta

The Royal Entomological Society Handbook for the Identification of British Insects is being issued in parts, of which the following had appeared by the end of 1961—

VOL. I

Part 2. DELANY, M. J., *Thysanura and Diplura* (1954).

Part 5. HINKS, W. D., *Dermaptera and Orthoptera* (1949).

Part 6. KIMMINS, D. E., *Plecoptera* (1950).

Part 9. KIMMINS, D. E., *Ephemeroptera* (1950).

Part 10. FRAZER, F. C., *Odonata* (1949).

Part 12 and 13. FRASER, F. C., *Mecoptera, Megaloptera and Neuroptera* (1959).

Part 16. SMIT, F. G. A. M., *Siphonaptera* (1959).

VOL. II.

Part 3. LeQUESNE, W. J., *Hemiptera-Homoptera: Fulgoromorpha* (1960).

Vol. IV. *Coleoptera:*

Part 1. CROWSON, R. A. *Coleoptera, Introduction and Key to Families* (1959).

Part 3. BROWN, F. BALFOUR, *Hydradephaga* (1953).

Part 8a. TOTTENHAM, C. E., *Coleoptera: Staphylinidae* (part) (1959).

Part 9. PEARCE, E. J., *Coleoptera: Pselaphidae* (1959).

Vol. V. *Coleoptera:*

Part 5b. THOMPSON, R. T., *Coleoptera: Phalaceridae* (1959).

Part 7. POPE, R. D., *Coccinellidae and Sphingidae* (1953).

Part 9. BUCK, F. O., Various small families (1954).

Part 11. BRITTON, E. B., *Coleoptera: Scarabeoidea* (1959).

Part 12. DUFFEY, E. A. J., *Cerambycidae* (1952).

Part 15. DUFFEY, E. A. J., *Scolytidae and Platypodidiae* (1953).

Vol. VI. *Hymenoptera:*

Part 1. RICHARDS, O. W., *Hymenoptera: Introduction and Key to Families* (1959).

Part 2. BENSON, R. B., *Symphyta and Aculeata* (1951–2).

Vol. VII

Part 2. PERKINS, J. F., *Ichneumonidinae* (1959).

Vol. VIII

Part 2a. FERRIÈRE, CH. and KERRICH, G. J., *Hymenoptera: Chalcidoidea* (part) (1959).

Part 3a. NIXON, G. E. J., *Hymenoptera: Proctotrupoidea* (part).

Vol. IX. *Diptera, Nematocera:*

OLDROYD, H., *Introduction and Key to Families* (1949).

COE, R. L., *et al.*, *Nematocera Part 1* (1950).

Vol. X. *Diptera, Cyclorhapha:*

Part 1. COE, R. L., *Syrphidae* (1953).

Part 4a. VAN EMDEN, F. I., *Tachinidae and Calliphoridae* (1954).

HINTON, H. E. and CORBET, A. S., Common insect pests of stored-food products: a guide to their identification, *Brit. Mus. (Nat. Hist.) Econ. Ser.*, No. 15 (1943). Covers species in the majority of insect orders.

CRYSTAL, R. N., *Insects of the British Woodlands*. Useful for larvae (Warne, 1937).

SKEDMORE, P., *British Insects. A Simplified Key to the Orders*, 19 pp. (Flatters and Garnett Ltd., Manchester, 1958).

MORETON, B. D., *Guide to British Insects*. Useful for larvae (Macmillan 1958).

The following series of foreign taxonomic works contain volumes of all insect orders and are often the most authoritative works available—

Faune de France (Lechevalier, Paris).
Die Tierwelt Deutschlands (Dahl. Fischer, Jena).
Die Tierwelt Mitteleuropas (Verlag von Quelle and Meyer, Leipzig).
Das Tierreich (de Gruyter, Berlin and Leipzig).
Danmarks Fauna (Gads Forlag, Copenhagen).

Quite indispensable for the serious invertebrate ecologist is the following which is generally taken as the authority for insect taxonomy—

KLOET, G. S. and HINKS, W. D., *A Check List of British Insects* (published privately, 1945).

Other works relating to specific orders are—

Collembola

HANDSCHIN, E., *In die Tierwelt Deutschlands*, **16**, 143 pp. (1929).

GISIN, H., *Collembolenfauna Europas* (Geneva, 1960).

WOMERSLEY, H., *Primitive insects of South Australia*, Govt. Pub., Adelaide, 200 pp. (1939).

MEYNARD, E. A., *The Collembola of New York State* (Comstock, New York, 1951).

STRENZKE, K., Thalassobionte u. thalassophile Collembola, in Remane, A. *Tierwell. N.u. Ostsee.*, **36**, 52 pp. (1955). Invaluable for the much-neglected shore Collembola.

Protura

STRENZKE, K., Norddeutsche Proturen, *Zool. Jahrb.* (Syst., Ökol. u. Geog. der Tiere), **75**, 73–102 (1942).

HANDSCHIN, E., *In die Tierwelt Deutschlands*, **16** (1929).

WOMERSLEY, H., Notes on the British Species of Protura, *Ent. Mon. Mag.*, **63**, 140–8 (1927).

Additional notes, ibid., **64**, 113–15 and 230–3 (1928).

TUXEN, S. L., Danske Protura, *Entomol. Medd.*, **17**, 306–11 (1931).

Orthoptera

BURR, M., *British Grasshoppers and their Allies* (Philip Allen, London, 1936).

PICKARD, B. C., *Grasshoppers and Crickets of Great Britain* (published privately, 1954).

RICHARDS, O. W. and WALOFF, N., Studies on the Ecology . . . of British Grasshoppers, *Anti-Locust Bulletin*, No. 17. Contains keys to all stages (London, 1954).

Odonata

LONGFIELD, C., *The Dragonflies of the British Isles* (Warne, 1937).

CORBET, P. S., LONGFIELD, C. and MOORE, N. W., *Dragonflies* (Collins). Includes a key to larvae. (1960).

Trichoptera

KIMMINS, D. E., British Trichoptera. A modified family key. *Ent. Gaz.*, 10 pp. (1956).

MOSELEY, M. E., *The Caddis Flies: a Collector's Handbook* (1939).

Thysanoptera

MORRISON, G. D., Thysanoptera of the London area, *Supplement to the London Naturalist*, Nos. **26**, 1–36, **27**, 37–75, **28**, 77–131 (1946–7). Reissued as "reprint No. 59" 131 pp. (1958–9).

Hemiptera–Homoptera

EVANS, J. W., A natural classification of the leaf-hoppers, *Trans. R. Ent. Soc. Lond.*, 3 parts, 207 pp. (1946–7).

Hemiptera–Heteroptera

JONES, H. P., An account of the Hemiptera-Heteroptera of Hampshire and the Isle of Wight. . . . A synopsis of the British Fauna, *Entomologist's Record*, **40–2** (1938).

SOUTHWOOD, T. R. E. and LESTON, D., *Land and Water Bugs of the British Isles* (Warne, 1959).

Coleoptera

DIBB, J. R., *Field Book of Beetles* (1948).

JOY, N. H., *A Practical Handbook of British Beetles* (Witherby, 1932).

LINSSEN, E. F., *Beetles of the British Isles*, 2 Vols. (Warne, 1959).

VAN EMDEN, R. L., A series of papers on beetle larvae in *Ent. Mon. Mag.* (**75–85**), *Proc. Zool. Soc. Lond.*, **122**, 651–797, and *Trans. R. Ent. Soc. Lond.*, **87**, 1 (1938–52).

Hymenoptera

STEP, E., *Bees, Wasps and Ants and Allied Orders* (Warne).

DONISTHORPE, H. ST. K., *British Ants* (Routledge, 1927).

MORLEY, D. W., *Ants* (Collins, 1953).

SLADEN, F. W. L., *The Honey Bee.* Out of Print (Macmillan, 1912).

RICHARDS, O. W., The specific characters of the British humblebees (Hymenoptera), *Trans. Ent. Soc. Lond.*, 233–68 (1927).

MORLEY, D. W., *Ants* (London, 1954).

COLLINGWOOD, C. A., The ants of the genus *Myrmica* in Great Britain, *Proc. R. Ent. Soc. Ser. A.*, **33**, 65–75 (1958).

FREE, J. B. and BUTLER, C. G., *Bumblebees* (Collins, 1959).

Diptera

COLYER, C. N. and HAMMOND, C. O., *Flies of the British Isles* (Warne).

MARSHALL, J. F., The British Mosquitoes, *Brit. Mus.* (*Nat. His.*) (1938).

STRENZKE, K., Systematik, Morphologie und Ökologie der terrestrischen Chironomiden, *Arch. f. Hydrobiol. Suppl.-Bund.*, **28**, 207–414 (1950).

NYE, I. W. B., . . . dipterous larvae living in Graminiae . . . *Trans. R. Ent. Soc.* **110**, 411–487 (1958).

MALLOCH, J. R., . . . classification of Diptera . ., on larval and pupal characteristics . . . Part I (all published but useful), *Bull. Illinois State Lab. Hist.*, **12**, 161–409 (1917).

BRAUNS, A., *Terricole Dipterenlarven. Puppen terricoler Dipterenlarven* (1954). See main Bibliography.

Trichoptera

HICKIN, N. E., *Caddis* (Methuen, 1952).

Vertebrata

A List of British Vertebrates, *Brit. Mus.* (*Nat. Hist.*), 66 pp. (1935).

SANDARS, E., *A Beast Book for the Pocket* (Oxford, 1937).

BARRET HAMILTON, G. E. H., *A History of British Mammals*, 3 vols., incomplete (London, 1910).

MATTHEWS, L. HARRISON, *The British Amphibia and Reptiles* (Methuen).

MATTHEWS, L. HARRISON, *British Mammals* (London, 1952).

SMITH, M., *The British Amphibians and Reptiles*, Rev. ed., 322 pp (Collins, 1954).

REFERENCES AND INDEX OF AUTHORS

Page numbers refer to position in this book

PAGE

1. AGRELL, I. (1942) Zur Ökologie der Kollembolen, *Opusc. Ent.*, Suppl. **3**, 62 194
2. AGRELL, I. (1945) An objective method for the characterization of Animal and Plant communities, *K. fysiogr. Sällsk. Lund Förh.*, N.F., **15**, 1 . . . . 191, 194
3. AGRELL, I. (1945) The Collemboles in nests of warm-blooded animals with a method for sociological analysis, *Acta Univ. lund.*, N.F., Ard. 2, **41**, 19 pp. 194
4. AGRELL, I. (1948) A dubious biocenological method, *Opusc Ent.*, **13**, 57-8 194
5. ALBRITTON, E. C. (1953) Ed. *Standard Values in Nutrition and Metabolism* (A.I.B.S. and Wright Air Development Centre, Ohio), 380 pp. 72, 241
6. ALLEE, W. C. (1939) *The Social Life of Animals* (London) . 135, 261
7. ALLEE, W. C. *et al.* (1949) *Principles of Animal Ecology* (New York), p. 436 refers. 135, 179
8. ALLEN, K. RADWAY (1951) *The Horokiwi Stream*, New Zealand Marine Dept. Fish. Bull. No. 10, 239 pp. . 74, 159, 162, 164, 241
9. ALLEN, K. RADWAY (1953) A method for computing the optimum size-limit for a fishery, *Nature, Lond.*, **172**, 210 275
9a. ANDERSEN, J. (1950) Harer og frugttrager, *Dansk Jagttidende*, **67**, 225-8 78
10. ANDERSON, P. K. (1960) Ecology and evolution in island populations of salamanders in the San Francisco Bay region, *Ecol. Monogr.*, **30**, 359-85 126
11. ANDRASSY, I. (1956) Die Rauminhalts-und Gewichtsbestimmung der Fadenwürmen (Nematoden), *Acta zool. Acad. Sci. Hung.*, **2**, 1-15 . 80
12. ANDREWARTHA, H. G. (1952) Diapause in relation to the ecology of insects, *Biol. Rev.*, **27**, 50-107 8
13. ANDREWARTHA, H. G. (1957) The use of conceptual models in population ecology, *Cold Spring Harbor Symposia on Quantitative Biology*, **22**, 219-36 156
14. ANDREWARTHA, H. G. (1959) Self-regulating mechanisms in animal populations, Presidential Address, A.N.Z.A.A.S., *Aust. J. Sci.*, **22**, 200-5 . . . . 143, 156
15. ANDREWARTHA, H. G. (1959) Density-dependent factors in ecology, *Nature, Lond.*, **183**, 200 . . . . . . 123, 156
15a. ANDREWARTHA, H. G. (1961) *Introduction to the Study of Animal Populations* (London, Methuen) 115, 156

PAGE

16. ANDREWARTHA, H. G. and BIRCH, L. C. (1954) *The Distribution and Abundance of Animals*, 782 pp. (Chicago) . . . 156, 259

17. ANDREWARTHA, H. G. and BIRCH, L. C. (1960) Some recent contributions to the study of the distribution and abundance of insects, *Ann. Rev. Ent.*, **5**, 219–42 . . . . . 156, 207, 223

18. ANDREWS, C. H., THOMPSON, H. V. and WANSI, W. (1959) Myxomatosis: the present position and future prospects in Great Britain, *Nature, Lond.*, **184**, 179–80 265

19. ANONYMOUS (1951) What is stress? *Lancet*, **260**, 277–9 . . . 147

20. ANONYMOUS (1960) Chemical warfare in the orchard, *The New Scientist*, **7**, 727 276

21. ANSBACHER, F. and JASON, A. C. (1953) Effects of water vapour on the electrical properties of anodized aluminium, *Nature, Lond.*, **171**, 177–8 42

22. ANSCOMBE, F. J. (1950) Sampling theory of the negative binomial and logarithmic series distributions, *Biometrika*, **37**, 358–82 . 103, 104

23. ARCHEBALD, E. A. A. (1949) The specific character of plant communities. 1. A quantitative approach, *J. Ecol.*, **37**, 274–88 . . 197

24. ARMITAGE, K. B. (1958) Ecology of the riffle insects of the Firehole river, *Ecology*, **39**, 571–9 193

25. ARMSBY, H. P. (1917) *The Nutrition of Farm Animals* (New York), p. 454 refers 72

26. ASLYNG, H. C. (1958) Shelter and its effect on climate and water balance, *Oikos*, **9**, 282–310 . . . . . 23, 25, 43, 46

27. AUDY, J. R. (1948) Some ecological effects of deforestation and settlement, *Malay. Nat. J.*, **3**, 178–189 59

28. BACKLUND, H. O. (1945) Wrack fauna of Sweden and Finland, *Opusc. Ent.*, Suppl. **5**, 238 pp. 269

29. BAERMANN, G. (1917) Eine einfache Methode zur Auffindung von *Ankylostomum*-larven in Erdproben, *Tijdschr. Geneeskd. Ned.-Ind.*, **5**, 57 98

29a. BAILEY, N. T. J. (1952) Improvements in the interpretation of recapture data, *J. Anim. Ecol.*, **21**, 120–7 114

29b. BAILEY, N. T. J. (1959) *Statistical Methods in Biology* (London, English Universities Press), 200 pp. 100

30. BALDWIN, E. (1948) *Dynamic Aspects of Biochemistry* (Cambridge), pp. 20–2 refer. 77

32. BALOGH, J. (1958) *Lebensgemeinschaften der Landtiere* (Budapest) 94, 267

33. BALOGH, J. (1958) On some problems of production biology, *Acta Zoologica Academiae Scientiarum Hungaricae*, **4**, 89–114 . . . 75, 80, 169, 236, 240, 241

34. BANETT, E. W. (1951) A dewpoint hygrometer, *J. Met.*, **8**, 40–5   36, 43

PAGE

35. BARBERS, F. H. (1953) Chemical control and resistance to insecticides
by agricultural pests, *J. Econ. Ent.*, **46**, 869–73 276

35a. BARNES, H. and STANBURY, F. A. (1951) A statistical study of plant
distribution and the colonization and early development of
vegetation on china clay residues, *J. Ecol.*, **39**, 171–81. . . 110

36. BARNES, H. F. and WEIL, J. W. (1942) Baiting slugs using metal-
dehyde mixed with various substances, *Ann. Appl. Biol.*, **29**, 56 . 97

37. BATES, M. (1950) *The Nature of Natural History*, 309 pp. (New York) 52

39. BEAUCHAMP, R. S. A. (1933) Rheotaxis in *Planaria alpina*, *J. Exp.
Biol.*, **10**, 113–29 19

40. BEDFORD, T. (1946) Environmental warmth and its measurement,
Med. Res. Coun. War. Memo., **17**, 2nd edn. (London, H.M.S.O.),
40 pp. 35

41. BELAIRE, F. R. and ANDERSON, L. J. (1951) A thermocouple psychro-
meter for field measurements, *Bull. Amer. Met. Soc.*, **32**, 217–20 . 43

43. BENJAMIN, B. (1956) Demographic aspects of ageing, in *The Biology
of Ageing*, Institute of Biology 119

44. BERLESE, A. (1905) Apparechio per raccogliere presto ed in gran
numero picoli arthropodi, *Redia*, **2**, 85–9 97

45. BERTHET, P. (in press) The evaluation of the true weight of Oribatids,
in Murphy, P. W., *Progress in Soil Zoology*, cf. 80

46. BEVERTON, R. J. H. and HOLT, S. J. (1957) On the dynamics of
exploited fish populations, *Fish. Invest.*, Ser. 2, **19**, 533 pp.
(London) 142, 167, 219

47. BILHAM, E. G. (1938) *The Climate of the British Isles* (London, Macmillan) 35

47a. BIRCH, L. C. (1948) The intrinsic rate of natural increase of an
insect population, *J. Anim. Ecol.*, **17**, 15–26 . . 123, 124, 125

48. BIRCH, L. C. (1953) Experimental background to the study of the
distribution and abundance of insects. i. The influence of temperature, moisture and food on the innate capacity for increase of three
grain beetles, *Ecology*, **34**, 698–711 . . . 19, 126, 175, 212

49. BIRCH, L. C. (1953) Experimental background to the study of the
distribution and abundance of insects. ii. The relation between
innate capacity for increase in numbers and the abundance of three
grain beetles in experimental populations, ibid., 712–26 . .
125, 126, 134, 175, 212

50. BIRCH, L. C. (1953) Experimental background to the study of the
distribution and abundance of insects. iii. The relation between
innate capacity for increase and survival of different species of
beetles living together on the same food, *Evolution*, **7**, 136–44
126, 175, 212

PAGE

51. BIRCH, L. C. (1955) Selection in *Drosophila pseudobscura* in relation to crowding, *Evolution*, **12**, 358–64 7

52. BIRCH, L. C. (1957) The role of weather in determining the distribution and abundance of animals, *Cold Spring Harbor Symposia on Quantitative Biology*, **22**, 203–18 156

53. BIRCH, L. C. (1960) The genetic factor in population ecology, *Amer. Nat.*, **94**, 5–24 . . . . 127, 143, 149

53a. BIRCH, L. C. and CLARK, D. P. (1953) Forest soils as an ecological community with special reference to the fauna, *Quart. Rev. Biol.*, **28**, 13–36 162

54. BIRCH, L. C., PARK, T. and FRANK, M. B. (1951) The effect of intraspecies and interspecies competition on the fecundity of two species of flour beetles, *Evolution*, **5**, 116–32 . . 175, 210

55. BLACKITH, R. E. (in press) The handling of multiple measurements, in Murphy, P.W., *Progress in Soil Zoology*, q.v. 191

56. BLISS, D. E. (1953) Endocrine control of metabolism in the land crab *Gecarcinus lateralis*. 1. Differences in the respiratory metabolism of sinus-glandless and eyestalkless crabs, *Biol. Bull.*, *Wood's Hole*, **104**, 275–96 76

57. BLISS, C. I. and FISHER, R. (1953) Fitting the negative binomial distribution to biological data, *Biometrics*, **9**, 176–200 . . . 103

58. BODENHEIMER, F. S. (1938) *Problems of Animal Ecology* (Oxford) . 259

59. BONESS, M. (1953) Die Fauna der Wiesen unter besonderer Berücksichtigung der Mahd, *Z. Morph. Ökol. Tiere.*, **42**, 225–77 . . 64

59a. BONESS, M. (1958) Biozönotische Untersuchungen über die Tierwelt von Klee-und Luzernefelden, *Z. Morph. Ökol. Tiere*, **47**, 309–73 59

60. BORNEBUSCH, C. H. (1930) *The Fauna of Forest Soil* (Copenhagen) 77, 162, 234

61a. BORUTZKY, E. V. (1939) (Dynamics of *Chironomus plumosus* in the profundal of Lake Beloie), *Arb. Proc. limnol. Sta. Kossino*, **22**, 156–95, 196–218. In Russian, English Summary 162

62. BOYCE, J. M. (1946) The influence of fecundity and egg mortality on the population growth of *Tribolium confusum* Duval, *Ecology*, **27**, 290–302 144

63. BOYOUCOS, G. J. (1949) Nylon electrical resistance unit for continuous measurement of soil moisture in the field, *Soil Sci.*, **67**, 319–30 47

64. BOYOUCOS, G. J. (1954) Electrical resistance methods as finally perfected for making continuous measurement of soil moisture content under field conditions, *Quart. Bull.*, *Mich. Agric. Exper. Sta.*, **37**, 132–149 47

PAGE

65. BOYOUCOS, G. J. and MICK, A. H. (1940) An electrical resistance
method for the continuous measurement of soil moisture under
field conditions, *Tech. Bull. Mich. Agric. Exper. Sta.*, **172**, 12 pp. .   47

66. BRAUN-BLANQUET, J.(1932) *Plant Sociology*, trans. and ed. Fuller, G. D.
and Conrad, H. S. (New York) 179, 183, 190

67. BRAUNS, A. (1954) *Untersuchungen zur angewandten Bodenbiologie;
Bd. 1 Terricole Dipterenlarven. Bd. 2 Puppen der terricolen Dipterenlarven (Göttingen, Musterschmidt)*   226

69. BRAY, J. R. (1960) The chlorophyll content of some native and
managed plant communities in central Minnesota, *Canad. J. Bot.*,
38, 313–33 238

70. BRAY, J. D., LAWRENCE, D. B. and PEARSON, L. C. (1959) Primary
production in some Minnesota terrestrial communities for 1957,
Oikos, **10**, 38–49 239

70a. BRERTON, J. LE G. (1957) The distribution of woodland isopods,
Oikos, **8**, 85–106 56

71. BREWER, R. (1960) A brief history of ecology. Pt. 1 Pre-nineteenth
century to 1919, *Occasional papers C. G. Adams Center for Ecol.
Studs.*, Kalamazoo, **1**, 18 pp.   224

72. BRIAN, M. V. (1952) The structure of a dense natural ant population,
J. Anim. Ecol., **21**, 12–24 256

73. BROADBENT, L. (1950) The microclimate of the potato crop, *Quart.
J. R. Met. Soc.*, **76**, 439–54 38

74. BROADBENT, L. (1953) Aphids and virus diseases in potato crops,
Biol. Rev., **28**, 350–80 38

75. BROADHEAD, E. (1958) The psocid fauna of larch trees in Northern
England, an ecological study of mixed species populations exploiting a common resource, *J. Anim. Ecol.*, **27**, 217–64 .   . 261

76. BRODY, S. (1945) *Bioenergetics and Growth*, 1,023 pp. (New York)
72, 81

77. BROWN, A. W. A.(1958) *Insecticidal Resistance in Arthropods*, W. H. O.,
(Geneva)   276

78. BROWN, F. A. (1954) A simple automatic continuous recording
respirometer, *Rev. Sci. Instrum.*, **25**, 415–17   .   .   . 82

79. BROWN, M. E. (1957) *The Physiology of Fishes: Vol. 1 Metabolism.
Vol. 2 Behaviour* (New York, Academic Press)   .   .   . 72

80. BULLOCK, T. H. (1955) Compensation for temperature in the metabolism and activity of poikilotherms, *Biol. Rev.*, **30**, 311–42.   . 77

81. BUNT, J. S. and ROVIRA, A. D. (1954) Oxygen uptake and carbon
dioxide evolution in heat-sterilized soil, *Nature, Lond.*, **173**, 1242 . 269

82. BURGESS, A. (1960) Time and size as factors in ecology, *J. Anim. Ecol.*,
29, 1–14 271

PAGE

83. BURGESS, A. (1960) Dynamic equilibria in the soil, in Parkinson, D. and Waid, J. S. *The Ecology of Soil Fungi* (Liverpool), 185–91
270, 271

84. BUTLER, L. (1953) The nature of cycles in populations of Canadian mammals, *Canad. J. Zool.*, **31**, 242–62 254

85. BUXTON, P. A. (1926) The radiation integrator in Racus, an instrument for the study of radiant heat received from the sun, *J. Hyg., Camb.*, **25**, 285–94 43

86. CADMAN, W. A. (1953) *Shelterbelts for Welsh Hill-farms* (London, H.M.S.O.) 23

87. CAIN, A. J. (1953) Geography, ecology and coexistence in relation to the biological definition of the species, *Ecology*, **7**, 76–83 . . 8

88. CAIN, A. J. and SHEPPARD, P. M. (1954) Natural selection in *Cepea*, *Genetics*, **39**, 89–116 8

89. CAIN, S. A. (1939) The climax and its complexities, in Just, T. *Animal and Plant Communities* (cf.) pp. 146–81 . . . 179, 183

90. CAIN, S. A. (1947) Characterization of natural areas and factors in their development, *Ecol. Monogr.*, **17**, 185–200 . . . 179, 183

91. CAMBRIDGE INSTRUMENT CO. (1951) The development of the thermal conductivity method of gas analysis, *Cambridge Instrument Co. Ltd. Monograph* No. 3 (Cambridge, England) 84

92. CAPSTICK, C. K. (1959) The distribution of free-living Nematodes in relation to salinity in the middle and upper reaches of the River Blyth estuary, *J. Anim. Ecol.*, **28**, 189–210 . . . 95

93. CARPENTER, J. R. (1936) Quantitative community studies of land animals, *J. Anim. Ecol.*, **5**, 231–45 92

94. CASPERS, H. (1950) Der Biozönose und Biotopbegriff vom Blickpunkt der marinen und limnischen Synökologie, *Biol. Zentralbl.*, **69**, 43–63 108

95. CHAPMAN, D. G. (1954) The estimation of biological populations, *Ann. Math. Statist.*, **25**, 1–15 110

96. CHAPMAN, R. M. (1928) The quantitative analysis of environmental factors, *Ecology*, **9**, 111–22 . . . . 143, 173, 175

96a. CHAPMAN, R. M. (1934) An experimental analysis of the causes of population fluctuations, *Science*, **80**, 297 *et seq.* 143

97. CHESTERS, C. G. C. (1949) Concerning fungi inhabiting the soil, *Trans. Brit. Mycol. Soc.*, **32**, 197–216 209

98. CHITTY, H. (1948) The snowshoe rabbit inquiry, 1943–46, *J. Anim. Ecol.*, **17**, 39–44 254

99. CHITTY, D. (1952) Mortality among voles (*Microtus agrestis*) at Lake Vyrnwy, Montgomeryshire in 1936–9, *Phil. Trans. (B)*, **236**, 505–52 148

PAGE

100. CHITTY, D. (1955) Adverse effects of population density upon the viability of later generations, in Cragg, J. B. and Pirie, N. W. *The Numbers of Man and Animals* (London, Oliver and Boyd), 57–68   148

101. CHITTY, D. (1957) Population studies and scientific methodology (reviews), *Brit. J. Phil. Sci.*, **8**, 64–6 . . . . . 148, 219

102. CHITTY, D. (1957) Self-regulation of numbers through changes in viability, *Cold Spring Harbor Symposia on Quantitative Biology*, **22**, 277–80 . . . . 143, 148

103. CHITTY, D. (1959) A note on shock disease, *Ecology*, **40**, 728–31   . 147

104. CHITTY, D. (1960) Population processes in the vole and their relevance to general theory, *Canad. J. Zool.*, **38**, 99–113   . 7, 143, 148, 149

105. CHITTY, D., CHITTY, H., LESLIE, P. H., and SCOTT, J. C. (1956) Changes in the relative size of the nucleus in the intervertebral discs of stressed Orkney voles (*Microtus orcadensis*), *J. Path. Bact.*, **72**, 459–70 148

106. CHITTY, D. and KEMPSON, D. A. (1949) Prebaiting small mammals and a new design of live trap, *Ecology*, **30**, 536–42   . . . 97

106a. CHITTY, D. and SHORTEN, M. (1946) Techniques for the study of the Norway rat (*Rattus norvegicus*), *J. Mammal.*, **26**, 63–78   97, 115

107. CHOUARD, P. (1932) Associations végétales des fôrets de la vallée d'Anance (Haute Marne): Application de la méthode statistique à l'étude des groupements des plantes, *Bull. Soc. bot. Fr.*, **79**, 617 *et seq.* 197

108. CHRISTIAN, J. J. (1950) The adreno-pituitary system and population cycles in mammals, *J. Mammal.*, **31**, 247–59   147

110. CLARK, L. R. (1953) The ecology of *Chrysomela gemellata* Rossi and *C. hyperici* Forst., and their effects on St. John's wort in the Bright district, Victoria, *Austr. J. Zool.*, **1**, 1–69. . . 55, 245

111. CLARK, L. R. and CLARK, N. (1952) A study of the effect of *Chrysomela hyperici* Forst. on St. John's wort in the Manus valley, N.S.W., *Austr. J. Agric. Res.*, **3**, 29–59 55

112. CLARK, E. J. (1946) Studies in the ecology of British grasshoppers, *Trans. R. Ent. Soc. Lond.*, **99**, 173–222   . . . 178, 181, 259

113. CLARKE, G. L. (1946) Dynamics of production in a marine area, *Ecol. Monogr.*, **16**, 321–37 162

115. CLARKE, J. R. (1953) The general adaptation syndrome in the study of animal populations, *Brit. J. Phil. Sci.*, **3**, 350–3 148

116. CLARKE, J. R. (1953) The effect of fighting on the adrenals, thymus and spleen of the vole (*Microtus agrestis*), *J. Endocrin.*, **9**, 114–26   148

117. CLARKE, J. R. (1955) The influence of numbers on reproduction and survival in two experimental vole populations, *Proc. Roy. Soc. (B)*, **144**, 68–85 148

PAGE

117*a*. CLEMENS, W. A. *et al.* (1948) Production in bodies of water, *Progr. Fish Cult.*, **39**, 36–43 . . . . . . 159, 162

119. CLOUDSLEY-THOMPSON, J. L. (1951) Studies in diurnal rhythms. 1. Rhythmic behaviour of millipedes, *J. Exp. Biol.*, **28**, 165–72   60, 76, 77

120. CLOUDSLEY-THOMPSON, J. L. (1951) On the sensory responses to environmental stimuli, and the sensory physiology of the millipedes (Diplopoda), *Proc. Zool. Soc. Lond.*, **121**, 253–75   60, 76, 77

120*a*. CLOUDSLEY-THOMPSON, J. L. (1953) Diurnal rhythms in animals, *Science News* (Harmondsworth), **28**, 76–9 60

121. CLOUDSLEY-THOMPSON, J. L. (1956) The effect of rock cover on the diurnal range of microclimatic conditions, *Entomologist*, **89**, 1120 . 26

122. COLE, L. C. (1949) The measurement of interspecific association, *Ecology*, **30**, 411–24 189

123. COLE, L. C. (1954) Some features of random population cycles, *J. Wildlife Mgmt.*, **18**, 2–24 136

124. COLQUHOUN, M. K. (1940) The density of woodland birds determined by the sample count method, *J. Anim. Ecol.*, **9**, 53–67 . 90

125. COMFORT, A. (1957) Survival curves of mammals in captivity, *Proc. Zool. Soc. Lond.*, **128**, 349–64 121

126. CONNELL, J. H. (1961) Effects of competition, predation by *Thais lapillus* and other factors on natural populations of the barnacle, *Balanus balanoides*, *Ecol. Monogr.*, **31**, 61–104 221

127. CONOVER, J. (1960) The feeding behaviour and respiration of some marine planktonic crustacea, *Biol. Bull.*, **119**, 399–415 . . 76

128. CONWAY, E. J. (1947) *Microdiffusion Analysis and Volumetric Error*, 2nd edn. (London) 82

129. COSTLOW, J. D., JUN. and BOOKHOUT, C. G. (1958) Moulting and respiration in *Balanus amphitrite* var. *denticulata* Broch, *Physiol. Zoöl.*, **31**, 271–80 76

131. COUNCIL FOR NATURE (1961) Birds killed by poisonous seed dressings, *Monthly Press Bulletin*, **13** 276

132. COUTTS, J. H. R. (1955) Soil temperatures in an afforested area in Aberdeenshire, *Quart. J. R. Met. Soc.*, **81**, 72–9 . . 33, 36

133. COUTTS, J. R. H. (1958) Moisture and temperature conditions in afforested areas in Aberdeenshire, *Forestry*, **31**, 167–76 . . 33

134. CRAGG, J. B. (1953) Book review of Dice, L. R. *Natural Communities* in *Bull. Inst. Biol.*, **1**, 3 177

135. CROMBIE, A. C. (1943) The effect of crowding on the oviposition of grain-infesting insects, *J. Exp. Biol.*, **19**, 311–40 . 144, 175, 210

136. CROMBIE, A. C. (1943) The effect of crowding upon the natality of grain-infesting insects, *Proc. Zool. Soc. Lond.*, A, **113**, 77–98

144, 175, 210

PAGE

137. CROMBIE, A. C. (1944) On intraspecific and interspecific competition in larvae of graminivorous insects, *J. Exp. Biol.*, **20**, 135–51
175, 210

138. CROMBIE, A. C. (1945) On competition between different species of graminivorous insects, *Proc. Roy. Soc.*, (*B*), **132**, 362–95
175, 206, 210, 211

139. CROMBIE, A. C. (1947) Interspecific competition, *J. Anim. Ecol.*, **16**, 44–73 . . . . 175, 210, 211

140. CROWCROFT, P. (1957) *The Life of the Shrew* (London, Reinhardt) 166 pp. 61

141. CROWCROFT, P. and ROWE, F. F. (1958) The growth of confined colonies of the wild house-mouse (*Mus musculus L.*): the effect of dispersal on female fecundity, *Proc. Zool. Soc. Lond.*, **131**, 357–65 148

142. CROWCROFT, P. and ROWE, F. F. (1961) The weights of wild house-mice (*Mus musculus L.*) living in confined colonies, *Proc. Zool. Soc. Lond.*, **136**, 177–85 148

143. CUSHING, D. H. (1955) Production and a pelagic fishery, *Fishery Invest. Lond.*, Ser., 2, **18**, (7), 104 pp. 72, 227

144. CUSHING, D. H. (1959) The seasonal variation in oceanic production as a problem in population dynamics, *J. Cons. int. Explor. Mer.*, **24**, 455–64 . . . . 72, 79, 166

145. CUSHING, D. H. (1959) On the nature of production in the sea, *Fishery Invest. Lond.*, Ser. 2, **22**, (6) 40 pp. . 72, 166, 240, 269

146. CUTLER, D. W. and CRUMP, L. M. (1920) Daily periodicity in the numbers of active soil flagellates with a brief note on the relation of trophic amoebae and bacterial numbers, *Ann. Appl. Biol.*, **7**, 11–24 183

147. CUTTING, C. L., JASON, A. C. and WOOD, J. L. (1956) A capacitance-resistance hygrometer, *J. Sci. Instrum.*, **32**, 425–31 . . . 42

149. CZIHAK, G. (1959) Eine einfache Methode zur Bestimmung der Feuchtigkeit des Bodens, *Wett. u. Leben*, **6**, 31–7 . . . 47

150a. DAHL, E. (1949) A new apparatus for recording ecologic and climatic factors, *Science*, **110**, 506–607 40

150b. DAHL, E. (1949) A new apparatus for recording ecologic and climatic factors, *Physiol. Plant.*, **2**, 272–86 40

151. DAHL, E. (1956) Rondane–mountain vegetation in South Norway and its relation to the environment, *Skr. norske Vidensk. Akad.* Oslo, Mat.-Naturv., Kl. **3**, 374 pp. 193

152. DAHL, F. (1908) Die Lycosiden oder Wolfspinnen Deutschlands und ihre stellung im Haushalte der Natur, *Nova Acta Leop.*, *Carol. Dtsch. Akad. Naturforsch.*, **88**, 174–678 152

PAGE

153. DAKSHINAMURTY, S. (1948) The common housefly, *Musca domestica* (L.), and its behaviour to temperature and humidity, *Bull. Ent. Res.*, **39**, 339–57 . . . . 17, 23
154. DARLING, F. F. (1938) *Bird Flocks and the Breeding Cycle* (Cambridge) 135
155. DARLING, F. F. (1952) Mammals and forestry, *Advanc. Sci.* (May 1952) 274
156. DARLING, F. F. and LEOPOLD, A. S. (1953) What's happening in Alaska? *Anim. Kingd.* (New York), **55**, 170–4 274
157. DARWIN, C. (1859) *The Origin of Species by Means of Natural Selection* (London) 174, 205, 281
158. DARWIN, F. (1887) *Life and Letters of Charles Darwin*, Letter to Asa Gray, 5th Sept., 1857 (London) 174
159. DAVIDSON, J. and ANDREWARTHA, H. G. (1948) Annual trends in a natural population of *Thrips imaginis* (Thysanoptera), *J. Anim. Ecol.*, **17**, 193–9 257
160. DAVIDSON, J. and ANDREWARTHA, H. G. (1948) The influence of rainfall, evaporation and atmospheric temperature on fluctuations in the size of a natural population of *Thrips imaginis* (Thysanoptera), *J. Anim. Ecol.*, **17**, 200–22 257
161. DAVIES, J. L. (1953) Colony size and reproduction in the grey seal, *Proc. Zool. Soc. Lond.*, **123**, 327–32 135
162. DAVIES, L. (1947) Observations on the development of *Lucilia sericata* (Ing.) eggs in sheep fleeces, *J. Exp. Biol.*, **25**, 86–102 . 33
164. DAVIS, B. N. K. (1961) *A study of soil micro-arthropods and their relation to land reclamation after open-cast ironstone quarrying.* Ph.D. Thesis, Univ. Nottingham, March 1961 . . 95, 190, 193, 196
166. DAWSON, J. (1956) Splenic hypertrophy in voles, *Nature, Lond.*, **178**, 1183–4 148
168. DE BACH, P. and SMITH, H. S. (1941) Are population oscillations inherent in the host-parasite relation? *Ecology*, **22**, 363–9 . . 220
168a. DEEVEY, E. S. (1947) Life tables for natural populations of animals, *Quart. Rev. Biol.*, **22**, 283–314 . . . . . . 120, 121
169. DE LONG, D. M. (1932) Some problems encountered in the estimation of insect populations by the sweeping method, *Ann. Ent. Soc. Amer.* **25**, 13–17 92
170. DEMOLL, R. (1938) Betrachtungen über Produktionsberechnungen, *Arch. Hydrobiol.*, **18**, 460–3 162
171. DEMPSTER, J. P. (1960) A quantitative study of the predators on the eggs and larvae of the broom beetle, *Phytodecta olivacea* Forster, using the precipitin test, *J. Anim. Ecol.*, **29**, 149–68 . . . 79
172. DEMPSTER, J. P., RICHARDS, O. W and WALOFF, N. (1959) Carabidae as predators on the pupal stage of the Chrysomelid beetle *Phytodecta olivacea* (Forster), *Oikos*, **10**, 65–70 56

PAGE

173. DENTON, R. L. (1951) A thermocouple amplifier, *Bull. Amer. Met. Soc.*, **32**, 214–16 37

173a. DETHIER, V. G. (1947) *Chemical Insect Attractants and Repellents* (London) 17

174. DHILLON, B. S. and GIBSON, N. H. E. (1962) A study of the Acarina and Collembola of agricultural soils, *Pedobiologia*, **1**, 189–209 . 191

175. DIGBY, P. S. B. (1955) Factors affecting temperature excess of insects in sunshine, *J. Exp. Biol.*, **32**, 279–98 . . . . 37, 78

176. DIGBY, P. S. B. (1958) Flight activity in the blowfly *Calliphora erythrocephala* in relation to light and radiant heat, with special reference to adaptation, *J. Exp. Biol.*, **35**, 1–19 78

177. DIXON, A. F. G. (1958) The escape responses shown by certain aphids to the presence of the Coccinellid *Adalia decempunctata* (L.), *Trans. R. Ent. Soc. Lond.*, **110**, 319–34 . . . . . 56, 221

178. DIXON, A. F. G. (1959) An experimental study of the searching behaviour of the predatory Coccinellid beetle *Adalia decempunctata* (L.), *J. Anim. Ecol.*, **28**, 259–81 . . . . . 56, 221

179. DIXON, M. (1951) *Manometric Methods as Applied to the Measurement of Cell Respiration and other Processess*, 3rd edn. (Cambridge) 81, 82

180. DOBZHANSKY, T. (1948) Genetics of natural populations: XVI Altitudinal and seasonal changes produced by natural selection in certain populations of *Drosophila pseudobscura* and *D. persimilis*, *Genetics*, **33**, 158–76 7

180a. DOWDESWELL, W. H., FISHER, R. A. and FORD, E. B. (1940) The quantitative study of populations in the Lepidoptera. I. *Polyommatus icarus* Rott., *Ann. Eugen., Camb.*, **10**, 123–36 . . 114, 115

180b. DOWDESWELL, W. H. and HUMBY, S. R. (1953) A photo-voltaic light meter for school use, *Sch. Sci. Rev.*, **125**, 64–70 . . 44

181. DRUMMETER, L. F. and FASTIE, W. G. (1947) A simple resistance thermometer for blood temperature measurements, *Science*, **105**, 73–4 39

182. DUFFEY, E. (1953) *Trinophylum cribratum* Bates, a new Indian pest of British timber yards, *Entomol. Gaz.*, **4**, 254–64 . . . 13

183. DUFFEY, E. A. J. (1953) On a Lycosid spider new to Britain and a rare spider taken near Oxford, *Ann. Mag. Nat. Hist.*, Ser. 12, **6**, 149–57 12

184. DUFFEY, E. A. J., LOCKETT, G. and MILLIDGE, A. (1958) The spider fauna of the heaths and fens of West Suffolk, *Suffolk Nat. Trans.*, **10**, 1–11 15

185. DUNGER, W. (1960) Zu einigen Fragen der Leistung der Bodentiere bei der Umsetzung organischer Substanz, *Zbl. Bakt.*, **2**, 113 *et seq.* 73, 75, 269

PAGE

186. DUNMORE, F. W. (1940) An electrical hygrometer and its application
to radio meteorology, *J. Res. Nat. Bur. Stand.*, **20**, 723–44 . . 41

187. DUPLAKOV, S. N. (1933) (Materien zur Erforchung des Periphytons), *Arb. limnol. Sta. Kossino*, **16**, 9–136 (Russian, German summary, pp. 136–60) 50

188. DYSON-HUDSON, U. R. D. (1956) Daily activity rhythms of *Drosophila* species, *Ecology*, **37**, 562–7 60

190. ECCLES, J. C. and McINTIRE, A. K. (1951) Plasticity of mammalian monosynaptic reflexes, *Nature, Lond.*, **167**, 466–8 . . . 152

191. EDNEY, E. B. (1951) The evaporation of water from woodlice and the millipede *Glomeris*, *J. Exp. Biol.*, **28**, 91–115 . . 17, 35

192. EDNEY, E. B. (1953) The construction and calibration of an electrical hygrometer suitable for microclimate measurements, *Bull. Ent. Res.*, **44**, 333–42 41

193. EDWARDS, C. A. (1958) The ecology of Symphyla: Part 1 Populations, *Ent. Exp. et. Appl.*, **1**, 308–19 . . . . . 55, 95

194. EDWARDS, R. W. (1958) The relation of oxygen consumption to body size and to temperature in the larvae of *Chironomus riparius* Meigen, *J. Exp. Biol.*, **35**, 383–95 77

195. EGERTON, A. C. (1951) Energy in the service of man. Paper 1: *Civilization and the use of energy*, Paris, UNESCO. N.S./74, 89 pp. 72

196. ELSTER, H. J. (1944) Das Verhältnis von Produktion, Bestand, Befischung und Ertrag, *Z. Fisch.*, **42**, 169–357 162

197. ELTON, C. S. (1924) Periodic fluctuations in the numbers of animals and their causes and effects, *J. Exp. Biol.*, **3**, 119–63 . . 147, 175

198. ELTON, C. S. (1930) *Animal Ecology and Evolution* (Oxford) . . 57

199. ELTON, C. S. (1935) *Animal Ecology*, 2nd edn. (London) . 176, 224

200. ELTON, C. S. (1942) *Voles, Mice and Lemmings* (Oxford) . . 149, 254, 255, 260

201. ELTON, C. S. (1946) Competition and the structure of ecological communities, *J. Anim. Ecol.*, **15**, 54–68 261

202. ELTON, C. S. (1949) Movements of Arctic fox populations in the region of Baffin Bay and Smith Sound, *Polar Record*, **5**, 296–305 . 5

203. ELTON, C. S. (1949) Population interspersion: an essay on animal community patterns, *J. Ecol.*, **37**, 1–25 . . . . 56, 183

204. ELTON, C. S. (1958) *The Ecology of Invasions by Animals and Plants* (Methuen) 13, 298

205. ELTON, C., DAVIS, D. H. S. and FINDLAY, G. M. (1935) An epidemic among voles (*Microtus agrestis*) in the Scottish Border in the spring of 1934, *J. Anim. Ecol.*, **4**, 277–88 93

PAGE

206. ELTON, C. S., FORD, E. B., BAKER, J. R. and GARDNER, A. D. (1931) Health and parasites of a wild mouse population, *Proc. Zool. Soc. Lond.*, 657–721 15

207. ELTON, C. S. and MILLER, R. (1954) The ecological survey of animal communities: with a practical system of classifying habitats by structural characters, *J. Ecol.*, **42**, 460–96 . 5, 200, 204

208. ELTON, C. S. and NICHOLSON, M. (1942) Fluctuations in numbers of muskrat (*Ondatra zibethica*) in Canada, *J. Anim. Ecol.*, **11**, 96–126 254

209. ELTON, C. S. and NICHOLSON, M. (1942) The ten-year cycle in the numbers of the lynx in Canada, *J. Anim. Ecol.*, **11**, 215–44 . . 254

210. EMERSON, A. (1939) Social co-ordination and the super-organism, in Just, T. (1939) cf. pp. 182–209 . . . 178, 179, 183, 184

210a. EMERSON, A. E. (1961) The evolution of adaptation in population systems, in Tax, S. Ed. *Evolution after Darwin* (Chicago), pp. 307–48
143

211. ERRINGTON, P. L. (1945) Some contributions of a fifteen-year study of the Northern bobwhite to a knowledge of population phenomena, *Ecol. Monogr.*, **15**, 1–34 165

213. EVANS, A. C. and GUILD, J. McL. (1948) Studies on the relation between earthworms and soil fertility. 5. Field populations, *Ann. Appl. Biol.*, **35**, 485–93 96

213a. EVANS, D. G. (1961) A portable visual photometer for the measurement of very low light intensities, *Ecology*, **42**, 402–3 . . 44

213b. EVANS, F. C. and SMITH, F. E. (1953) The intrinsic rate of natural increase for the human louse, *Pediculus humanus* (L.), *Amer. Nat.*, **86**, 299–310 123

214. EVANS, G. O. and COOMBE, D. E. (1959) Hemispherical and woodland canopy photography and the light climate, *Ecology*, **47**, 103–13 44

215. EVANS, G. O. (1953) On a collection of Acari from Kilimanjaro (Tanganyika), *Ann. Mag. Nat. Hist.*, Ser. 12, **64**, 258–81 . . 95

216. EVANS, G. O. and SHEALS, J. G. (1959) Three new mesostigmatic mites associated with millipedes in Indonesia, *Ent. Ber. Amst.*, **19**, 107–11 15

217. FAGER, E. W. (1957) Determination and analysis of recurrent groups, *Ecology*, **38**, 586–95 . . . . 189, 191, 194, 198

218. FAIRBROTHER, H. G. (1957) On an electrical resistance technique for the study of soil moisture problems in the field. Pt. 1, *Emp. Cott. Gr. Rev.*, **34**, 71–89 47

219. FENNER, F. (1953) Changes in the mortality rate due to myxomatosis in the Australian wild rabbit, *Nature, Lond.*, **172**, 228–30 . . 265

PAGE

221. FENTON, F. A. and HOWELL, D. E. (1956) A comparison of five methods of sampling alfalfa fields for Arthropod populations. *Ann. Ent. Soc. Amer.*, **50**, 606–11 92

222. FINDLAY, J. D. (1950) The effects of temperature, humidity and air movement and solar radiation on the behaviour and physiology of cattle and other farm animals, *Hanna Dairy Res. Inst. Bull.*, **9**, 178 pp. 22, 77

222a. FISHER, R. A. (1938) *Statistical Methods for Research Workers*, 7th edn. (Edinburgh) 100, 115

223. FLANDERS, S. E. and BADGLEY, M. E. (1960) A host parasite interaction conditioned by predation, *Ecology*, **41**, 363–5 . . 223

223a. FLEMMING, W. E. and BAKER, F. E. (1936) A method for estimating populations of larvae of the Japanese beetle in the field, *J. Agric. Res.*, **53**, 319–31 . . . . 106, 110

224. FOGG, G. E. (1951) The mechanism of photosynthesis, *New Biol.*, **11**, 27–49 . . . . 228, 240

226. FOGG, G. E. (1959) Dissolved organic matter in oceans and lakes, *New Biol.*, **29**, 31–48 . . . . . . 268, 270

227. FORD, H. D. and FORD, E. B. (1930) Fluctuation in numbers and its influence on variation in *Melitaea aurinia*, *Trans. R. Ent. Soc. Lond.*, **78**, 345–51 6

229. FOX, D. L. (1955) Organic detritus in the metabolism of the sea, *Sci. Mon. N.Y.*, **80**, 256–9 269

230. FOX, H. M. and WINGFIELD, C. A. (1938) A portable apparatus for the determination of oxygen dissolved in a small quantity of water, *J. Exp. Biol.*, **15**, 437–45 . . . . . 82, 237

231. FRANK, P. W. (1952) A laboratory study of intraspecies and intraspecies competition in *Daphnia pulicaria* (Forbes) and *Simocephalus vetulus* O.F. Müller, *Physiol. Zoöl.*, **25**, 178–204 . . . 211

232. FRANK, P. W. (1957) Coactions in laboratory populations of two species of *Daphnia*, *Ecology*, **38**, 510–19 211

233. FRANK, P. W. (1960) Prediction of population growth form in *Daphnia pulex* cultures, *Amer. Nat.*, **44**, 357–72 126, 127, 168, 212

234. FRANK, P. W., BOLL, C. D. and KELLY, R. W. (1957) Vital statistics of laboratory cultures of *Daphnia pulex* De Geer as related to density, *Physiol. Zoöl.*, **30**, 287–305 123

236. FRIEDERICHS, K. (1927) Grundsätzliches über die Lebenseinheiten höher Ordnung und den Ökologischen Einheitsfaktor, *Naturwissenschaften*, **15**, 153–7, 182–6 . . . . . 178, 186, 267

236a. FRIEND, D. T. C. (1961) A simple method of measuring integrated light values in the field, *Ecology*, **42**, 577–9 44

237. FROST, W. E. (1954) The food of pike, *Esox lucius* (L.), in Windermere, *J. Anim. Ecol.*, **23**, 339–60 79

PAGE

238. FROST, W. E. and SMYLY, W. J. P. (1952) The brown trout of a moorland fish-pond, *J. Anim. Ecol.*, **21**, 62–86 79

239. FRY, F. E. J. (1947) Effects of the environment on animal activity, *Univ. Toronto Stud. Biol.*, **68**, *Publ. Ont. Fish. Res. Lab.* **55**, 62 pp. . 18

240. FRY, F. E. J. (1958) Temperature compensation, *Annu. Rev. Physiol.* **20**, 207–24 . . . . 67, 77

241. GAJEVSKAYA, N. S. (1959) Sur l'étude quantitative de l'alimentation des animaux aquatiques, *Proc. XV Int. Cong. Zool. Lond.* 769–72 . . . . 79, 166, 269

242. GARDINER, B. G. (1958) Some observations on the respiration of young nymphs of *Schistocerca gregaria* (Forsk) in relation to phase and rearing density, *Proc. R. Ent. Soc. A*, **33**, 159–66 . . . 149

243. GAUSE, G. F. (1934) *The Struggle for Existence* (Baltimore). . . 143, 150, 175, 176, 181, 205, 207, 214, 222, 223

244. GAUSE, G. F. (1935) Vérifications expérimentales de la théorie mathématique de la lutte pour la vie, *Actualités Scientifiques*, No. 277 (Paris) 143, 150, 205, 214, 222

245. GAUSE, G. F. (1936) (On certain basic problems of biocenology) Russian, English Summary, *Zool. Zhurn.*, **15**, 363–381 . 175, 222

246. GAUSE. G. F. (1936) Principles of Biocenology, *Quart. Rev. Biol.*, **11**, 320–36 50

247. GEIGER, R. (1951) Das Klima der bodennahen Luftschicht (Die Wissenschaft, Braunschweig 1927, 2nd edn., 1942). Translation of 2nd edn. revised by author entitled *The Climate Near the Ground* (Harvard University Press) 21, 26, 27

248. GEIGER, R., (1951) Der künstliche Windschutz als meteorologisches Problem, *Erdkunde*, **5**, 106–114 23

249. GEORGE, J. L. (1957) *The Pesticide Problem*, 67 pp. (New York, The Conservation Foundation) 276

250. GERE, G. (1956) Investigations concerning the energy turn-over of the *Hyphantria cunea* Drury caterpillars, *Opusc. Zoologica* **1**, 29–32 . 73

251. GERE, G. (1956) Investigations into the laws governing the growth of *Hyphantria cunea* Drury caterpillars, *Acta Biol. Hung.*, **7**, 43–72 73

252. GERE, G. (1957) Productive biologic grouping of organisms and their role in ecological communities, *Ann. Univ. Sci. Budapest. Roland Eötvös nom.*, Sect. Biol., **1**, 61–9 . . . 73, 74, 241, 269

253. GESSNER, F., (1949) Der Chlorophyllgehalt in See und seine photosythetische Valenz als geophysikalisches Problem, *Schweiz. Z. Hydrol.*, **11**, 378–410 239

254. GIER, J. T. and BOELTER, L. M. K. (1941) The silver-constantan plated thermopile, in *Temperature Measurement and Control* (Amer. Inst. Phys., Reinhold), pp. 1284–92 43

PAGE

255. GILBERT, O. *et. al.* (1952) Gause's Hypothesis: an examination, *J. Anim. Ecol.*, **21**, 310–12 206

256. GILLBRICHT, M. (1952) Untersuchungen zur Produktionsbiologie des Planktons in der Kieler Bught, I. *Kieler Meersforsch.*, **8**, 173 . 238

257. GISIN, H. (1947) Analyses et synthèses biocénotiques, *Arch. Sci. phys. nat.*, **29**, 42–75 . . . . 193, 194

258. GISIN, H. (1948) Divergences à propos de la méthode biocénotique, *Opusc. ent.*, **13**, 1 *et seq.* 193

259. GISIN, H. (1949) L'écologie, *Acta biotheoretica*, **9**, 89–100 . . . 193

260. GISIN, H. (1949) Example du dévelopement d'une biocénose dans un tas des feuilles en décomposition, *Mitt. schweiz. ent. Ges.*, **22**, 422 *et seq.* 193

261. GISIN, H. (1950) La biocénotique, *Ann. Biol.*, *Paris*, **27**, 82–8 . . 193

262. GISIN, H. (1950) La faune du sol, in Symposium on "*La biologie du sol*," *Actes Soc. Helv. Sci. nat.*, 92–4 193

263. GISIN, H. (1951) Neue Forschung über Systematik und Ökologie der Kollembolen, *Naturwissenschaften*, **23**, 549 4

264. GISIN, H. (1952) Die ökologische Forschung und die Lebensgemein-schaften, *Scientia*, **6**, 151–5 193

265. GLASGOW, J. P. (1939) A population study of subterranean soil Collembola, *J. Anim. Ecol.*, **8**, 323–53 191

266. GLASGOW, J. P. (1953) The extermination of animal populations by artificial predation and the estimation of populations, *J. Anim. Ecol.*, **22**, 32–46 261

267. GLYNNE-WILLIAMS, J. and HOBART, J. (1952) Studies in the crevice fauna of a selected shore in Anglesey, *Proc. Zool. Soc. Lond.*, **122**, 797–824 225

268. GODFREY, G. K. (1954) Tracing field voles (*Microtus agrestis*) with a Geiger-Müller counter, *Ecology*, **35**, 5–10 115

269. GODFREY, G. and CROWCROFT, P. (1960) *The Life of the Mole* (*Talpa europaea* (L.)), (London, Museum Press) . . . 61, 115

270. GOLDMAN, C. R. (1960) Primary production and limiting factors in three lakes of the Alaska peninsula, *Ecol. Monogr.*, **30**, 207–30 . 238

271. GOLLEY, F. B. (1960) Energy dynamics of food chains of an old field community, *Ecol. Monogr.*, **30**, 187–206 . . . 231, 236, 240

272. GOLLEY, F. B. (1960) An index to the rate of cellulose decomposition in the soil, *Ecology*, **41**, 551–2 239

273. GOMPEL, M. (1938) Récherches sur la consommation d'oxygène de quelques animaux aquatiques littoraux: rythme des oxydations et rythme des marées, *Ann. Physiol.*, **14**, 914–31 . . . 76

274. GOODALL, D. W. (1952) Quantitative aspects of plant distribution, *Biol. Rev.*, **27**, 194–245 . . . . 105, 197

PAGE

275. GOODALL, D. W. (1953) Objective methods for the classification of vegetation, *Aust. J. Bot.*, **1**, 434–56 190

276. GOODE, J. E. and HYRYCZ, K. J. (1960) The soil moisture tensiometer: its practical value for field use in fruit crops and its construction, *Ann. Rep. E. Malling Res. Sta.*, 47th Year, 78–84 . . . 46

277. GOULDEN, C. H. (1952) *Methods of Statistical Analysis*, 2nd edn. (New York, Wiley), 467 pp. 191

278. GRAINGER, J. N. R. (1956) Effects of changes of temperature on the respiration of certain crustacea, *Nature, Lond.*, **178**, 930–31 . . 77

279. GRAINGER, J. N. R. (1958) First stages in the adaptation of poikilotherms to temperature change, in *Physiological Adaptation* (Pub. Amer. Physiol. Soc.), pp. 79–91 77

280. GREEN, F. H. W. (1956) A year's observations of potential evapotranspiration in *Rothiemurchus, J. Inst. Water Eng.*, **10** (5) . . 46

281. GREEN, R. G. and EVANS, C. A. (1940) Studies on a population cycle of snowshoe hares in the Lake Alexander area, *J. Wildlife Mgmt.*, **4**, 220–38, 267–78, 347–58 147

282. GREEN, R. G. and LARSON, C. L. (1938) A description of shock disease in the snowshoe hare, *Amer. J. Hyg.*, **28**, 190–212 . . . 147

282a. GREENBERG, B. G. (1951) Why randomize? *Biometrika*, **7**, 309–32 . 106

283. GREIG-SMITH, P. (1957) *Quantitative Plant Ecology* (London, Butterworth) 105

284. GRETSCHY, E. (1952) *Veröff. Bundesanst. alp. Landw. Admont.*, **6**, 25–85 50

285. GRIFFIN, D. G. (1952) Bird navigation: with an appendix by Ernst Mayr, *Biol. Rev.*, **27**, 359–400 55

286. GRIM, J. (1950) Zur Klärung einiger Produktionsbiologischer Begriffe in der Seekunde, *Arch. Hydrobiol.*, **44**, 1–14 . . . 162

287. GRIM, J. (1950) Versuche zur Ermittlung der Produktionskoeffizienten einiger Planktophyten in einem flachen See, *Bio. Zbl.*, **69**, 147–174 162

288. GUILD, W. J. McL. (1951) The distribution and population density of earthworms (*Lumbricidae*) in Scottish pasture fields, *J. Anim. Ecol.*, **20**, 88–97 96

289. GUTMANN, F. and SIMMONDS, L. M. (1949) Electrolytic thermistors, *Rev. Sci. Instrum.*, **20**, 674–5 39

290. HAARLØV, N. (1947) A new modification of the Tullgren apparatus, *J. Anim. Ecol.*, **16**, 115–21 97

291. HAARLØV, N. (1955) Vertical distribution of mites and Collembola in relation to soil structure, in Kevan, D. K. Mc. E. *Soil Zoology* (London, Butterworth), 167–179 89

292. HAARLØV, N. (1960) Microarthropods of Danish soils, *Oikos*, Suppl. **3**, 176 pp., 17 pl. (pp. 25–6 refer) 31

PAGE

293. HAARLØV, N. and PETERSEN, B. (1952) Measurement of temperature in bark and wood of Sitka spruce, *Forstl. Forsv. Danm.* **21**, 43–91   29

294. HAARLØV, N. and WEIS-FOGH, T. (1953) A microscopical technique for studying the undisturbed texture of soils, *Oikos*, **4**, 44–57   .   89

295. HAISTON, N. G. (1958) Observations on the ecology of *Paramecium* with comments on the species problem, *Evolution*, **12**, 440–50   .   208

296. HAIRSTON, N. G. (1959) The soil zoology of a Belgian Oak woods, *Ecology*, **40**, 168   .   .   .   .   236, 267, 340

297. HAIRSTON, N. G. (1959) Species abundance and community organization, *Ecology*, **40**, 404–16   .   .   .   198, 199, 236, 241

298. HAIRSTON, N. G., HUBENDICK, B., WATSON, J. M. and OLIVIER, L. J. (1958) An evaluation of techniques used in estimating snail populations, *Bull. World Hlth Org.*, **19**, 661–672   93

299. HAIRSTON, N. G., SMITH, F. E. and SLOBODKIN, L. B. (1960) Community structure, population control and competition, *Amer. Nat.*, **94**, 421–5   241

299a. HALDANE, J. B. S. (1953) Some animal life tables, *J. Inst. Actu.*, **79**, 83–9   120

300. HAMILTON, A. G. (1959) The infra-red gas analyser as a means of measuring the carbon dioxide output of individual insects, *Nature, Lond.*, **184**, 367–9   84

301. HARKER, J. E. (1956) Factors controlling diurnal activity rhythm of *Periplaneta americana*, *J. Exp. Biol.*, **33**, 224–34   60

302. HARPER, J. L. (1959) Factors controlling plant numbers, in The biology of weeds, *Brit. Ecol. Soc. Symp.* (Oxford)   .   .   156, 261

302a. HARPER, J. L. (1961) Approaches to the study of plant competition, *Symp. Soc. Exp. Biol.*, **XV**, 39 pp. 204, 261

303. HARRISSON, L. E. (1957) An inexpensive instrument for the determination of the electrical resistance of soil moisture units, *Emp. Cott. Gr. Rev.*, **34**, 89–92   47

304. HARRIT, T. van (1952) An experimental study of habitat selection by prairie and forest races of the deermouse, *Peromyscus maniculatus*, *Contrib. Lab. Biol. Michigan* (56), 53 pp.   55

305. HARTENSTEIN, R. (1961) On the distribution of forest soil microarthropods and their fit to contagious distribution factors, *Ecology*, **42**, 190–4   105

306. HARTLEY, P. T. H. (1948) Food and feeding relationships in a community of freshwater fishes, *J. Anim. Ecol.*, **17**, 1–14   .   .   79, 207

307. HARTLEY, P. T. H. (1953) An ecological study of the feeding habits of the English titmice, *J. Anim. Ecol.*, **22**, 261–88   .   205, 206, 207

308. HARVEY, H. W. (1942) Production of life in the sea, *Biol. Rev.*, **17**, 221–46   162

PAGE

309. HASLETT, A. W. (1952) Underwater television, *Science News* (Harmondsworth), **25**, 91–6 89

311. HAWKES, H. A. (1951) A study of the biology and control of *Anisopus fenestralis* (Scop, 1763) a fly associated with sewage filters, *Ann. Appl. Biol.*, **38**, 592–605 255

312. HAWKES, H. A. (1952) The ecology of *Anisopus fenestralis* Scop. (Diptera) in sewage bacteria beds, *Ann. Appl. Biol.*, **39**, 181–92 . 255

313. HAWKINS, A. E., JEWELL, P. A. and THOMLINSON, G. (1960) The metabolism of some British shrews, *Proc. Zool. Soc. Lond.*, **135**, 99–103 75

315. HEALY, M. J. R. (In press) Some basic statistical techniques in soil zoology, in Murphy, Ed. *Progress in Soil Zoology* (London, Butterworth) 100, 101, 105

316. HECHT, O. (1931) On the heat sense of mosquitoes at egg laying, *Veröff dtsch. Ges. angew. Ent.*, **8**, 26–9 19

317. HEMMINGSEN, A. M. (1950) The relation of standard (basal) energy metabolism to total fresh weight of living organisms, *Rep. Steno. Mem. Hosp.*, **4**, 1–58 75

318. HESSE, R. (1924) *Tiergeographie auf ökologischer Grundlage* (Jena) 178, 186

319. HEYDEMANN, B. (1956) Über die Bedeutung der "Formalinfallen" für die zoologische Landforschung, *Faun. Mitt. aus Norddeutschl.*, **6**, 19–24 96

320. HEYDEMANN, B. (1958) Erfassungsmethoden für die Biozönosen der Kulturbiotop, in Balogh, J. *Lebensgemeinschaften der Landtiere* (Budapest) 96

321. HEYDEMANN, B. (1960) Zum Ökologie von *Sorex araneus* (L.) und *S. minutus* (L.), *Zeits. f. Säugertierkunde*, **25**, 24–9 . . . 96

322. HILSUM, C. (1960) Progress in developing solar batteries, *The New Scientist*, **7**, 96 240

322a. HOEL, P. G. (1943) The accuracy of sampling methods in ecology, *Ann. Math. Stat.*, **14**, 289–300 110

323. HOFFMANN, R. S. (1958) The role of reproduction and mortality in population fluctuations of voles (*Microtus*), *Ecol. Monogr.*, **28**, 79–109 148

324. HOLDAWAY, F. G. (1932) The growth of populations of the flour beetle as affected by atmospheric moisture, *Ecol. Monogr.*, **2**, 261–304 . . . . 143, 150, 175

325. HOLTER, H. (1943) Technique of the Cartesian Diver, *C.R. Lab. Carlsberg Ser. Chim.*, **24**, 399–478 82

327. HOWARD, L. O. and FISKE, W. F. (1911) The importation into the United States of the parasites of the Gipsy Moth and the Brown-tail Moth, *U.S. Dept. Agric. Ent. Bull.*, **91**, 312 pp. . . 153, 327

PAGE

328. HÜBER, B. (1950) Registierung des CO_2-Gefalles und Berechnung des CO_2 Stromes über Pflanzengesellschaften, *Ber. dtsch. Bot. Ges.*, **63**, 53–64 84

329. HUFFAKER, C. B. (1958) Experimental studies on predation. II Dispersion factors in predator prey oscillations, *Hilgardia*, **27**, 343–83 223

330. HUFFAKER, C. B. and KENNETT, C. E. (1956) Experimental studies on predation: predation and cyclamen mite populations on strawberries in California, *Hilgardia*, **26**, 191–222 223

331. HUGHES, R. D. (1955) The influence of the prevailing weather on the numbers of *Meromyza variegata* Meigen (Dipt. Chloropidae) caught with a sweep net, *J. Anim. Ecol.*, **24**, 324–35 . . . 92

332. HUGHES, R. D. (1959) The natural mortality of *Erioischia brassicae* (Bouché) (Dipt. Anthomyidae) during the egg stage of the first generation, *J. Anim. Ecol.*, **28**, 343–57 260

333. HUGHES, R. D. (In press) The study of aggregated populations, in Murphy, P. W. *Progress in Soil Zoology*, (London, Butterworth) 106

334. HUKILL, W. V. (1941) Characteristics of thermocouple anemometers, in *Temperature: its Measurement and Control* (Amer. Inst. Phys. Reinhold), 666–72 45

336. HUTCHINSON, G. E. (1944) Limnological studies in Connecticut VII, *Ecology*, **25**, 3–26 206

337. HUTCHINSON, G. E. (1948) Circular causal systems in ecology, *Ann. N.Y. Acad. Sci.*, **50**, 221–46 138

338. HUTCHINSON, G. E. (1954) Theoretical notes on oscillatory populations, *J. Wildlife Mgmt.*, **18**, 107–9 . . . . . 139, 266

339. HUTCHINSON, G. E. and DEEVEY, E. S. (1949) Ecological studies on populations, *Surv. Biol. Progr.*, **1**, 325–59 . . . . 206, 261

340. HUXLEY, J. S. (1938) Species formation and geographical isolation, *Proc. Linn. Soc. Lond.*, **150**, 253 *et seq.* 7

341. HUXLEY, J. S. (1940) *The New Systematics* (Oxford) . . . 8

343. HYATT, K. H. (1959) Mesostigmatic mites associated with *Geotrupes stercorarius* (L.) (Col, Scarabaeidae), *Ent. Mon. Mag.*, **95**, 22–3 . 15

344. IVLEV, V. S. (1934) Eine Mikromethode zur Bestimmung des Kaloriengehaltes von Nährstoffen, *Biochem. Z.*, **275**, 49–55 . 81

345. IVLEV, V. S. (1945) (The biological productivity of water.) *Uspekhi Sovremennoi Biologii*, **19**, 98–120. In Russian. Translation by W. E. Ricker available in Bureau Anim. Population, Oxford . 162

345a. JACKSON, C. H. N. (1939) The analysis of an animal population, *J. Anim. Ecol.*, **8**, 238–46 114

345b. JACKSON, C. H. N. (1948) The analysis of a tetse fly population, *Ann. Eugen. Lond.*, **14**, 91–108 114

PAGE

346. JAMES, W. O. and JAMES, A. L. (1940) The respiration of barley germinating in the dark, *The New Phytologist*, **39**, 145–76 . . 82

347. JANETSCHEK, H. (1949) Tierische Successionen auf hochalpinen Neuland, *Ber. naturw.-med. Ver. Innsbruck*, **49**, 1–215 . . . 48

348. JASON, A. C. and ANSBACHER, F. (1952) *Improvements in and relating to the Measurement of Moisture*, Brit. Pat. Appl, 2936/52 . . 37

349. JEHN, K. H. (1949) Wet bulb temperatures without a wick, *Rev. Sci. Instrum.*, **20**, 668–73 43

350. JOHNSON, C. G. (1940) The maintenance of high atmospheric humidities for entomological work with Glycerol-water mixtures, *Ann. Appl. Biol.*, **27**, 295–9 17

351. JÓNASSON, P. M. (1954) An improved funnel trap for capturing emerging aquatic insects, with some preliminary results, *Oikos*, **5**, 179–88 96

352. JÓNASSON, P. M. (1955) The efficiency of sieving techniques for sampling freshwater bottom fauna, *Oikos*, **6**, 183–207 . . 93

354. JONES, P. C. T. and MOLLISON, J. F. (1948) A technique for quantitative estimation of soil microorganisms, *J. Gen. Microbiol.*, **2**, 54 . 105

355. JUST, T. (1939) (Ed.) Animal and plant communities, *Amer. Midl. Nat.*, **21**, 1–255 183

357. KALLE, K. (1948) Zur Frage der Produktionsleistung des Meeres, *Dtsch. hydrogr. Zeits.*, **1**, 1–17 . . . . . 162, 239, 240

358. KAWANABE, H. (1958) On the significance of social structure for the mode of density effect in a salmon-like fish, "Ayu," *Plecoglossus altivelis*, *Mem. Coll. Sci. Univ. Kyoto (B)*, **25**, 171–80 . . 149

359. KENDALL, M. G. (1955) *Rank Correlation Methods*, 2nd edn. (London, Griffin), 196 pp. 190

360. KENDALL, M. G. (1957) *A Course in Multivariate Analysis* (London, Griffin), 185 pp. 191

361. KENNINGTON, G. S. (1953) The effects of reduced atmospheric pressure on populations of *Tribolium castaneum* and *Tribolium confusum*, *Physiol. Zoöl.*, **26**, 179–203 134

362. KERKUT, G. A. and TAYLOR, B. J. R. (1956) Effect of temperature on the spontaneous activity from the isolated ganglia of slug, cockroach and crayfish, *Nature, Lond.*, **178**, 426 . . . 77

363. KERSHAW, K. A. (1957) The use of cover and frequency in the detection of pattern in plant communities, *Ecology*, **38**, 291–9 . 198

364. KERSHAW, K. A. (1959) An investigation of the structure of a grassland community, *J. Ecol.*, **47**, 31–54 198

365. KERSHAW, K. A. (1960) The detection of pattern and association, *J. Ecol.*, **48**, 233–42 198

PAGE

366. KEVAN, D. K. MC. E. (1955) (Ed.) *Soil Zoology:* proceedings of the University of Nottingham Second Easter School in Agricultural Science (London, Butterworth) 93, 96, 98

367. KINNE, O. (1960) Growth, food intake and food conversion in a euryplastic fish exposed to different temperatures and salinities, *Physiol. Zoöl.,* **33,** 288–317 . . . . . . 72, 79

368. KITAZAWA, Y. and KURASAWA, H. (1951) Studies on the biological production of Lake Suwa. I. Standing Crop of herbivorous zoobenthos, *Misc. Rep. Res. Inst. Nat. Resour. Tokyo* (**24**), 15 pp. . 241

369. KITCHING, J. A., SLOANE, J. F. and EBLING, F. J. (1959) The ecology of Lough Ine. VIII. Mussels and their predators, *J. Anim. Ecol.,* **28,** 331–41 222

370. KLUIJVER, H. N. (1951) The population ecology of the great tit, *Parus major* (L.) *Ardea,* **39,** (1/3) 135 pp. 255

371. KOHN, A. J. (1959) The ecology of *Conus* in Hawaii, *Ecol. Monogr.,* **29,** 47–90 15

372. KØIE, K. (1948) A portable A.C. bridge and its use for microclimatic temperature, and humidity measurements, *J. Ecol.,* **36,** 269–82 41, 43

373. KØIE, M. E. (1954) A self recording light integrator and a portable integrator for light percentage measurements, *Oikos,* **4,** 178– 86 44

374. KONTKANEN, P. (1950) Sur les diverses méthodes de groupement des recoltes dans la biocenotique animale, *Vie et Milieu,* **1,** 121– 30 194

375. KONTKANEN, P. (1950) Quantitative and seasonal studies on the leaf hopper fauna of the field stratum on open areas in North Karelia, *Ann. (Bot-Zool.) Soc. zool.-bot. Fenn. Vanoma,* **13,** 1–91 92, 196, 194

376. KONTKANEN, P. (1957) On the delimation of communities in research on animal biocenotics, *Cold Spring Harbor Symposia on Quantitative Biology,* **22,** 373–8 196

377. KRISTENSEN, K. T. (1959) Temperature and heat balance of soil, *Oikos,* **10,** 103–20 33

378. KROGERUS, R. (1932) Über die Ökologie und Verbreitung der Arthropoden der Triebsandgebiete an den Küsten Finnlands, *Acta zool. Fenn.,* **12,** 1–308 26

379. KROGH, A. (1914) The quantitative relation between temperature and standard metabolism in animals. *Int. Z. phys.-chem. Biol.,* **1,** 491–508 . . . . 18, 77, 234

380. KROGH, A. (1916) *The Respiratory Exchange in Man and Animals* (London) 77, 234

381. KROGH, A. (1940) A microclimatic recorder, *Ecology,* **21,** 275–9 . 39

PAGE

382. KROGH, A. and WEIS-FOGH, T. (1951) The respiratory exchange of the desert locust (*Schistocerca gregaria*) before, during and after flight, *J. Exp. Biol.*, **28**, 344–57 70

383. KUBIËNA, W. L. (1938) *Micropedology* (Iowa, Ames) . . . 89

384. KUBIËNA, W. H. (1953) *The Soils of Europe* (London, Musby) . . 270

385. KÜHNELT, W. (1943) Die Lietformen-methode in der Ökologie der Landwebeltiere, *Biologia generalis*, **17**, 106–46 . . . 200

386. KÜHNELT, W. (1948) Ein Beitrag zur Kenntnis des Bodentierwelts einiger Waldtypen Kärntens, *Mitt. naturw. Ver. Kärnten.*, **137–8**, 165–73 194

387. KULCZYNSKI, ST. M. (1927) Die Pflanzenassoziationen der Pieninen, *Bull. int. Acad. Pol. Sci. Lett.*, Suppl. **2**, 57–204 . . . 194, 196

388. LACK, D. (1933) Habitat selection in birds, *J. Anim. Ecol.*, **2**, 239–62
55

388a. LACK, D. (1937) The psychological factor in bird distribution, *Brit. Birds*, **31**, 130–6 . . . . 55, 90

390. LACK, D. (1954) Cyclic mortality, *J. Wildlife Mgmt.*, **18**, 25–37. . 264

390a. LACK, D. (1955) *The Natural Regulation of Animal Numbers* (Oxford) 154, 264, 265

391. LACK, D. (1955) The mortality factors affecting adult numbers, in Gragg, J. B. and Pirie, N. W. (Eds.) *The Numbers of Man and Animals* (London, Oliver and Boyd) 47–56 143

392. LACK, D. (1956) Variations in the reproductive rate of birds, *Proc. Roy. Soc. B.*, **145**, 329–33 7

393. LACK, D. and LACK, L. (1933) Territory reviewed, *Brit. Birds*, **27**, 179–99 264

394. LACK, D. and SOUTHERN, H. N. (1949) Birds on Teneriffe, *Ibis*, **91**, 607–26 11

395. LADELL, W. R. S. (1936) A new apparatus for separating insects and other Arthropods from the soil, *Ann. Appl. Biol.*, **23**, 862–79 . . 94

396. LAKE, J. V. (1956) The temperature profile above bare soil on clear nights, *Quart. J. R. Met. Soc.*, **82**, 187–97 26

397. LAURENCE, B. R. (1954) The larval inhabitants of cowpats, *J. Anim. Ecol.*, **23**, 234–60 . . . . 51, 95

398. LEATON, E. J. (1949) High speed thermocouple temperature reading equipment, *J. Sci. Instrum.*, **62**, 161–2 37

399. LE CREN, E. D. (1949) The interrelationships between population, production and growth-rate in freshwater fish, *Proc. Linn. Soc. Lond.*, **161**, 131–40 . . . . 72, 194

400. LEOPOLD, A. S. and DARLING, F. E. (1953) Effects of land use on moose and caribou in Alaska, *18th N. Amer. Wildlife Conf.*, 553–60 274

PAGE

401. LESLIE, P. H. (1945) On the use of matrices in certain population mathematics, *Biometrika*, **33**, 183–212 . . . 123, 127, 138

402a. LESLIE, P. H. (1952) The estimation of population parameters from data obtained by means of the capture-recapture method. II. The maximum likelihood equations for estimating total numbers, *Biometrika*, **39**, 363–88 114

403. LESLIE, P. H. (1957) An analysis of the data for some experiments carried out by Gause with populations of the Protozoa, *Paramecium aurelia*, and *Paramecium caudatum*, *Biometrika*, **44**, 314–27 . 175

404. LESLIE, P. H. (1959) The properties of a certain lag type of population growth and the influence of an external random factor on a number of such populations, *Physiol. Zoöl.*, **32**, 151–9 . 139, 150

404a. LESLIE, P. H. and CHITTY, D. (1951) The estimation of population parameters from data obtained by means of the capture-recapture method. I. The maximum-likelihood equations for the estimation of the death rate, *Biometrika*, **38**, 269–92 114

405. LESLIE, P. H., CHITTY, D. and CHITTY, H. (1953) The estimation of population parameters . . . III. An example of the practical applications of the method, *Biometrika*, **40**, 137–69 . . . 114

405a. LESLIE, P. H. and PARK, T. (1949) The intrinsic rate of natural increase of *Tribolium castaneum* Herbst, *Ecology*, **30**, 469–77 . 123, 125

405b. LESLIE, P. H. and RANSON, R. M. (1940) The mortality, fertility and rate of natural increase of the vole (*Microtus agrestis*) as observed in the laboratory, *J. Anim. Ecol.*, **9**, 27–52 . . 121, 123

405c. LESLIE, P. H. et al. (1952) The fertility and population structure of the brown rat (*Rattus norvegicus*) in corn ricks and some other habitats, *Proc. Zool. Soc. Lond.*, **122**, 187–238 . . . 123, 124

406. LEVER, R. J. A. W. (1957) The diet of the fox since myxomatosis, *J. Anim. Ecol.*, **28**, 359–74 265

407. LEWIS, T. and SIDDORN, J. W. (1959) A simple portable recorder for direction and speed of wind, *J. Anim. Ecol.*, **28**, 377–80 . 44

408. LINDE, VAN DER R. J. and WONDENBERG, J. P. M. (1951) On the microclimatic properties of sheltered areas, *Meded. Inst. Toegep. Biol. Onderz. Nat.* **10**, 151 pp. 23

409. LINDEMANN, R. L. (1942) The trophic-dynamic aspect of ecology, *Ecology*, **23**, 399–418 . . . . . 162, 230, 241, 267

410. LINDERSTRØM-LANG, K. (1943) On the theory of the Cartesian Diver micro-respirometer, *C.R. Lab. Carlsberg Ser. Chim.*, **24**, 333–98

82

411. LINDQUIST, A. W., YATES, W. W., HOFFMAN, R. A. and BUTTS, J. S. (1951) Studies on the flight habits of three species of flies tagged with radioactive phosphorus, *J. Econ. Ent.*, **44**, 397–400 . . 115

PAGE

412. LLOYD, M. (1960) Statistical analysis of Marchant's data on breeding
success and clutch size, *Ibis*, **102**, 600–11 221

413. LONG, D. B. (1953) Effects of population density on larvae of
lepidoptera, *Trans. R. Ent. Soc. Lond.*, **104**, 541–54 . . . 149

414. LOOMAN, J. and CAMPBELL, J. B. (1960) Adaptation of Sørensen's K
(1948) for estimating unfit affinities in prairie vegetation, *Ecology*,
41, 409–16 198

415. LOTKA, A. J. (1925) *Principles of Physical Biology* (Baltimore), re-
printed as *Principles of Mathematical Biology* (Dover, 1959) . .
122, 134, 147, 174, 181, 213, 215

415a. LOTKA, A. J. (1945) Population analysis as a chapter in the mathematical theory of evolution, in Le Gros, Clark, W. E. and Medawar,
P. B. *Essays on Growth and Form* (Oxford) 122

416. LOUCH, C. D. (1957) Adrenocortical activity in relation to density
and dynamics of three confined populations of *Microtus pensyl-
vanicus*, *Ecology*, **38**, 701–13 147

417. LOUCH, C. D. (1958) Adrenals and voles, *J. Mammal.*, **39**, 109–16 . 147

418. LOUSLEY, J. E. (1950) *Wild flowers of Chalk and Limestone* (London,
Collins) 192

419. LOWRY, W. P. (1956) Evaporation from forest soils and a proposed
field method for estimating evaporation, *Ecology*, **37**, 419–30 . 45

420. LOWRY, W. P. (1957) An inexpensive field instrument for non-selective net radiation measurements, *Ecology*, **38**, 152–5 . . . 43

421. LUCAS, C. E. (1947) The ecological effects of external metabolites,
Biol. Rev., **22**, 270–95 270

422. LUDWIG, J. W. and HARPER, J. L. (1958) The influence of the environment on seed and seedling mortality. VIII. The influence of soil
colour, *J. Ecol.*, **46**, 481–90 26

423. MACAN, T. T. (1938) Evolution of aquatic habitats with special
reference to the distribution of Corixidae, *J. Anim. Ecol.*, **7**, 1–19 61, 193

423a. MACAN, T. T. (1939) The Culicidae of the Cambridge district,
Parasitology, **31**, 263–9 201

424. MACAN, T. T. (1954) A contribution to the study of the ecology of
the Corixidae (Hemipt.), *J. Anim. Ecol.*, **23**, 115–41 . . 61, 193

425. MACAN, T. T. (1958) Methods of sampling the bottom fauna of
stony streams, *Mitt. int. Ver. Limnol.*, **8**, 21 pp. 92

427. MACARTHUR, R. H. (1957) On the relative abundance of bird
species, *Proc. Nat. Acad. Sci.*, *Wash.*, **43**, 293–5 198

429. McCULLOCH, J. S. G. and PENMAN, H. L. (1956) Heat flow in the
soil, *Ext. Rap. VI Cong. Sci. Sol*, Paris, **1**, 275–80 . . . 33

431. MACFADYEN, A. (1948) The meaning of productivity in biological
systems, *J. Anim. Ecol.*, **17**, 75–80 159

PAGE

432. MACFADYEN, A. (1949) A simple device for recording mean temperatures in confined spaces, *Nature, Lond.*, **164**, 965 . . 33, 39

433. MACFADYEN, A. (1950) Biologische Produktivität, *Arch. Hydrobiol.*, **43**, 166–170 159

434. MACFADYEN, A. (1952) The small Arthropods of a *Molinia* fen at Cothill, *J. Anim. Ecol.*, **21**, 87–117 . . . . 57, 109, 116

435. MACFADYEN, A. (1953) Notes on methods for the extraction of small soil Arthropods, *J. Anim. Ecol.*, **22**, 65–77 . . 88, 95, 97, 98

436. MACFADYEN, A. (1954) The invertebrate fauna of Jan Mayen Island (East Greenland), *J. Anim. Ecol.*, **23**, 261–97 50, 58, 183, 194, 195

437. MACFADYEN, A. (1955) A comparison of methods for extracting soil Arthropods, in Kevan, D. K. Mc. E. (Ed.) *Soil Zoology* (London, Butterworth), 315–32 97

438. MACFADYEN, A. (1956) The use of a temperature integrator in the study of soil temperature, *Oikos*, **7**, 56–81 . . . 33, 39

439. MACFADYEN, A. (1961) Metabolism of soil invertebrates in relation to soil fertility, *Ann. Appl. Biol.*, **49**, 216–19 . . 68, 240, 271

440. MACFADYEN, A. (1961) Improved funnel-type extractors for soil animals, *J. Anim. Ecol.*, **30**, 171–84 97

441. MACFADYEN, A. (1961) A new system for continuous respirometry of small air breathing invertebrates in near-natural conditions, *J. Exp. Biol.*, **38**, 323–41 . . . . . 68, 76, 82

441a. MACFADYEN, A. (In press) Soil arthropod sampling, in Cragg, J. B. (Ed.), *Adv. Ecol. Res.*, **1** (London and New York, Acad. Press) . 98

442. MACFADYEN, A. and KEMPSON, D. K. (1954) An inexpensive multipoint recorder for field use, *J. Anim. Ecol.*, **23**, 376–80 . . 39

442a. McINTIRE, G. A. (1953) Estimation of plant density using line transects, *J. Ecol.*, **41**, 319–30 107

443. MACLEOD, J. (1943) A survey of British sheep blowflies, *Bull. Ent. Res.*, **34**, 65–88 51

444. MACLEOD, J. (1958) The estimation of numbers of mobile insects from low-incidence recapture data, *Trans. Roy. Ent. Soc. Lond.*, **110**, 363–92 115

445. MACMILLAN, R. H. (1951) *An Introduction to the Theory of Control* (Cambridge) 137

445a. MADGE, D. S. (1961) "Prefered temperatures" of land Arthropods, *Nature, Lond.*, **190**, 106–7 17

445b. MADGE, D. S. (1961) The control of relative humidity with aqueous solutions of Sodium hydroxide, *Ent. Exp. et Appl.*, **4**, 143–7 . 16

446. MALTHUS, T. R. (1803) *Essay on Population* (London, Rev. edn.) . 132

447. MANN, K. H. (1952) A revision of the British leeches of the family Erpobdellidae, *Proc. Zool. Soc. Lond.*, **122**, 395–406 . . . 61

PAGE

447*a*. MANN, K. H. (1956) A study of the oxygen consumption of five species of leech, *J. Exp. Biol.*, **33**, 615–26 . . . 75, 76, 82

448. MANNING, W. M. and JUDAY, R. E. (1941) The chlorophyll content and productivity of some lakes in Northwestern Wisconsin, *Trans. Wis. Acad. Sci. Arts Lett.*, **33**, 363–93 238

449. MARGALEF, D. R. (1957) (Information theory in ecology) Translation of a paper in *Memorias de la Real Acad. Cien. Art. Barcelona*, **23**, 373–449, by L. B. Slobodkin 197

450. MARQUARDT, G. (1950) Die schleswig-holsteinische Knicklandschaft, *Schr. geogr. Inst. Univ. Keil*, **13**, 90 pp. 23

450*a*. MASSEE, A. M. (1951) in *Synopsis of World Literature on the Fruit-tree Red-spider-mite* (Commonw. Inst. Ent., London) . . . 275

451. MATTHEWS, G. V. T. (1953) Navigation on the Manx shearwater, *J. Exp. Biol.*, **30**, 370–96 55

451*a*. MATTHEWS, G. V. T. (1955) *Bird Navigation* (Cambridge) . . 55

452. MAYR, E. (1942) *Systematics and the Origin of Species from the Viewpoint of a Zoologist* (New York) 8

453. MAYR, E. (1947) Ecological factors in speciation, *Evolution*, **1**, 263 *et seq.* 7

453*a*. MEDAWAR, P. B. (1952) *An Unsolved Problem of Biology*, 24 pp. Inaug. Lect. Univ. Coll. Lond. 126

454. MERRELL, D. J. (1953) Gene-frequency changes in small laboratory populations of *Drosophila melanogaster*, *Evolution*, **7**, 95–101 . 8, 13

455. MIDDLETON, A. D. (1931) *The Grey Squirrel* (London) . . . 10

456. MILBURN, T. R. and BEADLE, L. C. (1960) Determination of total carbon dioxide in water, *J. Exp. Biol.*, **37**, 444–60 . . . 84

457. MILLER, R. S. (1955) Activity rhythms in the wood mouse, *Apodemus sylvaticus* and the bank vole, *Clethrionomys glareolus*, *Proc. Zool. Soc. Lond.*, **125**, 505–19 61

458. MILNE, A. (1957) The natural control of insect populations, *Canad. Ent.*, **89**, 193–213 154

459. MILNE, A. (1957) Theories of natural control of insect populations, *Cold Spring Harbor Symposia Quantitative Biology*, **22**, 253–71 . 154

460. MILNE, A. (1958) Perfect and imperfect density dependence in population dynamics, *Nature, Lond.*, **182**, 1251–2 . . . 154

461. MILNE, A. (1960) On a theory of natural control of insect population, *Internat. Un. For. Res. Org.* Zurich 154

462. MILNE, S. (1960) Studies on the life histories of various species of Arthropleone Collembola, *Proc. Roy. Ent. Soc. Lond. (A)*, **35**, 133–40 76

463. MÖBIUS, K. (1877) *Die Auster und die Austerwirtschaft* (Berlin) 48, 178, 267

464. MONTEITH, J. L. (1958) A thermocouple method for measuring relative humidity in the range 95–100 per cent. *J. Sci. Instrum.*, **35**, 443–6 43

PAGE

465. MOONEY, H. A. and BILLINGS, W. D. (1961) Comparative physiological ecology of arctic and alpine populations of *Oxyria digina*,
Ecol. Monogr., **31**, 1–29 84
466. MORAN, P. A. P. (1949) The statistical analysis of the sunspot and
lynx cycles, *J. Anim. Ecol.*, **18**, 115–16 .   .   .   . 136, 260
467. MORAN, P. A. P. (1952) The statistical analysis of game-bird records,
J. Anim. Ecol., **21**, 154–8 136
468. MORAN, P. A. P. (1954) The logic of the mathematical theory of animal
populations, *J. Wildlife Mgmt.*, **18**, 60–6 136
469. MORISITA, M. (1954) The estimation of population density by the
spacing method, *Mem. Fac. Sci. Kyushu.* (*E*), **1**, 187–97 .   . 106
470. MORISITA, M. (1957) A new method for the estimation of density
by the spacing method applicable to non-randomly distributed
populations, *Physiol. and Ecol. Tokyo.* **7**, 134–44.   .   .   . 106
471. MORISITA, M. (1959) Measuring the dispersion of individuals and
analysis of the distributional patterns, *Mem. Fac. Sci. Kyushu.*
(*E*), **2**, 215–35 105
472. MORISITA, M. (1959) Measuring of interspecific association and
similarity between communities, *Mem. Fac. Sci. Kyushu.* (*E*), **3**,
65–80 189
472*a*. MORRIS, R. F. (1954) A sequential sampling technique for spruce
budworm egg surveys, *Canad. J. Zool.*, **32**, 302–13 .   .   . 113
473. MORRIS, R. F. (1955) The development of sampling techniques for
forest insect defoliators, *Canad. J. Zool.*, **33**, 225–94 .   .   . 113
473*a*. MORTIMER, C. H. (1956) The oxygen content of air-saturated
fresh waters and aids in calculating percentage saturation, *Mitt.
int. Ver. Limnol.*, **6**, 20 pp. 237
474. MORTIMER, C. H. and MOORE, W. H. (1953) The use of thermistors
for the measurement of lake temperatures, *Mitt. int. Ver. Limnol.*,
2, 42 pp. 38
475. MOUNTFORD, M. D. (In press) An index of similarity and its application to classificatory problems, in Murphy, P. W. *Progress in
Soil Zoology* (London, Butterworth) 196
476. MÜLLER, D., MØLLER, C. M. and NIELSEN, J. (1960) The dry matter
production of European beech, *Forstl. Forsøksv. Danm.*, **21**,
253–335 239
477. MÜLLER, P. (1960) Kreislauf des Kohlenstoffs, *Handb. Pflanzenphy-
siol.* **5**, 255–68, **12**, (2) 934–48 239
478. MUNDIE, J. H. (1956) Emergence traps for aquatic insects, *Mitt. int.
Ver. Limnol.*, **7**, 13 pp. 96
479. MURPHY, P. W. (1953) The biology of forest soils with special
reference to the mesofauna or meiofauna, *J. Soil Sci.*, **4**, 155–93 . 95

PAGE

480. NATIONAL PHYSICAL LABORATORY (1953) *Measurement of Humidity*, Notes on applied science (4) (London, H.M.S.O.), 18 pp. . . 43

482. NAYLOR, A. F. (1959) An experimental analysis of dispersal in the flour beetle, *Tribolium confusum, Ecology*, **40,** 453–65 . . . 105

483. NAYLOR, E. (1958) Tidal and diurnal rhythms of locomotory activity in *Carcinus maenas* (L.), *J. Exp. Biol.*, **35,** 602–10 . . 60

484. NEEDHAM, P. R. (1940) Production in inland waters, *Proc. 6th Pac. Sci. Cong.*, **3,** 353–8 162

485. NESS, J. and DUGDALE, R. C. (1959) Computation of production for populations of aquatic midge larvae, *Ecology*, **40,** 425–30 . 165

486. NEWELL, L. M. (1948) Quantitative methods in biological and control studies of orchard mites, *J. Econ., Ent.*, **40,** 683–9 . . . 92

487. NICHOLSON, A. J. (1927) A new theory of mimicry in insects, *Aust. Zool.* **5,** 10–104 153

488. NICHOLSON, A. J. (1933) The balance of nature in animal populations, *J. Anim. Ecol.*, **2,** 132–78 . 144, 156, 174, 181, 217, 251

489. NICHOLSON, A. J. (1934) The influence of temperature on the activity of sheep blowflies, *Bull. Ent. Res.*, **25,** 85–99 . . . 17, 18

490. NICHOLSON, A. J. (1937) The role of competition in determining animal populations, *J. Coun. Sci. Ind. Res.*, **10,** 101–6 . . 156

492. NICHOLSON, A. J. (1947) *Fluctuations of Animal Populations*, Pres. Address Aust. N. Z. Assoc. Adv. Sci. Perth. 156

493. NICHOLSON, A. J. (1950) Population oscillations caused by competition for food, *Nature, Lond.*, **165,** 476–7 . . 139, 144, 175

494. NICHOLSON, A. J. (1950) Competition for food among *Lucilia cuprina* larvae, *8th Int. Cong. Ent., Stockholm*, 277–81 . 144, 150, 175

495. NICHOLSON, A. J. Experimental demonstrations of balance in populations, *Nature, Lond.*, **173,** 862–3 175

496. NICHOLSON, A. J. (1954) Compensatory reactions of populations to stress and their evolutionary significance, *Austr. J. Zool.*, **2,** 1–8 . . . . 145, 156, 168

497. NICHOLSON, A. J. (1954) An outline of the dynamics of animal populations, *Austr. J. Zool.*, **2,** 9–65 . . . 150, 156, 262

498. NICHOLSON, A. J. (1955) Density governed· reaction, the counterpart of selection in evolution, *Cold Spring Harbor Symposia Quantitative Biology*, **20,** 288–93 156

499. NICHOLSON, A. J. (1955) An outline of the dynamics of animal populations, *Austr. J. Zool.*, **2,** 9–65 156

500. NICHOLSON, A. J. (1957) The self-adjustment of populations to change, *Cold Spring Harbor Symposia Quantitative Biology*, **22,** 153–73

7, 145, 150, 156, 168

PAGE

501. NICHOLSON, A. J. (1958) Dynamics of insect populations, *Ann. Rev. Ent.*, **3**, 107–36 . . . . 156, 257

502. NICHOLSON, A. J. and BAILEY, V. A. (1935) The balance of animal populations, Part I. *Proc. Zool. Soc. Lond.*, 551–98 . . 156, 249

503. NICOL, H. (1943) *The Biological Control of Insects* (Penguin) . . 263

504. NIELSEN, C. OVERGAARD, (1948) An apparatus for quantitative extraction of Nematodes and Rotifers from soil and moss, *Natura Jutlandica*, **1**, 271–7 98

505. NIELSEN, C. OVERGAARD, (1949) Free living Nematodes and soil microbiology, *4th Internat. Congr. Microbiol.*, Copenhagen, 1947, 483–4 74

506. NIELSEN, C. OVERGAARD (1949) Studies on the soil microfauna. II. The soil-inhabiting Nematodes, *Natura Jutlandica*, **2**, 1–131 77, 80

507. NIELSEN, C. OVERGAARD (1953) Studies on Enchytraeidae. A technique for extracting Enchytraeidae from soil samples, *Oikos*, **4**, 187–96 . . . . 98, 238

508. NIELSEN, C. OVERGAARD Personal communication . . . 270

509. NIELSEN, C. OVERGAARD (1961) Respiratory metabolism of some populations of Enchytraeid worms and freeliving Nematodes, *Oikos*, **12**, 17–35 234

510. NIELSEN, E. STEEMANN (1951) Measurement of the production of organic matter in the sea by means of Carbon 14, *Nature, Lond.*, **167**, 684–5 237

511. NIELSEN, E. STEEMANN (1952) Production of organic matter in the sea, *Nature, Lond.*, **169**, 956–7 237

512. NIELSEN, E. STEEMANN (1952) The use of radioactive carbon for measuring organic production in the sea, *J. Cons. int. Exp. Mer.*, **18**, 117–140 237

513. NIELSEN, E. STEEMANN (1954) On organic production in the oceans. *J. Cons. int. Exp. Mer.*, **19**, 309–28 237

514. NIELSEN, E. STEEMANN (1959) Über primäreproduktion in einiger Alpenseen, *Oikos*, **10**, 24–37 237

515. NIELSEN, E. TETENS and NIELSENN, H. TETENS (1959) Temperatures preferred by the Pierid *Ascia monuste* (L.), *Ecology*, **40**, 181–5 . 19

516. NIELSEN, E. TETENS and THAMDRUP, H. M. (1939) Ein hygrometer für mikriklimatologische Untersuchungen, *Bioklim.Beibl.*, **6**, 180–4 41

517. NIESCHULZ, O. (1933) On the determination of the temperature preferenda of insects, *Zool. Anz.*, **103**, 21–9 16

518. NIESCHULZ, O. (1934) On the temperature preferendum of *Stomoxis calcitrans*, *Z. angew. Ent.*, **21**, 224–38 18

518a. NØRDBERG, S. (1936) Biologisch-ökologische Untersuchungen über die Vogelnidicolen, *Acta zool. fenn.*, **21**, 1–168 . . . 65

PAGE

520. Nørgaard, E. (1934) Okologiske undersøgelser over nogle danske Jagtedderkopper, *Flora og Fauna*, **51**, 1–38 . . 19, 29, 39, 63

521. Nørgaard, E. (1948) Bidrag til danske edderkoppers biologi. 1. *Lithyphantes albomaculatus* (De Geer), *Flora og Fauna*, **54**, 1–14 19, 63

522. Nørgaard, E. (1951) Notes on the biology of *Filistata insidiatrix* (Forsk.), *Ent. Medd.*, **26**, 170–84 . . . . . 19, 63

523. Nørgaard, E. (1951) On the ecology of two Lycosid spiders *Pirata piraticus* and *Lycosa pullata* from a Danish sphagnum bog, *Oikos*, **3**, 1–21 . . . . 18, 19, 63

524. Nørgaard, E. (1952) The habits of the Danish species of *Pirata*, *Ent. Medd.*, **3**, 415–23 . . . . 19, 63

525. O'Brien, F. E. M. (1948) The control of humidity by saturated salt solution, *J. Sci. Instrum.*, **25**, 73–6 16

526. Odum, E. P. and Odum, H. T. (1959) *Introduction to Ecology*, 2nd edn. (Philadelphia, Saunders) . . 73, 75, 163, 231, 239, 240

528. Odum, E. P. and Pontin, H. J. (1961) Population density of the underground ant *Lasius flavus*, as determined by tagging with P³², *Ecology*, **42**, 186–9 115

529. Odum, E. P. and Smalley, A. E. (1959) Comparison of population energy flow of a herbivorous and a deposit-feeding invertebrate in a salt marsh ecosystem, *Proc. Nat. Acad. Sci. Wash.*, **45**, 617–22
169, 231

530. Odum, H. T. (1956) Efficiencies, size of organisms and community structure, *Ecology*, **37**, 592–7 . . . . . . 240, 267

531. Odum, H. T. (1957) Trophic structure and productivity of Silver Springs, Florida, *Ecol. Monogr.*, **27**, 55–112 . . . 231, 241

532. Odum, H. T., Abbott, W. and Selander, R. (1958) Studies on the productivity of the lower montane rain forest of Puerto Rico, *Bull. Ecol. Soc. Amer.*, **39**, 85 . . . . 231, 236, 238, 239

533. Odum, H. T., Cantlon, J. E. and Kornicker, L. S. (1960) An organizational hierarchy postulate for the interpretation of species-individual distribution, species entropy, ecosystem evolution and the meaning of a species-variety index, *Ecology*, **41**, 395–9 . 198

534. Odum, H. T. and Odum, E. P. (1956) Corals as producers, herbivores, carnivores and possibly decomposers, *Ecology*, **37**, 385 . 231

535. Ogden, J. Gordon, (1960) A phototube solar radiation integrator for environmental studies, *Ecology*, **41**, 560–2 44

536. Oliff, W. D. (1953) The mortality, fecundity and intrinsic rate of natural increase of the multimammate mouse, *Rattus (Mastomys) natalensis* (Smith) in the laboratory, *J. Anim. Ecol.*, **22**, 217–26 . 123

537. Orians, G. H. and Leslie, P. H. (1958) A capture-recapture analysis of a shearwater population, *J. Anim. Ecol.*, **27**, 71–84 . . . 115

PAGE

Overgaard Nielsen, see Nielsen, C. Overgaard

540. Ovington, J. D. (1957) Dry matter production by *Pinus sylvestris*, *Ann. Bot.*, **21**, 287–314 239

541. Ovington, J. D. and Heitkamp, D. (1960) The accumulation of energy in forest plantations in Britain, *J. Ecol.*, **48**, 639–48 . .
239, 240, 242

542. Ovington, J. D. and Pearsall, W. H. (1956) Production ecology. II. Estimates of average production by trees, *Oikos*, **7**, 202–5 . . 239

543. Palmgren, P. (1930) Quantitative Untersuchungen über die Vogelfauna in den Wälden Südfinnlands, *Acta zool. Soc. fenn.*, **7**, 1–218 178

544. Palmgren, P. (1942) Die Populationsgrösse der Vögel als Evolutionsfaktor, *Naturwissenschaft*, **30**, 217–20 162

545. Park, T. (1932) Studies in population physiology: 1. The relation of numbers to initial population growth in the flour beetle *Tribolium confusum* Duval, *Ecology*, **13**, 172–81 . . 135, 175, 208

546. Park, T. (1933) Studies in population physiology: 2. Factors regulating the initial growth of *Tribolium confusum* populations, *J. Exp. Zool.*, **65**, 17–42 . . . . 175, 208

547. Park, T. (1934) Studies in population physiology; 3. The effect of conditioned flour upon the productivity and population decline of *Tribolium confusum*, *J. exp. Zool.*, **68**, 167–83 144, 175, 208

548. Park, T. (1935–1941) Studies in population physiology. Further papers in *Ecology*, *J. Exp. Zool.*, *Physiol. Zoöl.* and in *J. Cell. Comp. Physiol.* 175, 208

549. Park, T. (1946) Some observations on the history and scope of population ecology, *Ecol. Monogr.*, **16**, 313–30 . . 134, 175, 208

550. Park, T. (1948) Experimental studies of interspecies competition. I. Competition between populations of the flour beetles, *Tribolium confusum* Duval and *Tribolium castaneum* Herbst, *Ecol. Monogr.*, **18**, 265–308 . . . . 144, 175, 207, 208, 210

551. Park, T. (1954) Experimental studies of interspecies competition. II. Temperature, humidity and competition between two species of *Tribolium*, *Physiol. Zoöl.*, **27**, 177–238 . . . . 175, 210

552. Park, T. (1954) Competition: an experimental and statistical study, in: Kempthorne, O. *et al.* (Ed.) *Statistics and Mathematics in Biology* (Iowa) 175, 210

553. Park, T. (1957) Experimental studies of interspecies competition. III. Relation of initial species proportions to competitive outcome in populations of *Tribolium*, *Physiol Zoöl.*, **30**, 22–40 . 175, 210

554. Park, T. and Frank, M. B. (1948) The fecundity and development of the flour beetles *Tribolium confusum* and *T. castaneum* at three constant temperatures, *Ecology*, **29**, 368–74 . . 175, 210, 212

PAGE

555. PARK, T. and LESLIE, P. H. (1949) The intrinsic rate of natural increase of *Tribolium castaneum* Herbst, *Ecology*, **30**, 469–77
126, 152, 175, 210

556. PARKINSON, D. and WAID, J. S. (1960) *The Ecology of Soil Fungi* (Liverpool) 271

557. PARRY, D. A. (1951) Factors determining the temperature of terrestrial Arthropods in sunlight, *J. Exp. Biol.*, **28**, 445–62 . . 34

558. PATTEN, B. C. (1959) An introduction to the cybernetics of the ecosystem: the trophic-dynamic aspect, *Ecology*, **40**, 221–31 73, 231

559. PAVIOUR-SMITH, K. (1960) The invasion of Britain by *Cis bilamellatus* Fowler (Coleoptera: Ciidae), *Proc. R. Ent. Soc. Lond. (A)*, **35**, 145–55 13

560. PAVIOUR-SMITH, K. (1960) The fruiting bodies of macrofungi as habitats for beetles of the family Ciidae (Coleoptera), *Oikos*, **11**, 43–71 15

561. PEACHEY, J. E. (1959) *Studies of the Enchytraeidae of moorland soils*, Ph. D. Thesis, Durham University 98, 106

562. PEARL, R. and PARKER, S. L. (1922) On the influence of population upon the rate of reproduction in *Drosophila*, *Proc. Nat. Acad. Sci. Wash.*, **8**, 212–19 . . . . . . 133, 150, 174

563. PEARL, R. and REED, L. J. (1920) On the rate of growth of the population of the United States. *Proc. Nat. Acad. Sci. Wash.*, **6**, 275–88 . . . . 133, 174

564. PEARSALL, W. H. (1945) Leaf fall in Hertfordshire woodlands, *Trans. Herts. Nat. Hist. Soc.*, **22**, 97–8 242

565. PEARSALL, W. H. (1961) The Isle of Rhum: a laboratory for conservationists, *The New Scientist*, **9**, 860–2 278

568. PENMAN, H. L. (1955) *Humidity* (London, Institute of Physics) . 43

569. PENMAN, H. L. and LONG, I. (1949) A portable thermistor bridge for micro meteorology among growing crops, *J. Sci. Instrum.*, **26**, 77–8 . . . . 38, 43, 44

569a. PENNAK, R. W. (1949) The microscopic fauna of the sandy beaches, *Amer. Assoc. Adv. Sci.* (10), 94–106 58

569b. PETERSON, C. G. J. (1918–1924) *The Sea-bottom and its Production of Food* (Copenhagen) 114

570. PHILIP, J. R. (1955) Note on the mathematical theory of population dynamics and a recent fallacy, *Austr. J. Zool.*, **3**, 287–94 . . 208

571. PHILLIPSON, J. (1960) A contribution to the feeding biology of *Mitopus morio* (F.) (Phalangida), *J. Anim. Ecol.*, **29**, 35–43 73, 84, 166, 227

572. PHILLIPSON, J. (1960) The food consumption of different instars of *Mitopus morio* (F.) (Phalangida) under natural conditions, *J. Anim. Ecol.*, **29**, 299–307 . . . . 73, 75, 84

PAGE

573. PHILIPSON, J. Personal communication 76

574. PICKETT, A. D. (1953) A critique of insect chemical control methods, *Canad. Ent.*, **81**, 67–76 276

575. PIELOU, E. C. (1959) The use of point to plant distances in the study of pattern of plant populations, *J. Ecol.*, **47**, 607–14 . . . 106

577. PIRIE, N. W. (1958) Unconventional production of foodstuffs, *Science News*, **49**, 17–38 277

578. PITELKA, F. A. (1958) Population studies of lemmings and lemming predators in Northern Alaska, *XV Int. Cong. Zool., Lond.*, 757–9 . 149

579. PLATT, R. B. (1958) The ultimate subdivisions of the environment and species adjustment, *Bull. Georgia Acad. Sci.*, **16**, 84–91 . .7, 19

580. PLATT, R. B., COLLINS, L. L. and WITHERSPOON, J. P. (1957) Reactions of *Anopheles quadrimaculatus* say to moisture, humidity and light, *Ecol. Monogr.*, **27**, 303–24 17

581. POHL, H. A. (1951) Super-sensitive thermoelements, *Rev. Sci. Instrum.*, **22**, 345 40

582. POHL, H. A. (1952) Super-sensitive thermo-and vapour-sensing elements and their useful temperature range, *Rev. Sci. Instrum.*, **23**, 770 40

582a. PONTIN, A. J. (1961) Population stabilization and a comparison between the ants *Lasius flavus* (F.) and *L. niger* (L.), *J. Anim. Ecol.*, **30**, 47–54 257

583. POORE, M. E. D. (1955) The use of phytosociological methods in ecological investigations: 1. The Braun-Blanquet system, *J. Ecol.*, **43**, 226–44 193

584. POORE, M. E. D. (1955) The use of phytosociological methods in ecological investigations: 2. Practical issues, *J. Ecol.*, **43**, 245–60 . 193

585. POORE, M. E. D. (1955) The use of phytosociological methods in ecological investigations: 3. Practical applications, *J. Ecol.*, **43**, 606–51 193

587. POTTER, L. D. (1956) Yearly soil temperatures in Eastern North Dakota, *Ecology*, **37**, 62–9 33

588. POWELL, R. W. (1936) The use of thermocouples for psychrometric purposes, *Proc. Phys. Soc. Lond.*, **48**, 406 43

589. PRATT, H. (1954) Analyse microcalorimetrique des variations de la thermogenèse chez divers insectes, *Canad. J. Zool.*, **32**, 172–94 . 81

590. PRINGLE, J. W. S. (1950) The instrumentation of the living body, *Science News*, **17**, 100–14 137

591. PRINGLE, J. W. S. and WILSON, V. J. (1952) The response of a sense organ to a harmonic stimulus, *J. Exp. Biol.*, **29**, 220–34 . . 137

592. QUENOUILLE, M. H. (1950) *Introductory Statistics* (London, Butterworth) 100, 104

PAGE

593. QUENOUILLE, M. H. (1952) *Associated Measurements* (London, Butterworth), 242 pp. 192

594. RANWELL, D. S. (1960) Newborough warren, Anglesey: III Changes in the vegetation on parts of the dune system after the loss of rabbits by myxomatosis, *J. Ecol.*, **48**, 385–96 265

595. RAO, C. R. (1952) *Advanced Statistical Methods in Biometrical Research* (New York, Wiley), 390 pp. 192

596. RAW, F. (1955) A flotation extraction process for soil micro-arthropods, in Kevan, D. K. Mc. E., *Soil Zoology* (London, Butterworth), 341–6 95

597. RAW, F. (1960) Earthworm population studies: a comparison of sampling methods, *Nature, Lond.*, **187**, 257 97

597a. RAW, F. (1961) In a paper read to Association of Applied Biologists, January 1961. 236

598. REMANE, A. (1952) Die Bedeutung des Sandbodens im Meere und die Bedeutung der Lebensformtypen für der Ökologie, *Zool. Anz.*, **16**, Suppl. 327–59 200

599. RENKONNEN, O. (1938) Statistisch-ökologisch Untersuchungen über die terrestrische Käferwelt der finnischen Brachmeere, *Ann. (bot- zool.) Soc. zool.-bot. fenn. Vanamo, sect. zool.*, **6**, 1 *et seq.* 189

600. RESVOY, P. D. (1924) Zur Definition des Biocönose-Begriffs, *Russ. hydrobiol. Zeitschr.*, **3**, 204–9 . . . . . 178, 186

601. REYNOLDSON, T. B. (1948) An ecological study of the Enchytraeid worm population of sewage bacteria beds, *J. Anim. Ecol.*, **17**, 27–38

255

602. REYNOLDSON, T. B. (1957) Population fluctuations in *Urceolaria mitra* (Peritricha) and *Enchytraeus albidus* (Oligochaeta) and their bearing on regulation, *Cold Spring Harbor Symposia Quantitative Biology*, **22**, 313–27 157

603. REYNOLDSON, T. B. (1958) The quantitative ecology of lake dwelling triclads in Northern Britain, *Oikos*, **9**, 94–138 . . . 93, 193

604. REYNOLDSON, T. B. (1958) Triclads and lake typology in northern Britain: qualitative aspects, *Verh. int. Ver. Limnol.*, **13**, 320–30 . 193

606. RICHARDS, O. W., WALOFF, N. and SPRADBERY, J. P. (1960) The measurement of mortality in an insect population in which recruitment and mortality widely overlap, *Oikos*, **11**, 306–10 . 220

607. RICHMAN, S. (1958) The transformation of energy by *Daphnia pulex*, *Ecol. Monogr.*, **28**, 273–91 166

608. RICKER, W. E. (1954) Stock and recruitment, *J. Fish. Res. Bd., Canada.* **11**, 559–623 . . . . 140, 165

609. RICKER, W. E. (1954) Effects of compensatory mortality upon population balance, *J. Wildlife Mgmt.*, **18**, 45–51 . . . 140

PAGE

609a. RICKER, W. E. and FOERSTER, R. E. (1948) Computation of fish production, *Bull. Bingham Oceanog. Coll. Yale.*, **11**, 173–211
159, 162, 163

610. RIGLER, F. H. (1956) A tracer study of the phosphorus cycle in lake water, *Ecology*, **37**, 550–61 79

611. RIHA, G. (1951) Zur Ökologie der Oribatiden in Kalksteinböden, *Zool. Jb. (Syst.)*, **80**, 189–450 78

612. RILEY, G. A. (1941) Plankton studies. 5. Regional summary, *J. Mar. Res.*, **4**, 162–71 162

614. RIPPER, W. E. (1956) Effect of pesticides on balance of Arthropod populations, *Ann. Rev. Ent.*, **1**, 403–38 277

615. ROBINSON, I. (1953) On the fauna of a brown flux of an elm tree, *Ulnus procera* Salisb., *J. Anim. Ecol.*, **22**, 149–53 . . . 225, 226

616. ROHDE, W. (1958) The primary production in lakes: some results and restrictions of the 14C method, *Rapp. Proc.-Verb. Cons. Internat. Explor. de la Mer*, **144**, 122–8 . . . . 237, 238

617. ROHDE, W. (1958) Primärproduktion und Seetypen, *Verh. int. Ver. Limnol.*, **13**, 121–41 237

617a. ROSE, R. E. and MILLER, J. G. (1954) Some sampling variations in soil fungal numbers, *J. Gen. Microbiol.*, **10**, 1–10 . . . 110

618. ROSE, S. M. (1960) A feedback mechanism of growth control in tadpoles, *Ecology*, **41**, 188–99 149

620. ROSS, R. (1910) *The prevention of Malaria* (London), 174 . . 213

621. ROTHSCHILD, M. and MARSH, H. (1956) Increase of hares (*Lepus europaeus*) Pallas at Ashton Wold, with a note on the reduction in numbers of the Brown Rat (*Rattus norvegicus* Berkenhout), *Proc. Zool. Soc. Lond.*, **127**, 441–5 265

622. RYTHER, J. H. (1956) The measurement of primary production, *Limnol. Oceanog.*, **1**, 72–84 . . . . 84, 236, 237, 238

624. SALMON, J. T. (1946) A portable apparatus for extracting from leaf mould of Collembola and other minute organisms, *Dom. Mus. Reccs. Ent.*, **1**, 5–8 98

625. SALT, G. and HOLLICK, F. S. K. (1944) Studies of wireworm populations: a census of wireworms in pasture, *Ann. Appl. Biol.*, **31**, 52–64 95

626. SALT, G., HOLLICK, F. S. K., RAW, F. and BRIAN, M. V. (1948) The Arthropod population of pasture soil, *J. Anim. Ecol.*, **17**, 139–50 95

627. SANG, J. H. (1950) Population growth in *Drosophila* cultures, *Biol. Rev.*, **25**, 188–219 . . . . . . 134, 143, 150

628. SATCHELL, J. E. (1955) Some aspects of earthworm ecology, in Kevan, D. K. Mc. E. *Soil Zoology* (London, Butterworth), 180–201
191, 200

PAGE

629. SATCHELL, J. E. (1955) An electrical method of sampling earthworm populations, in Kevan, D. K. Mc. E. *Soil Zoology* (London, Butterworth), 356–64 97

630. SATCHELL, J. E. (1955) The effects of B.H.C., D.D.T. and Parathion on soil fauna, *Soils and Fertilizers* (Comm. Bur. Soil Sci.), **18**, 279–85 277

631. SATCHELL, J. E. (1958) Earthworm biology and soil fertility, *Soils and Fertilizers*, **21**, 209–19 . . . . . . 199, 200

632. SATCHELL, J. E. (1960) Earthworms and soil fertility, *The New Scientist*, **7**, 79 et seq. 200

633. SAVAGE, R. MAXWELL, (1961) *The Ecology and Life History of the Common Frog (Rana temporaria temporaria)* (London, Pitman), 221 pp. 149

633a. SCHALLER, F. (1950) Zur Ökologie der Kollembolen des mainzer Sandes, *Zool. Jahrb. Syst. Ökol, Geog.*, **78**, 449–513 . . . 64

634. SCHMITSCHEK, E. (1931) Entomologische Untersuchungen aus der Gebiete von Lunz, 1. *Z. angew. Ent.*, **18**, 460–91 . . . 33

635. SCHMIDT, R. L. and MARSHALL, J. R. (1960) A wind-direction recorder for remote stations, *Ecology*, **41**, 541–3 44

637. SCHUSTER, R. (1956) Der Anteil der Oribatiden an den Zersetzungsvorgängen im Boden, *Z. Morph. Ökol. Tiere*, **45**, 1–33 . . 78

638. SCHWERDTFEGER, (1935) Studien über ein Massenwechsel einiger Forstschädlinge, *Z. Forst- u. Jagdw.*, **67**, 15–38, 85–104, 449–82, 513–40
25, 251

639. SCHWERDTFEGER, (1941) Über die Ursuchen des Massenwechsel der Insekten, *Z. angew. Ent.*, **28**, 254–303 . . . . 26, 251

640. SCOTT, J. C. (1955) Stress factor in the disc syndrome. *J. Bone J. Surg.*, **37B**, 107–11 148

641. SEALANDER, J. A. et al. (1958) A technique for studying behavioural responses of small mammals, *Ecology*, **39**, 541–2 . . . 97

642. SEARLE, S. A. (1953) *The Measurement of Plant Climate* (Pub. privately, Chichester, England) 36

643. SEDGLEY, R. H. and MILLINGTON, R. J. (1957) A rapidly equilibrating soil moisture tensiometer, *Soil Sci.*, **84**, 215–17 . . . 46

644. SELLECK, G. W. and SCHUPPERT, K. (1957) Some aspects of microclimate in a pine forest, *Ecology*, **38**, 650–3 34

645. SEYLE, H. (1950) *The Physiology and Pathology of Exposure to Stress* (Montreal) 147

646. SHEPPARD, P. M. (1956) Ecology and its bearing on population genetics, *Proc. Roy. Soc. B*, **145**, 308–15 7

647. SHORTEN, M. (1946) A survey of the distribution of the American grey squirrel (*Sciurus carolinensis*) and the British red squirrel (*S. vulgaris leucourus*) in England and Wales in 1944–1945, *J. Anim. Ecol.*, **15**, 82–92 10

PAGE

648. SHORTEN, M. (1953) Notes on the distribution of the grey squirrel (*Sciurus carolinensis*) and the Red squirrel (*S. vulgaris leucourus*) in England and Wales from 1945–1952, *J. Anim. Ecol.*, **22**, 134–40 . 10

649. SKELLAM, J. G. (1951) Random dispersal in theoretical populations, *Biometrika*, **38**, 196–218 . . . . 8, 208

651. SKELLAM, J. G. (1958) The mathematical foundations underlying the use of line transects in animal ecology, *Biometrics*, **14**, 385–400 112

652. SKUHRAVÝ, V. (1957) Bewegungsareal einiger Carabidenarten, *Acta Soc. ent. Cechoslov.*, **53**, 171–9 . . . . . . 96, 115

654. SLOBODKIN, L. B. (1954) Population dynamics in *Daphnia obtusa* Kurz, *Ecol. Monogr.*, **24**, 69–88 . . . . . 72, 166

655. SLOBODKIN, L. B. (1955) Conditions for population equilibrium, *Ecology*, **36**, 530–3 72

656. SLOBODKIN, L. B. (1957) A laboratory study of the effect of removal of newborn animals from a population, *Proc. Nat. Acad. Sci. Wash.*, **43**, 780–2 . . . . 72, 166

657. SLOBODKIN, L. B. (1958) Metamodels in theoretical ecology, *Ecology*, **39**, 550–1 169

658. SLOBODKIN, L. B. (1959) Energetics in *Daphnia pulex* populations, *Ecology*, **40**, 232–43 . . . . 72, 84, 127, 166, 269

659. SLOBODKIN, L. B. (1960) Ecological relationships at the population level, *Amer. Nat.*, **94**, 213–36 . 72, 73, 79, 166, 167, 230, 231, 241

660. SLOBODKIN, L. B. and RICHMAN, S. (1960) The availability of a miniature bomb calorimeter for ecology, *Ecology*, **41**, 784–5 . . 80

662. SMITH, C. A. B. (1954) *Biomathematics: the Principles of Mathematics for Students of Biological Science* (London, Griffin,), 3rd edn., 712 pp. 127

663. SMITH, F. E. (1961) Density dependence in the Australian thrips, *Ecology*, **42**, 403–7 . . . . 153, 257, 258

664. SMITH, H. S. (1935) The role of biotic factors in the determination of population densities, *J. Econ. Ent.*, **28**, 873–98 . 175, 219, 259

665. SMITH, H. S. (1942) Biological control of black scale, *Calif. Citrogr.* **27**, 266, 290, 291 259

666. SMITH, H. S. (1943) A race of *Comperiella bifasciata* successfully parasitizes California red scale, *J. Econ. Ent.*, **35**, 809–12 . . 259

667. SMITH, H. S. and DE BACH, P. (1953) Artificial infestation of plants with pests as an aid in biological control, *Proc. 7th Pacific Sci. Congr.*, **4**, 255–9 . . . . 274, 276

668a. SNEDECOR, G. W. (1949) *Statistical Methods*, 4th edn. (Iowa) 100, 104, 115

669. SOLOMON, M. E. (1945) The use of cobalt salts as indicators of humidity and moisture, *Ann. Appl. Biol.*, **32**, 75–85 . . . 41

670. SOLOMON, M. E. (1949) The natural control of animal populations, *J. Anim. Ecol.*, **18**, 1–35 . . . . . . 259, 265

PAGE

671. SOLOMON, M. E. (1951) Control of humidity with potassium
hydroxide, sulphuric acid and other solutions, *Bull. Ent. Res.*,
42, 543–54 . . . . 16, 41

672. SOLOMON, M. E. (1953) The population dynamics of storage pests,
Trans. 9th Int. Ent. Congr. Amsterdam, **2**, 235–48 . . . 135

674. SOLOMON, M. E. (1953) Insect population balances and chemical
control of pests, *Chem. and Ind.*, 1143–7 276

675. SOLOMON, M. E. (1957) Estimation of humidity with cobalt thiocyanate papers and permanent colour standards, *Bull. Ent. Res.*,
48, 489–506 . . . . 17, 41

676. SOLOMON, M. E. (1957) Ecology of stored products pests: progress
of a long-term project, *Z. PflKrankh.* **64**, 606–612 . . . 19

678. SOLOMON, M. E. (1957) Dynamics of insect populations, *Ann. Rev.
Ent.*, **2**, 121–42 . . . . . . 156, 157, 257, 260

680. SOLOMON, M. E. (1958) Meaning of density dependence and related terms in population dynamics, *Nature, Lond.*, **181**, 1778–81
153, 156

681. SOLOMON, M. E. (1958) Perfect and imperfect density dependence in
population dynamics, *Nature, Lond.*, **182**, 1252 153

682. SÖRENSEN, T. (1948) A method of stabilizing groups of equivalent
amplitude in plant sociology based on the similarity of species
content and its application to analyses of the vegetation on Danish
commons, *kanske vid. Selsk. Bot. Skr.*, **5**, 1–34 . . 194, 196, 198

683. SOUTHERN, H. N. (1953) Balance of numbers in owls and small
mammals, *J. Anim. Ecol.*, **22**, 426–7 . . . . . 78, 247

684. SOUTHERN, H. N. (1959) Mortality and population control, *Ibis*,
101, 429–36 . . . . 246, 260, 265

685. SOUTHERN, H. N. Personal communication . . . 97, 115

686. SOUWICK, C. (1958) Population characteristics of house mice living
in English corn ricks: density relationships, *Proc. Zool. Soc.
Lond.*, **131**, 163–75 153

687. SPEMBLEY LTD. (1960) Capacitor discharge welding, *Welding and
Metal Fabrication*, April 37

689. SPRAGUE, V. G. and WILLIAMS, E. M. (1941) An inexpensive
light recorder, *Plant Physiol.* **16**, 679–85 44

689a. SPRAGUE, V. G. and WILLIAMS, E. M. (1943) A simplified light
recorder for field use, *Plant Physiol.*, **18**, 131–3 . . . 44

690. SPURWAY, H. (1953) Territory and evolution in sticklebacks, *New
Biol.*, **14**, 33–43 55

690b. STERN, V. M., SMITH, R. F., VAN DEN BOSCH, R. and HAGEN, K. S.
(1959) Integration of chemical and biological control of the
spotted alfalfa aphid, *Hilgardia*, **29**, 81–154 277

PAGE

691. STERRETT, S. J. (1961) Improved manufacturing technique for blood-flow probes, *J. Sci. Instrum.*, **38**, 59 37

692. STILES, W. and LEECH, W. (1931) On the use of the katharometer for the measurement of respiration, *Ann. Bot.*, **45**, 461–88 . . 84

693. STÖCKLI, A. (1945) Die biologische Komponente der Vererdung der Gäre und der Nährstoffpufferung, *Schweiz. land. Mh.*, **24**, 3–19 4

694. STRENZKE, K. (1952) Untersuchungen über die Tiergemeinschaften des Bodens: Die Oribatiden und ihre Synusien in den Böden Norddeutschlands, *Zoologica*, **104**, 173 pp. (Stuttgart) 57, 65, 193, 194

695. STRENZKE, K. (1960) Die systematische und ökologische Differenzierung der Gattung *Chironomus*, *Ann. ent. fenn.*, **26**, 111–38 . 7

696. STRICKLAND, J. D. H. (1958) Solar radiation penetrating the ocean, *J. Fish. Res. Bd. Canada*, **15**, 453–93 240

697. STRØM, K. M. (1932) Tyrifjord, a limnological study. *Skr. utgitt ar Norske Vidensk.-Akad. i Oslo, Math.-Naturw. Klasse*, **1**, 1–84 162

698. SYMPOSIUM ON MARKING (1956) *Ecology*, **37**, 665–86 . . . 115

699. TANNER, J. T. (1957) A wet-bulb and dry-bulb recording thermometer, *Ecology*, **38**, 530–1 43

700. TANSLEY, A. G. (1929) Succession, the concept and its values, *Proc. Int. Cong. Plant Sci.*, Ithaca., **1**, 677–86 . . . . 179, 183

700a. TANSLEY, A. G. (1935) The use and abuse of vegetational concepts and terms, *Ecology*, **16**, 284–307 . . . . . 162, 267

701. TANSLEY, A. G. (1947) The early history of modern plant ecology in Britain, *J. Ecol.*, **35**, 130–7 183

702. TAYLOR, C. B. (1936) Short period fluctuations in the numbers of bacterial cells in soil, *Proc. Roy. Soc. B.* **119**, 269–95 . . . 183

702a. TAYLOR, L. R. (1960) The distribution of insects at low levels in the air, *J. Anim. Ecol.*, **29**, 45–63 45

703. TAYLOR, L. R. (1961) Aggregation, variance and the mean, *Nature, Lond.*, **189**, 732–5 105

704. TAYLOR, R. H. (1956) The use of pellet counts for estimating the density of populations of the wild rabbit, *Oryctolagus cuniculus* (L.), *N.Z. J. Sci. Tech. B*, **38**, 236–56. 93

705. TAYLOR, T. H. C. (1937) *The Biological Control of an Insect in Fiji. An account of the coco-nut leaf mining beetle and its parasite complex*, 239 pp. (Imp. Inst. Ent. Lond.) . . . . . 251 ff.

706. TEAL, J. M. (1957) Community metabolism in a temperature cold spring, *Ecol. Monogr.*, **27**, 283–302 . . . 72, 74, 165, 231, 241

707. THIENEMANN, A. (1926) Die Nährungskreislauf im Wasser, *Verh. dtsch. zool. Ges.*, **31**, 29–79 267

PAGE

708. THIENEMANN, A. (1931) Der Produktionsbegriff in der Biologie, *Arch. Hydrobiol.*, **22**, 616–22 . . . . . . 159, 227

709. THIENEMANN, A. (1947) Zur Klärung einiger wichtiger Begriffe der allgemeinen Ökologie, *Arch. Hydrobiol.*, **41**, 626–9 . . . 159

710. THIENEMANN, A. (1954) Tropical freshwater plankton, *Symp. Mar. Freshw. Plank. in the Indo-Pacific* (Madras) 269

711. THOMAS, A. S. (1960) Changes in vegetation since the advent of myxomatosis, *J. Ecol.*, **48**, 287–306 265

712. THOMAS, M. (1949) A generalization of Poisson's binomial limit for use in ecology, *Biometrika*, **36**, 18–25 110

713. THOMPSON, W. R. (1922) 4 papers in *C. R. Acad. Sci. Paris*, **174** 174, 213

714. THOMPSON, W. R. (1924) Théorie mathématique de l'action des parasites entomophages et le facteur du hasard, *Ann. Fac. Sci. Marseille*, **2**, 69 *et seq.* 174, 213

715. THOMPSON, W. R. (1927–1930) Five papers in *Bull. Ent. Res.*, **17–20** and four papers in *Parasitology*, **20–21** 174, 213

716. THOMPSON, W. R. (1939) Biological control and the theories of the interactions of populations, *Parasitology*, **31**, 299–388 . 156, 219

717. THOMPSON, W. R. (1951) The time factor in biological control, *Canad. Ent.* **83**, 230–40 156

718. THOMPSON, W. R. (1956) The fundamental theory of natural and biological control, *Ann. Rev. Ent.*, **1**, 379–402 156

719. THOMSEN, M. (1938) Steufluen of Stickfluen. . . . *Beretn. Forsøks-Lab.*, *København* (176), 352 pp. 12

720. THORTON, I. W. B. (1957) Faunal succession in the umbels of *Cyperus papyrus* (L.) on the upper White Nile, *Proc. R. Ent. Soc., Lond.* (*A*), **32**, 119–31 201

721. THORPE, W. H. (1940) Ecology and the future of systematics, in Huxley, J. S. *The New Systematics* (London), 341–64 . . . 8

722. THORPE, W. H. (1945) On the evolutionary significance of habitat selection, *J. Anim. Ecol.*, **14**, 67–70 8

724. THORSEN, G. (1950) Reproductive and larval ecology of marine bottom invertebrates, *Biol. Rev.*, **25**, 1–45 . . . 18, 77

725. TINBERGEN, L. (1946) Die Sperwer als roofvijand van Zangvogels, *Ardea*, **34**, 1–213 248

726. TINSLEY, J. (1950) The determination of organic carbon in soils by dichromate mixtures. *Int. Cong. Soil. Sci.*, **1**, 161–4 . . . 81

727. TISCHLER, W. (1950) Vergleichend-biozönotische Untersuchungen am Waldrand und Feldhecke. *Zool. Anz. Supp.* **145**, 1000–15 . 59

727a. TISCHLER, W. (1952) Biozönotische Untersuchungen am Ruderal-stellen, *Zool. Jahrb.* (*Syst. Ökol. u. Geog.*), **81**, 122–74 . . 64

PAGE

728a. TISCHLER, W. (1959) Studien zur Bionomie und Ökologie der Schmalwanze *Ischnodemus sabulei* Fall (Hem. Lygeidae), *Z. f. wiss. Zool.*, **163**, 168–209 15

729. TODD, V. (1949) The habits and ecology of the British harvestmen (Arachnida, Opiliones) with special reference to those of the Oxford district, *J. Anim. Ecol.*, **18**, 209–16 . . . 19, 63, 76

731. TRELOAR, A. E. and GRAY, H. E. (1935) Note on the enumeration of insect populations by the method of net collection, *Ecology*, **16**, 122–4 92

735. TUFT, P. (1950) A new micro-respirometer with automatic setting and recording apparatus, *J. Exp. Biol.*, **27**, 334–9 . . . 82

736. TULLGREN, A. H. (1918) Ein sehr einfacher Ausleseapparat für terricole Tierfaunen. *Z. ang. Ent.*, **4**, 149–50 97

737. TURNER, F. B. (1960) Tests of randomness in recaptures of *Rana pretiosa*, *Ecology*, **41**, 237–9 115

738. TURNER, F. B. (1960) Size and dispersion of a Louisiana population of the cricket frog *Acris gryllus*, *Ecology*, **41**, 258–68 . . 115

738a. TURNER, F. B. (1961) The relative abundance of snake species, *Ecology*, **42**, 600–3 199

739. TUXEN, S. L. (1944) The hot springs and their animal communities and their zoogeographical significance, *Zool. Iceland*, **1**, (ii) (Copenhagen and Reykjavik) 183

740. UMBREIT, W. W., BURRIS, R. H. and STAUFFER, J. F. (1957) *Manometric Techniques*, 3rd edn., 338 pp. (Minneapolis, Burgess) . 81, 82

741. UVAROV, B. P. (1949) The migratory locust in England in 1947 and 1948, *Proc. R. Ent. Soc. (A.)*, **24**, 20–5 13

743. VAN DER DRIFT, J. (1951) Analysis of the animal community of a beech forest floor, *Tijdschr. Ent.*, **94**, 1–68 80

744. VAN DER DRIFT, J. (1959) Field studies on the surface fauna of forests, *I.T.B.O.N. Medd.*, **41**, 79–103 . . . . . 55, 60

745. VAN DER DRIFT, J. and WITKAMP, M. (1959) The significance of the breadkown of oak litter by *Enoicyla pusilla* Burm., *Arch. neerl. de Zool.*, **13**, 486–92 . . . . 270, 271

746. VAN HEERDT, P. F. and BRUYNS, M. F. MÖRZER, (1960) A biocenological investigation in the yellow dune region of Terschelling, *Tijdschr. Ent.*, **103**, 225–75 50

747. VAN HEERDT, P. F., ISINGS, J. and NIJENHUIS, L. E. (1956) Temperature and humidity preferences of various Coleoptera from the duneland of Terschelling, *Koninkl. Nederl. Akad. Wetensch. Amsterdam Proc. (C.)*, **59**, 668–76 and **60**, 99–106 . . . . . 17, 18, 19

747a. VAN SLYKE, D. D. and FOLCH, J. (1940) Manometric carbon determination, *J. Biol. Chem.*, **136**, 509–41 81

PAGE

748. VARLEY, G. C. (1947) The natural control of population balance in the knapweed gallfly (Urophora jaceana), J. Anim. Ecol., 16, 139–87
176, 249, 250, 258

749. VARLEY, G. C. (1948) Population instability. Review of Voûte, A.D. (1946) (q.v.) J. Anim. Ecol., 17, 82–3. 251

750. VARLEY, G. C. (1949) Population changes in German forest pests, J. Anim. Ecol., 18, 117–22 251

751. VARLEY, G. C. (1953) Ecological aspects of population regulation, Trans. 9th Int. Ent. Congr., 2, 210–14 . . . . 153, 262

752. VARLEY, G. C. (1957) Ecology as an experimental science, J. Ecol., 45, 639–48 and J. Anim. Ecol., 26, 251–60 251

754. VARLEY, G. C. (1958) Meaning of density dependence and related terms in population dynamics, Nature, Lond., 181, 1778–81 . 153

755. VARLEY, G. C. (in press) A note on density dependent factors and their effects, Int. Union. For. Res. Org. Zurich. 155

756. VARLEY, G. C. (1961) Demonstration reported in Proc. R. Ent. Soc. Lond. (C.), 26, 11 72

757. VARLEY, G. C. and EDWARDS, R. L. (1957) The bearing of parasite behaviour on the dynamics of insect host and parasite populations, J. Anim. Ecol., 26, 471–7 220

758. VARLEY, G. C. and GRADWELL, G. R. (1960) Key factors in population studies, J. Anim. Ecol., 29, 399–402 . . . 221, 258, 260

759. VERDUIN, J. (1956) Primary production in lakes, Limnol. Oceanog., 1, 85–91 237

760. VERDUIN, J. (1956) Energy fixation and utilization by natural communities in Western Lake Erie, Ecology, 37, 40–50 . . . 237

761. VERDUIN, J. (1959) Use of an aerated reference sample when measuring dissolved carbon dioxide, Ecology, 40, 322–3 84

762. VERDUIN, J. (1959) Photosynthesis by aquatic communities in Northwestern Ohio, Ecology, 40, 377–83 . . . . . 84, 237

764. VERHULST, P. F. (1844) Récherches mathématiques sur la loi d'accroissement de la population, Mem. Acad. Roy. Bruxelles, 18, 1–58 . . . . 123, 174

765. VERHULST, P. F. (1846) Deuxième mémoire sur la loi d'accroissement de la population, Mem. Acad. Roy. Bruxelles, 20, 1–52 . 123, 174

767. VERZAR, F., KEITH, J. and PARCHET, V. (1953) Temperatur und Feuchtigkeit der luft in den Atemwegan, Pflügers Archiv, 257, 400–16 . 42

768. VOLTERRA, V. (1926) Variazioni e fluttuazioni del numero d'individui in specie animali conviventi, Mem. Acad. Lincei., 2, 31–113
147, 174, 181, 204, 216

769. VOLTERRA, V. (1931) Translation of the above, an appendix to Chapman's Animal Ecology (New York) . . . 147, 214, 216

PAGE

770. VOLTERRA, V. (1931) Leçons sur la théorie mathématique de la lutte pour la vie, *Cahiers Scientifiques* (7) (Paris, Gauthier-Villars) . 204

771. VOÛTE, A. D. (1937) Bevolkerungsproblemen. II. Emigratie van *Calandra oryzae* (L.) *Naturkundig Tijdsch. voor Ned.-Indie*, **97**, 210–13 144

772. VOÛTE, A. D. (1938) Bevolkerungsproblemen III. *Naturkundig Tijdsch. voor Ned.-Indie*, **98**, 97–102 144

773. VOÛTE, A. D. (1946) Regulation of the density of the insect populations in virgin forests and cultivated woods, *Arch. néerl. Zool.*, **7**, 435–70 251

775. WALKER, T. J. (1957) Ecological studies of the Arthropods associated with certain decaying materials in four habitats, *Ecology*, **38**, 262–76 . . . . 51, 96

777. WALLACE, M. M. H. (1959) Insecticides for the control of the lucerne flea, *Aust. J. Agric. Res.*, **10**, 160–70 277

778. WALLIS, G. W. and WILDE, S. A. (1957) A rapid method for the determination of carbon dioxide evolved from forest soils, *Ecology*, **38**, 359–61 238

779. WALLWORK, J. A. (1958) Notes on the feeding behaviour of some forest soil Acarina, *Oikos*, **9**, 260–71. 270

781. WANGERIN, W. (1925) Beiträge zur pflanzensoziologischen Begriffsbildung und Terminologie, *Repertorium Speciarum novum regni vegetabilis, Beiheft*, **36**, 1–59 . . . . . . 178, 186

782. WANGERSKY, P. J. and CUNNINGHAM, W. J. (1957) Time lag in predator-prey population models, *Ecology*, **38**, 136–9 . . . 219

783. WATERHOUSE, F. L. (1950) Humidity and temperature in grass microclimates with reference to insolation, *Nature, Lond.* **166**, 232 . 29

784. WATERHOUSE, F. L. (1951) Body temperature in small insect larvae, *Nature, Lond.*, **168**, 340 . . . . 31, 35

785. WATERHOUSE, F. L. (1955) Microclimatological profiles in grass cover in relation to biological problems, *Quart. J. R. Met. Soc.*, **81**, 63–71 . . . . 29, 33

786. WATERS, W. E. (1955) Sequential sampling in forest insect surveys, *Forest Science.*, **1**, 68–79 . . . . 104, 113

787. WATT, A. S. (1947) Pattern and process in the plant community, *J. Ecol.*, **35**, 1–22 . . . . 109, 182

788. WATT. K. E. F. (1955) Studies on population productivity. I. Three approaches to the optimum yield problem in populations of *Tribolium confusum, Ecol. Monogr.*, **25**, 269–90 . . . 167, 241

789. WATT, K. E. F. (1956) The choice and solution of mathematical models for productivity and maximizing the yield of a fishery, *J. Fish. Res. Bd.*, *Canada.*, **13**, 613–45 167

PAGE

790. Watt, K. E. F. (1959) A mathematical model for the effect of densities of attacked and attacking species on the number attacked, *Canad. Ent.*, **91**, 129–144 220

791. Watt, K. E. F. (1959) Studies on population productivity. II. Factors governing productivity in a population of smallmouth bass, *Ecol. Monogr.*, **29**, 367–92 168

792. Watt, K. E. F. (1960) The effect of population density on fecundity of insects, *Canad. Ent.*, **92**, 674–95 . . . . . 142, 221

793. Watt, K. E. F. (1961) Mathematical models for use in insect pest control, *Canad. Ent.*, **93** (Supply 19), 62 pp. . . . 142, 277

795. Weis-Fogh, T. (1952) Weight economy of flying insects, *Trans. 9th Int. Ent. Congr.*, **1**, 341–7 70

796. Welch, H. E. (1960) Two applications of a method of determining the error of population estimates of mosquito larvae by the mark and recapture technique, *Ecology*, **41**, 228–9 115

797. Wellington, W. G. (1957) Synoptic approach to studies of insects and climate, *Ann. Rev. Ent.*, **2**, 143–62 92

798. Wellington, W. G. (1957) Individual differences as a factor in population dynamics: the development of a problem, *Canad. J. Zool.*, **35**, 293–323 7

799. Wellington, W. G. (1960) Qualitative changes in natural populations during change in abundance, *Canad. J. Zool.*, **38**, 289–314 . 149

800. Wellington, W. G. (1960) The need for direct observation of behaviour in studies of temperature effects on light reaction, *Canad. Ent.*, **92**, 438–48 17

801. Wendt, H. (1931) Der Einfluss der Hecken auf den landwirtschaftlichen Ertrag, *Erdkunde*, **5**, 115–25 23

802. Wheeler, L. R. (1948) *Harmony of Nature: a Study in Co-operation for Existence* (London, Arnold) 135

803. Whitehead, A. N. (1925) *Science and the Modern World* (Cambridge) 180, 184

804. Wittie, P. (1956) The estimation of age specific infection rates from a curve of relative infection, *Biometrics*, 154–62 . . . 220

806. Wigglesworth, V. B. (1949) The utilization of reserve substances in *Drosophila* during flight, *J. Exp. Biol.*, **26**, 150–63 . . 70, 130

807. Wigglesworth, V. B. (1960) The fauna of the orchard, *Ann. Rep. E. Malling Res. Sta.*, 39–47 277

808. Williams, C. B. (1944) Some applications of the logarithmic series and the index of diversity to ecological problems, *J. Ecol.*, **32**, 1–44 . . . . 104, 198

808a. Williams, C. B. (1947) The logarithmic series and its application to biological problems, *J. Ecol.*, **34**, 253–72 . . . 104, 261

PAGE

809. WILLIAMS, G. (1959) The seasonal and diurnal activity of the fauna sampled by pitfall traps in different habitats, *J. Anim. Ecol.*, **28**, 1–14 . . . . 60, 96

810. WILLIAMS, G. (1959) Seasonal and diurnal activity of Garabidae, with particular reference to *Nebria*, *Notiophilus* and *Feronia*, *J. Anim. Ecol.*, **28**, 309–30 60

811. WILLIAMS, R. W. (1960) A new simple method for the isolation of freshwater invertebrates from soil samples, *Ecology*, **41**, 573–4 97

812. WILLIAMS, W. T. and LAMBERT, J. M. (1959) Multivariate methods in plant ecology. I. Association analysis in plant communities, *J. Ecol.*, **47**, 83–102 . . . . 108, 196

813. WILLIAMS, W. T. and LAMBERT, J. M. (1960) Multivariate methods in plant ecology. II. The use of an electronic computer for association analysis, *J. Ecol.*, **48**, 689–711 196

814. WILLIAMSON, M. H. (1957) An elementary theory of interspecific competition, *Nature, Lond.*, **180**, 422–5 . . . . 208, 218

817. WILLIAMSON, M. H. (1958) Selection, controlling factors and polymorphism, *Amer. Nat.*, **92**, 329–35 6

818. WILLIAMSON, M. H. (1959) The separation of molluscs from woodland leaf litter, *J. Anim. Ecol.*, **28**, 153–5 93

819. WILSON, F. (1946) Interaction of insect infestation, temperature and moisture content in bulk-depot wheat, *Bull. Coun. Sci. Ind. Res. Austr.* (**209**), 31 pp. 244

820. WILSON, J. W. (1959) Notes on wind and its effects on arctic-alpine vegetation, *J. Ecol.*, **47**, 415–27 . . . . . 34, 45

821. WINDBERG, G. C. and IAROVITZINA, L. L. (1939) (Daily changes in the quantity of dissolved oxygen as a method of measuring primary production) Russian, English Summary, *Proc. Kossino limnol. Sta.*, **22**, 128–34 162

822. WINSTON, P. W. (1956) The acorn microsere, with special reference to Arthropods, *Ecology*, **37**, 120–32 201

823. WITKAMP, M. (1960) Seasonal fluctuations of the fungus flora in mull and mor of an oak forest, *I.T.B.O.N. Medd.*, **46** (Arnhem) . . 271

824. WOODGER, J. H. (1929) *Biological Principles* (London) . . . 183

825. WRIGHT, S. (1940) The statistical consequences of Mendelian heredity in relation to speciation, in Huxley, J. S. *The New Systematics* (Oxford), 161–84 7

826. WRIGHT, S. (1959) Physiological generics, ecology of populations and natuaral selection, *Persp. Biol. Med.*, **3**, 107–51 . . . 7

827. YAPP, W. B. (1955) The theory of line transects, *Bird Study*, **3**, 93–104 III

PAGE

827a. YATES, F. (1949) *Sampling Methods for Censuses and Surveys* (London)
    318 pp. 106, 110
827b. YATES, W. W., LINDQUIST, A. W. and BUTTS, J. S. (1952) Further
    studies of dispersion of flies tagged with radioactive phosphoric
    acid, *J. Econ. Ent.*, **45**, 547–8 115
828. YONGE, C. M. (1961) Nutrition and growth in corals, *The New
    Scientist*, **9**, 338–40   231
829. ZEUTHEN, E. (1947) Body-size and metabolic rate in the animal
    kingdom, *C. R. Lab. Carlsberg.*, *Ser. Chim.*, **26**, 17–165   . 75, 80
830. ZEUTHEN, E. (1953) Oxygen uptake as related to body size in organ-
    isms, *Quart. Rev. Biol.*, **28**, 1–12   .   .   .   .   . 75, 80

INDEX

References to illustrations are in bold type